Everyman, I will go with thee, and be thy guide,
In thy most need to go by thy side.

EVERYMAN'S LIBRARY

No. 927

ESSAYS & BELLES-LETTRES

OUR VILLAGE
BY MARY RUSSELL MITFORD
EDITED, WITH AN INTRO-
DUCTION, BY SIR JOHN SQUIRE

MARY RUSSELL MITFORD was born at Alresford, Hampshire, on 16th December 1787. She won £20,000 in a lottery at the age of ten, but the extravagances of her father eventually reduced her to poverty. In 1820 she went to live in a small cottage at Three Mile Cross, on the road between Reading and Basingstoke, which was her home for more than thirty years, her one luxury being her flower garden. She was awarded a Civil List pension in 1837, and died near Reading on 10th January 1855.

OUR VILLAGE

MARY RUSSELL MITFORD

LONDON: J. M. DENT & SONS LTD.
NEW YORK: E. P. DUTTON & CO. INC.

Y 266/8 m

INTRODUCTION

Mary Russell Mitford was born on 16th December 1787 at Alresford, Hants. Her mother was the daughter of a Dr. Russell, rector of Ash, vicar of Overton, a county magistrate, and a cadet of the Bedford family; she inherited, besides landed property, £28,000 in money. Her father, Dr. George Mitford, who had an Edinburgh medical degree, but made scant use of it, was a younger son of a younger brother of Mitford of Mitford (or Bertram) Castle in Northumberland, and an attractive, extravagant man who, by dint of gambling and high living, went through first his wife's fortune and then his daughter's, but was beloved by his daughter to the end, when, as an ageing but cheerful spinster in the country, she was working her fingers to the bone to keep him out of the clutches of his creditors. Except for brief intervals at boarding-school, in London lodgings, or staying with rich relations, Miss Mitford spent the whole of her life in county towns or small villages, now in a handsome house with an upkeep of thousands a year, now in a humble cottage with the roof falling in. The area of her wanderings was the borderland of Berkshire and Hampshire, with Reading on the north and Basingstoke on the south—not very far from the haunts of Jane Austen and White of Selborne, neither of whom was a more exact observer than she or acquainted with as wide a range of rural life. Circumstances had given her personal knowledge of prosperity and poverty, elegance and squalor, and she was directly acquainted with the houses of the great and the hovels of the labourers, as well as with those middle sorts of abodes which the mind of Jane Austen chose entirely to frequent. She herself said, late in life, of Jane Austen: 'Your admiration of Jane Austen is so far from being a heresy, that I never met any high literary people in my life who did not prefer her to any female prose writer!' So far as novelists are concerned, that may still stand; but amongst essayists, recorders of character and custom, and sensitive painters of natural scenery, Miss Mitford ranks as high as Miss Austen ranks among novelists.

Hers was a very quiet life, but much less secluded than Miss Austen's, for all her days she had streams of visitors and correspondents, from B. R. Haydon to Mrs. Browning; her letters (strung together to make a *Life*) fill three volumes, and might have filled more. She was, for a time, a successful dramatist; her interests were universal, and she must definitely be called a learned woman. She could read at three, and was mastering Percy's Ballads shortly afterwards; and the lists that were kept of the books she read each month are astonishing, though there is enough light literature in them to prevent them from being terrifying. From early years she had strong and even pugnacious views, and the reader of her *Life* will come across many amusing, many shrewd, and many wrong opinions about her contemporaries. In 1798 she was sent to a school in Hans Place kept by a French *émigré*, M. St. Quentin. No sooner is she there than we find her correcting her head master on a point of grammar, the correction being referred to an umpire and then gracefully accepted. At twelve she begins a letter to her father (it must be remembered that they were always on the closest terms):

> MY DEAR PAPA,
>
> I sit down in order to return you thanks for the parcels I received. My uncle called on me twice while I stayed in London, but he went away in five minutes both times. He said that he only went to fetch my aunt, and would certainly take me out when he returned. I hope that I may be wrong in my opinion of my aunt; but I again repeat, I think she has the most hypocritical drawl that I ever heard.

But, lest it should be thought that at this stage she was too grown-up, I may quote a passage from a note-book written only two months later:

> *Nov.* 30, 1800—Where shall I be this day month? At home! How happy I shall be! I may do what I like then, and shall be ready to jump out of my skin for joy.

Home was always the centre of her affections; the humblest collection of square habitations took a radiance from her eye and the most ordinary of neighbours revealed characteristics worth studying. Her love of home had to stand many tests, considering how reckless was her charming father and how dim and helpless, if devoted, her mother.

Her mother's patrimony had all gone, and the house at Alresford, within eight or nine years of the marriage; a year at Lyme Regis followed, and then lodgings across Blackfriars Bridge and a refuge from creditors within the rules of King's Bench. The next escape cannot be better told than in the words of the Revs. Harness and L'Estrange, who wrote the official *Life*:

> From this depressed state of their affairs the family were delivered by a prize in the lottery. The circumstances under which the ticket in this lottery was purchased were curious.

> The doctor took his little girl with him to the lottery office to choose the number, and a quantity of tickets were laid down on the counter for her to select from. She at once fixed upon the number 2,224. . . . The sixteenth she had fixed her heart upon she carried home with her; the remaining shares of the number were bought up from the other offices, at a considerable advance in price; and the doctor, on the drawing of the lottery, received £20,000, the largest prize that was then given, as the fruit of—we cannot say, his wisdom and discretion.

This prize, amounting to about £100,000 in our money, might, one would think, have sufficed for even Mr. Micawber or Mr. Skimpole to keep the duns at bay. Not in the least. Off went the doctor to a new house at Reading: once more the family prosperity soon hung in fearful hazards on the fleetness of the doctor's greyhounds or the number of his trumps at whist. By 1802 we see the family not merely purchasing a Tudor house and seventy acres at Grasely, near Reading, but pulling the strong old place down to build a correct residence in the Georgian manner, named Bertram House, after the family castle. That year Mary left school, and by 1804 she and her mother, though not always her father, were settled in the new house. By 1820 the family were once more penniless, except for a reserved fragment of Mrs. Mitford's dowry and what could by that time be earned by the daughter. They moved to a cottage—'no, not a cottage—it does not deserve the name'—at Three Mile Cross, near Reading, consisting of 'a series of closets, the largest of which may be about eight feet square. . . . On one side a public house, on the other a village shop, and right opposite a cobbler's stall.' Even that did not depress Miss Mitford, at any rate externally. 'Notwithstanding all this,' she wrote to her friend Sir William Elford, the painter:

> the cabin, as Bobadil says, is convenient. It is within reach of my dear old walks; the banks where I find my violets; the meadows full of cowslips; and the woods where the wood-sorrel blows. We are all beginning to get settled and comfortable, and resuming our usual habits. Papa has already had the satisfaction of setting the neighbourhood to rights by committing a disorderly person, who was the pest of the Cross, to Bridewell. Mamma has furbished up an old dairy and made it into a not incommodious store room. I have lost my only key, and stuffed the garden with flowers. My little dog Molly, after a good deal of staring and squeaking and running about (she seemed conscious of some degradation from the change), has at last pitched upon a chair to lie on when I turn her out of my lap; and the great white cat, who was likewise very eloquent and out of his wits, has given this very evening most satisfactory proofs of finding himself at home, by resuming his ancient

predatory habits and stealing all the milk for our tea. (N.B.— We were forced to go without.) Moreover, it is an excellent lesson in condensation—one which we all wanted.

There, at the end of 1829, Mrs. Mitford died, and in December 1842 Dr. Mitford. He was in debt, and his daughter wrote: 'Everybody shall be paid, if I sell the gown off my back or pledge my little pension'—£120 a year from the Civil List. Friends, however, raised a subscription of over a thousand pounds, Queen Victoria privately contributing. There was one move more, to Swallowfield (six miles from Reading) in 1850. There Miss Mitford died, on 10th January 1855, and after a life of hard work, illness, and vicissitude, she was but three days from her grave when she could write a letter about robins and sparrows and thank God that she had preserved 'my love of poetry and literature, my cheerfulness, and my enjoyment of little things.'

Her poems and plays are unlikely to return to favour, even though *Rienzi, Charles I*, and the other dramas (oddly, for her, full of dukes and desperadoes) were successful in their day. Her letters and recollections will always be read by the sagacious, and *Our Village* is a classic. The sketches contained in it were first published in the *Lady's Magazine* and appeared in five volumes (1824–32), and in two volumes, not quite complete, in Paris in 1839.

They are uneven, though I hope the best of them are here. They are not all about one village or indeed any village: she drew on her memory for scenes and characters of all kinds and from all periods of her early life. But mostly she stayed round Reading, dwelling upon familiar rustic people, places, and seasons. She is equally felicitous painting portraits (not least of people with humours), describing domestic backgrounds, and taking 'country walks' in all weathers. He who should wish to recover the 'interiors' of the period, the furniture, china, and fabrics in whatever rank of house, can find more in her than in any novelist; she is as faithful and full with the 'low life' of labourers and publicans, keepers, poachers, and milkmaids, as George Morland himself; to read her is to live in her village. But her finest prose is to be found in those papers such as *Frost and Thaw*, and *The First Primrose*, in which she united the detail of Richard Jefferies with a quiet perfection of prose all her own.

And, not least, the reader of these papers gets to know Miss Mitford herself—the charming little plain woman with beautiful eyes and speech; wise, witty, humorous, intellectual, plain-spoken, modest, satirical, and tender, who lives on every page. Small she was and delicate, and no Diana: she was once on a donkey which threw her into a pond: her sporting exploits consisted in watching village cricket, which thoroughly excited her. But she was countrywoman by nature and choice, loving bird, beast, and flower, storm and sunshine, all the pageant of the seasons and the beauties and queernesses which, in man as elsewhere, spring direct from the soil—and English soil at that. She found all she wanted in a few square miles, and knew it. 'Even in books,' she said, 'I like a confined locality.'

J. C. SQUIRE.

The following is a list of the works of Mary Russell Mitford with the dates of their first publication in book form:

Poems, 1810; *Christina: the Maid of the South Seas* (a poem), 1811; *Blanche of Castile,* 1812; *Watlington Hill* (a poem), 1812; *Narrative Poems on the Female Character* (Vol. I only; no more published), 1813; *Julian: a Tragedy,* 1823; *Our Village: Sketches of Rural Character and Scenery* (5 vols.), 1824, 1826, 1828, 1830, 1832; *Foscari: a Tragedy,* 1826; *Dramatic Scenes, Sonnets, and other Poems,* 1827; *Rienzi: a Tragedy,* 1828; *Mary Queen of Scots: a Scena in Verse,* 1831; *Charles the First: an Historical Tragedy,* 1834; *Belford Regis: Sketches of a Country Town* (3 vols.), 1835; *Sadak and Kalasrade, or the Waters of Oblivion: a Romantic Opera,* 1835; *Country Stories,* 1837; *Recollections of a Literary Life* (3 vols.), 1852; *Atherton and other Tales* (3 vols.), 1854.

Mary Russell Mitford edited *Stories of American Life,* 1830; *Lights and Shadows of American Life,* 1832; and *Finden's Tableaux* (an annual), 1838–41. She also contributed to *The Edinburgh Tales,* conducted by Mrs. C. I. Johnstone, 1845–6; and to the *London Magazine* and the *Reading Mercury.*

Collected editions: *The Works of Mary Russell Mitford, Prose and Verse,* 1841 (published in Philadelphia); *Dramatic Works* (2 vols.), 1854.

Biographies, etc.: *The Life of Mary Russell Mitford* (related in a selection from her letters to her friends), edited by the Rev. A. G. L'Estrange, 1870. *Letters, Second Series,* edited by Henry Chorley, 1872. *The Friendships of Mary Russell Mitford* (as recorded in letters from her literary correspondents), edited by the Rev. A. G. L'Estrange, 1882. *Mary Russell Mitford: the Tragedy of a Blue Stocking,* by W. J. Roberts, 1913. *Correspondence with Charles Boner and John Ruskin,* 1914. *Mary Russell Mitford and her Surroundings,* by Constance Hill, 1920. *Selected Letters,* edited by R. Brimley Johnson, 1925. *Mary Russell Mitford: Her Circle and Her Books,* by Marjorie Astin, 1930. *Mary Russell Mitford,* by James Agate, 1940. *Mary Russell Mitford,* by Vera Watson, 1949,

CONTENTS

TO

HER ONLY SURVIVING RELATIVE
AND MOST CHERISHED FRIEND,

HER BELOVED AND VENERABLE FATHER,

These Volumes

FULL OF ENDEARING RECOLLECTIONS OF THE
BEAUTIFUL SCENERY WHERE THEY HAVE
SO OFTEN WANDERED, AND OF THE VILLAGE HOME
WHERE FOR SO MANY YEARS
THEY HAVE DWELT TOGETHER IN WEAL OR IN WOE,
ARE

VERY AFFECTIONATELY INSCRIBED

BY

THE AUTHOR

PREFACE TO THE FIRST EDITION

THE following pages contain an attempt to delineate country scenery and country manners, as they exist in a small village in the south of England. The writer may at least claim the merit of a hearty love of her subject, and of that local and personal familiarity which only a long residence in one neighbourhood could have enabled her to attain. Her descriptions have always been written on the spot, and at the moment, and, in nearly every instance, with the closest and most resolute fidelity to the place and the people. If she be accused of having given a brighter aspect to her villagers than is usually met with in books, she cannot help it, and would not if she could. She has painted, as they appeared to her, their little frailties and their many virtues, under an intense and thankful conviction that, in every condition of life, goodness and happiness may be found by those who seek them, and never more surely than in the fresh air, the shade, and the sunshine of nature.

CHAPTER I

OUR VILLAGE

OF all situations for a constant residence, that which appears to me most delightful is a little village far in the country; a small neighbourhood, not of fine mansions finely peopled, but of cottages and cottage-like houses, 'messuages or tenements,' as a friend of mine calls such ignoble and nondescript dwellings, with inhabitants whose faces are as familiar to us as the flowers in our garden; a little world of our own, close-packed and insulated like ants in an ant-hill, or bees in a hive, or sheep in a fold, or nuns in a convent, or sailors in a ship; where we know every one, are known to every one, interested in every one, and authorized to hope that every one feels an interest in us. How pleasant it is to slide into these true-hearted feelings from the kindly and unconscious influence of habit, and to learn to know and to love the people about us, with all their peculiarities, just as we learn to know and to love the nooks and turns of the shady lanes and sunny commons that we pass every day! Even in books I like a confined locality, and so do the critics when they talk of the unities. Nothing is so tiresome as to be whirled half over Europe at the chariot-wheels of a hero, to go to sleep at Vienna and awaken at Madrid; it produces a real fatigue, a weariness of spirit. On the other hand, nothing is so delightful as to sit down in a country village in one of Miss Austen's delicious novels, quite sure before we leave it to become intimate with every spot and every person it contains; or to ramble with Mr. White [1] over his own parish of Selborne, and form a friendship with the fields and coppices, as well as with the birds, mice, and squirrels who inhabit them; or to sail with Robinson Crusoe to his island, and live there with him, and his goats, and his man

[1] White's *Natural History and Antiquities of Selborne*, one of the most fascinating books ever written. I wonder that no naturalist has adopted the same plan.

Friday—how much we dread any new-comers, any fresh importation of savage or sailor! we never sympathize for a moment in our hero's want of company, and are quite grieved when he gets away; or to be shipwrecked with Ferdinand on that other, lovelier island—the island of Prospero, and Miranda, and Caliban, and Ariel, and nobody else, none of Dryden's exotic inventions—that is best of all. And a small neighbourhood is as good in sober waking reality as in poetry or prose; a village neighbourhood, such as this Berkshire hamlet in which I write, a long, straggling, winding street, at the bottom of a fine eminence, with a road through it, always abounding in carts, horsemen, and carriages, and lately enlivened by a stage-coach from B—— to S——, which passed through about ten days ago, and will, I suppose, return some time or other. There are coaches of all varieties nowadays: perhaps this may be intended for a monthly diligence, or a fortnightly fly. Will you walk with me through our village, courteous reader? The journey is not long. We will begin at the lower end, and proceed up the hill.

The tidy, square, red cottage on the right hand, with the long well-stocked garden by the side of the road, belongs to a retired publican from a neighbouring town; a substantial person with a comely wife; one who piques himself on independence and idleness, talks politics, reads newspapers, hates the minister, and cries out for reform. He introduced into our peaceful vicinage the rebellious innovation of an illumination on the queen's acquittal. Remonstrance and persuasion were in vain; he talked of liberty and broken windows—so we all lighted up. Oh! how he shone that night with candles, and laurel, and white bows, and gold paper, and a transparency (originally designed for a pocket-handkerchief) with a flaming portrait of Her Majesty, hatted and feathered, in red ochre. He had no rival in the village, that we all acknowledged; the very bonfire was less splendid; the little boys reserved their best crackers to be expended in his honour, and he gave them full sixpence more than any one else. He would like an illumination once a month; for it must not be concealed, that in spite of gardening, of newspaper reading, of jaunting about in his little cart, and frequenting both church and meeting, our worthy neighbour begins to feel the weariness of idleness. He hangs over his gate, and tries to entice passengers to stop and chat; he volunteers little jobs all round, smokes cherry-trees to cure the blight, and traces and blows up all the wasp-nests in the parish. I have seen a great many wasps in our garden to-day, and shall enchant him with the intelligence. He even assists his wife in her sweepings and dustings. Poor man! he is a very respectable person, and would be a very happy one, if he would add a little employment to his dignity. It would be the salt of life to him.

Next to his house, though parted from it by another long garden with a yew arbour at the end, is the pretty dwelling of the shoemaker, a pale, sickly-looking, black-haired man, the very model of sober industry. There he sits in his little shop, from early morning till late at night. An earthquake would hardly stir him: the illumination did not. He stuck immovably to his last, from the first lighting up, through the long blaze and the slow decay, till his large solitary candle was the only light in the place. One cannot conceive anything more perfect than the contempt which the man of transparencies and the man of shoes must have felt for each other on that evening. There was at least as much vanity in the sturdy industry as in the strenuous idleness, for our shoemaker is a man of substance, he employs three journeymen, two lame, and one a dwarf, so that his shop looks like a hospital; he has purchased the lease of his commodious dwelling—some even say that he has bought it out and out; and he has only one pretty daughter, a light, delicate, fair-haired girl of fourteen, the champion, protectress, and playfellow of every brat under three years old, whom she jumps, dances, dandles, and feeds all day long. A very attractive person is that child-loving girl. I have never seen any one in her station who possessed so thoroughly that undefinable charm, the lady-look. See her on a Sunday in her simplicity and her white frock, and she might pass for an earl's daughter. She likes flowers too, and has a profusion of white stocks under her window, as pure and delicate as herself.

The first house on the opposite side of the way is the blacksmith's; a gloomy dwelling, where the sun never seems to shine; dark and smoky within and without, like a forge. The blacksmith is a high officer in our little state, nothing less than a constable; but, alas! alas! when tumults arise, and the constable is called for, he will commonly be found in the thickest of the fray. Lucky would it be for his wife and her eight children if there were no public-house in the land: an inveterate inclination to enter those bewitching doors is Mr. Constable's only fault.

Next to this official dwelling is a spruce brick tenement, red, high, and narrow, boasting, one above another, three sash-windows, the only sash-windows in the village, with a clematis on one side and a rose on the other, tall and narrow like itself. The slender mansion has a fine genteel look. The little parlour seems made for Hogarth's old maid and her stunted footboy; for tea and card-parties—it would just hold one table; for the rustle of faded silks, and the splendour of old china; for the delight of four-by-honours, and a little snug quiet scandal between the deals; for affected gentility and real starvation. This should have been its destiny; but fate has been unpropitious: it belongs to a plump, merry, bustling dame, with four fat, rosy, noisy children, the very essence of vulgarity and plenty.

Then comes the village shop, like other village shops multifarious as a bazaar; a repository for bread, shoes, tea, cheese, tape, ribbons, and bacon; for everything, in short, except the one particular thing which you happen to want at the moment, and will be sure not to find. The people are civil and thriving, and frugal withal; they have let the upper part of their house to two young women (one of them is a pretty blue-eyed girl) who teach little children their A B C, and make caps and gowns for their mammas—parcel school-mistress, parcel mantua - maker. I believe they find adorning the body a more profitable vocation than adorning the mind.

Divided from the shop by a narrow yard, and opposite the shoemaker's, is a habitation of whose inmates I shall say nothing. A cottage—no—a miniature house, with many additions, little odds and ends of places, pantries, and what not; all angles, and of a charming in-and-outness; a little bricked court before one half, and a little flower-yard before the other; the walls, old and weather-stained, covered with hollyhocks, roses, honeysuckles, and a great

apricot-tree; the casements full of geraniums (ah, there is
our superb white cat peeping out from amongst them!); the
closets (our landlord has the assurance to call them rooms)
full of contrivances and corner cupboards; and the little
garden behind full of common flowers, tulips, pinks, lark-
spurs, peonies, stocks, and carnations, with an arbour of
privet, not unlike a sentry-box, where one lives in a delicious
green light, and looks out on the gayest of all gay flower-
beds. That house was built on purpose to show in what an
exceeding small compass comfort may be packed. Well,
I will loiter there no longer.

The next tenement is a place of importance, the Rose
Inn; a whitewashed building, retired from the road behind
its fine swinging sign, with a little bow-window room coming
out on one side, and forming, with our stable on the other,
a sort of open square, which is the constant resort of carts,
wagons, and return chaises. There are two carts there
now, and mine host is serving them with beer in his eternal
red waistcoat. He is a thriving man and a portly, as his
waistcoat attests, which has been twice let out within this
twelvemonth. Our landlord has a stirring wife, a hopeful
son, and a daughter, the belle of the village; not so pretty
as the fair nymph of the shoe shop, and far less elegant, but
ten times as fine; all curl-papers in the morning, like a porcu-
pine, all curls in the afternoon, like a poodle, with more
flounces than curl - papers, and more lovers than curls.
Miss Phoebe is fitter for town than country; and, to do her
justice, she has a consciousness of that fitness, and turns her
step townward as often as she can. She is gone to B——
to-day with her last and principal lover, a recruiting sergeant
—a man as tall as Sergeant Kite, and as impudent. Some
day or other he will carry off Miss Phoebe.

In a line with the bow-window room is a low garden wall
belonging to a house under repair—the white house opposite
the collar-maker's shop, with four lime-trees before it, and
a wagon-load of bricks at the door. That house is the
plaything of a wealthy, well-meaning, whimsical person,
who lives about a mile off. He has a passion for brick and
mortar, and, being too wise to meddle with his own residence,
diverts himself with altering and realtering, improving
and reimproving, doing and undoing here. It is a perfect

Penelope's web. Carpenters and bricklayers have been
at work for these eighteen months, and yet I sometimes
stand and wonder whether anything has really been done.
One exploit in last June was, however, by no means equivocal. Our good neighbour fancied that the limes shaded
the rooms, and made them dark (there was not a creature
in the house but the workmen), so he had all the leaves
stripped from every tree. There they stood, poor miserable
skeletons, as bare as Christmas under the glowing midsummer sun. Nature revenged herself, in her own sweet
and gracious manner: fresh leaves sprang out, and at nearly
Christmas the foliage was as brilliant as when the outrage
was committed.

Next door lives a carpenter, 'famed ten miles round, and
worthy all his fame'; few cabinet - makers surpass him,
with his excellent wife, and their little daughter Lizzy, the
plaything and queen of the village, a child three years old
according to the register, but six in size and strength and
intellect, in power and in self-will. She manages everybody in the place, her schoolmistress included; turns the
wheeler's children out of their own little cart, and makes
them draw her; seduces cakes and lollipops from the very
shop window; makes the lazy carry her, the silent talk to
her, the grave romp with her; does anything she pleases;
is absolutely irresistible. Her chief attraction lies in her
exceeding power of loving, and her firm reliance on the love
and indulgence of others. How impossible it would be to
disappoint the dear little girl when she runs to meet you,
slides her pretty hand into yours, looks up gladly in your
face, and says, 'Come!' You must go: you cannot help
it. Another part of her charm is her singular beauty.
Together with a good deal of the character of Napoleon, she
has something of his square, sturdy, upright form, with the
finest limbs in the world, a complexion purely English, a
round laughing face, sunburnt and rosy, large merry blue
eyes, curling brown hair, and a wonderful play of countenance. She has the imperial attitudes too, and loves to stand
with her hands behind her, or folded over her bosom: and
sometimes, when she has a little touch of shyness, she clasps
them together on the top of her head, pressing down her
shining curls, and looking so exquisitely pretty! Yes, Lizzy

is queen of the village! She has but one rival in her dominions, a certain white greyhound called Mayflower, much her friend, who resembles her in beauty and strength, in playfulness, and almost in sagacity, and reigns over the animal world as she over the human. They are both coming with me, Lizzy and Lizzy's 'pretty May.' We are now at the end of the street; a cross-lane, a rope-walk, shaded with limes and oaks, and a cool clear pond overhung with elms, lead us to the bottom of the hill. There is still one house round the corner, ending in a picturesque wheeler's shop. The dwelling-house is more ambitious. Look at the fine flowered window-blinds, the green door with the brass knocker, and the somewhat prim but very civil person, who is sending off a labouring man with sirs and curtsies enough for a prince of the blood. Those are the curate's lodgings—apartments his landlady would call them: he lives with his own family four miles off, but once or twice a week he comes to his neat little parlour to write sermons, to marry, or to bury, as the case may require. Never were better or kinder people than his host and hostess: and there is a reflection of clerical importance about them, since their connection with the Church, which is quite edifying—a decorum, a gravity, a solemn politeness. Oh, to see the worthy wheeler carry the gown after his lodger on a Sunday, nicely pinned up in his wife's best handkerchief—or to hear him rebuke a squalling child or a squabbling woman! The curate is nothing to him. He is fit to be perpetual churchwarden.

We must now cross the lane into the shady rope-walk. That pretty white cottage opposite, which stands straggling at the end of the village in a garden full of flowers, belongs to our mason, the shortest of men, and his handsome, tall wife: he, a dwarf, with the voice of a giant; one starts when he begins to talk as if he were shouting through a speaking-trumpet; she, the sister, daughter, and granddaughter of a long line of gardeners, and no contemptible one herself. It is very magnanimous in me not to hate her; for she beats me in my own way, in chrysanthemums, and dahlias, and the like gauds. Her plants are sure to live; mine have a sad trick of dying, perhaps because I love them, 'not wisely, but too well,' and kill them with over-kindness. Half-way up the hill is another detached cottage, the residence of an officer and his beautiful family. That eldest boy, who is hanging over the gate, and looking with such intense childish admiration at my Lizzy, might be a model for a Cupid.

How pleasantly the road winds up the hill, with its broad green borders and hedgerows so thickly timbered! How finely the evening sun falls on that sandy excavated bank, and touches the farm-house on the top of the eminence! and how clearly defined and relieved is the figure of the man who is just coming down! It is poor John Evans, the gardener—an excellent gardener till about ten years ago, when he lost his wife, and became insane. He was sent to St. Luke's, and dismissed as cured; but his power was gone and his strength; he could no longer manage a garden, nor submit to the restraint, nor encounter the fatigue of regular employment, so he retreated to the workhouse, the pensioner and factotum of the village, amongst whom he divides his services. His mind often wanders, intent on some fantastic and impracticable plan, and lost to present objects; but he is perfectly harmless, and full of a childlike simplicity, a smiling contentedness, a most touching gratitude. Every one is kind to John Evans, for there is that about him which must be loved; and his unprotectedness, his utter defence-lessness, have an irresistible claim on every better feeling. I know nobody who inspires so deep and tender a pity; he improves all around him. He is useful, too, to the extent of his little power; will do anything, but loves gardening best, and still piques himself on his old arts of pruning fruit-trees and raising cucumbers. He is the happiest of men just now, for he has the management of a melon-bed—a melon-bed! —fie! What a grand pompous name was that for three melon-plants under a hand-light! John Evans is sure that they will succeed. We shall see: as the chancellor said, 'I doubt.'

We are now on the very brow of the eminence, close to the Hill House and its beautiful garden. On the outer edge of the paling, hanging over the bank that skirts the road, is an old thorn—such a thorn! The long sprays covered with snowy blossoms, so graceful, so elegant, so lightsome, and yet so rich! There only wants a pool under the thorn to give a still lovelier reflection, quivering and trembling, like a tuft of feathers, whiter and greener than the life, and more prettily mixed with the bright blue sky. There should indeed be a pool; but on the dark grass-plat, under the high bank, which is crowned by that magnificent plume, there is something that does almost as well—Lizzy and May-flower in the midst of a game at romps, 'making a sun-shine in the shady place'; Lizzy rolling, laughing, clapping her hands, and glowing like a rose; Mayflower playing about her like summer lightning, dazzling the eyes with her sudden turns, her leaps, her bounds, her attacks, and her escapes. She darts round the lovely little girl with the same momentary touch that the swallow skims over the water, and has exactly the same power of flight, the same match-less ease and strength and grace. What a pretty picture they would make; what a pretty foreground they do make to the real landscape! The road winding down the hill with a slight bend, like that in the High Street at Oxford; a wagon slowly ascending, and a horseman passing it at a full trot (ah! Lizzy, Mayflower will certainly desert you to have a gambol with that blood-horse!); half-way down, just at the turn, the red cottage of the lieutenant, covered with vines, the very image of comfort and content; farther down, on the opposite side, the small white dwelling of the little mason; then the limes and the rope-walk; then the village street, peeping through the trees, whose clustering tops hide all but the chimneys, and various roofs of the houses, and here and there some angle of a wall: farther on, the elegant town of B——, with its fine old church towers and spires; the whole view shut in by a range of chalky hills; and over every part of the picture, trees so profusely scattered that it appears like a woodland scene, with glades and villages intermixed. The trees are of all kinds and all hues, chiefly the finely shaped elm, of so bright and deep a green, the tips of whose high outer branches drop down with such a crisp and garland-like richness, and the oak, whose stately form is just now so splendidly adorned by the sunny colouring of the young leaves. Turning again up the hill, we find our-selves on that peculiar charm of English scenery, a green common divided by the road; the right side fringed by hedge-rows and trees, with cottages and farm-houses irregularly placed, and terminated by a double avenue of noble oaks;

the left, prettier still, dappled by bright pools of water, and islands of cottages and cottage gardens, and sinking gradually down to cornfields and meadows, and an old farm-house, with pointed roofs and clustered chimneys, looking out from its blooming orchard, and backed by woody hills. The common is itself the prettiest part of the prospect; half covered with low furze, whose golden blossoms reflect so intensely the last beams of the setting sun, and alive with cows and sheep, and two sets of cricketers: one of young men, surrounded by spectators, some standing, some sitting, some stretched on the grass, all taking a delighted interest in the game; the other, a merry group of little boys, at a humble distance, for whom even cricket is scarcely lively enough, shouting, leaping, and enjoying themselves to their hearts' content. But cricketers and country boys are too important persons in our village to be talked of merely as figures in the landscape. They deserve an individual introduction—an essay to themselves—and they shall have it. No fear of forgetting the good-humoured faces that meet us in our walks every day.

CHAPTER II

HANNAH

THE prettiest cottage on our village green is the little dwelling of Dame Wilson. It stands in a corner of the common, where the hedgerows go curving off into a sort of bay round a clear bright pond, the earliest haunt of the swallow. A deep, woody, green lane, such as Hobbema or Ruysdael might have painted, a lane that hints of nightingales, forms one boundary of the garden, and a sloping meadow the other; whilst the cottage itself, a low, thatched, irregular building, backed by a blooming orchard, and covered with honeysuckle and jasmine, looks like the chosen abode of snugness and comfort. And so it is.

Dame Wilson was a respected servant in a most respectable family, where she passed all the early part of her life, and which she quitted only on her marriage with a man of character and industry, and of that peculiar universality of genius which forms what is called, in country phrase, a handy fellow. He could do any sort of work; was thatcher, carpenter, bricklayer, painter, gardener, gamekeeper, 'everything by turns, and nothing long.' No job came amiss to him. He killed pigs, mended shoes, cleaned clocks, doctored cows, dogs, and horses, and even went as far as bleeding and drawing teeth in his experiments on the human subject. In addition to these multifarious talents, he was ready, obliging, and unfearing; jovial withal, and fond of good fellowship; and endowed with a promptness of resource which made him the general adviser of the stupid, the puzzled, and the timid. He was universally admitted to be the cleverest man in the parish; and his death, which happened about ten years ago, in consequence of standing in the water, drawing a pond for one neighbour, at a time when he was overheated by loading hay for another, made quite a gap in our village commonwealth. John Wilson had no rival, and has had no successor—for the

Robert Ellis, whom certain youngsters would fain exalt
to a co-partnery of fame, is simply nobody — a bell-
ringer, a ballad-singer — a troller of profane catches —
a fiddler — a bruiser — a loller on ale-house benches — a
teller of good stories — a mimic — a poet! What is all
this to compare with the solid parts of John Wilson?
Whose clock hath Robert Ellis cleaned?—whose windows
hath he mended?—whose dog hath he broken?—whose
pigs hath he ringed? —whose pond hath he fished? —
whose hay hath he saved?—whose cow hath he cured?—
whose calf hath he killed?—whose teeth hath he drawn?—
whom hath he bled? Tell me that, irreverent whipsters!
No! John Wilson is not to be replaced. He was missed
by the whole parish; and most of all, he was missed at home.
His excellent wife was left the sole guardian and protector
of two fatherless girls; one an infant at her knee, the other
a pretty handy lass about nine years old. Cast thus upon
the world, there must have been much to endure, much to
suffer; but it was borne with a smiling patience, a hopeful
cheeriness of spirit, and a decent pride, which seemed to
command success as well as respect in their struggle for
independence. Without assistance of any sort, by needlework, by washing and mending lace and fine linen, and
other skilful and profitable labours, and by the produce of
her orchard and poultry, Dame Wilson contrived to maintain herself and her children in their old comfortable home.
There was no visible change; she and the little girls were as
neat as ever; the house had still within and without the
same sunshiny cleanliness, and the garden was still famous
over all other gardens for its cloves, and stocks, and double
wallflowers. But the sweetest flower of the garden, the
joy and pride of her mother's heart, was her daughter
Hannah. Well might she be proud of her! At sixteen
Hannah Wilson was, beyond a doubt, the prettiest girl in
the village, and the best. Her beauty was quite in a different style from the common country rosebud—far more
choice and rare. Its chief characteristic was modesty. A
light youthful figure, exquisitely graceful and rapid in all
its movements; springy, elastic, and buoyant as a bird, and
almost as shy; a fair innocent face, with downcast blue
eyes, and smiles and blushes coming and going almost with

her thoughts; a low soft voice, sweet even in its mono-
syllables; a dress remarkable for neatness and propriety,
and borrowing from her delicate beauty an air of superiority
not its own;—such was the outward woman of Hannah.
Her mind was very like her person: modest, graceful,
gentle, affectionate, grateful, and generous above all. The
generosity of the poor is always a very real and fine thing;
they give what they want; and Hannah was of all poor
people the most generous. She loved to give; it was
her pleasure, her luxury. Rosy-cheeked apples, plums
with the bloom on them, nosegays of cloves and
blossomed myrtle — these were offerings which Hannah
delighted to bring to those whom she loved, or those
who had shown her kindness; whilst to such of her neighbours as needed other attentions than fruit and flowers,
she would give her time, her assistance, her skill; for Hannah
inherited her mother's dexterity in feminine employments,
with something of her father's versatile power. Besides
being an excellent laundress, she was accomplished in all
the arts of the needle, millinery, dressmaking, and plain
work, a capital cutter-out, an incomparable mender, and
endowed with a gift of altering, which made old things better
than new. She had no rival at a *rifacimento*, as half the
turned gowns on the common can witness. As a dairy-
woman, and a rearer of pigs and poultry, she was equally
successful: none of her ducks and turkeys ever died of
neglect or carelessness, or, to use the phrase of the poultry-
yard on such occasion, of 'ill-luck.' Hannah's fowls never
dreamed of sliding out of the world in such an ignoble way;
they all lived to be killed, to make a noise at their deaths
as chickens should do. She was also a famous 'scholar':
kept accounts, wrote bills, read letters, and answered them;
was a trusty accomptant, and a safe confidante. There was
no end to Hannah's usefulness or Hannah's kindness; and
her prudence was equal to either. Except to be kind or
useful, she never left her home; attended no fairs, or revels,
or mayings; went nowhere but to church; and seldom made
a nearer approach to rustic revelry than by standing at her
own garden gate, on a Sunday evening, with her little
sister in her hand, to look at the lads and lasses on the green.
In short, our village beauty had fairly reached her twentieth

year without a sweetheart, without the slightest suspicion of her having ever written a love-letter on her own account; when, all on a sudden, appearances changed. She was missing at the 'accustomed gate'; and one had seen a young man go into Dame Wilson's; and another had descried a trim elastic figure walking, not unaccompanied, down the shady lane. Matters were quite clear, Hannah had gotten a lover; and when poor little Susan, who, deserted by her sister, ventured to peep rather nearer to the gay group, was laughingly questioned on the subject, the hesitating 'No' and the half 'Yes' of the smiling child were equally conclusive.

Since the new Marriage Act,[1] we who belong to country magistrates have gained a priority over the rest of the parish in matrimonial news. We (the privileged) see on a workday the names which the sabbath announces to the generality. Many a blushing awkward pair hath our little lame clerk (a sorry Cupid!) ushered in between dark and light to stammer and hacker, to bow and curtsy, to sign or make a mark, as it pleases Heaven. One Saturday, at the usual hour, the limping clerk made his appearance; and walking through our little hall, I saw a fine athletic young man, the very image of health and vigour, mental and bodily, holding the hand of a young woman, who with her head half buried in a geranium in the window was turning bashfully away, listening, and yet not seeming to listen, to his tender whispers. The shrinking grace of that bending figure was not to be mistaken—'Hannah!' and she went aside with me, and a rapid series of questions and answers conveyed the story of the courtship. 'William was,' said Hannah, 'a journeyman hatter in B——. He had walked over one Sunday evening to see the cricketing, and then he came again. Her mother liked him. Everybody liked her William—and she had promised—she was going—was it wrong?' 'Oh, no! And where are you to live?' 'William has got a room in B——. He works for Mr. Smith, the rich hatter in the market-place, and Mr. Smith speaks of him—oh, so well! But William will not tell me where our room is. I suppose in some narrow street or lane,

---

[1] It is almost unnecessary to observe that this little story was written during the short life of that whimsical experiment in legislation.

which he is afraid I shall not like, as our common is so pleasant. He little thinks—anywhere——' She stopped suddenly; but her blush and her clasped hand finished the sentence—'anywhere with him!' 'And when is the happy day?' 'On Monday fortnight, madam,' said the bridegroom elect, advancing with the little clerk to summon Hannah to the parlour, 'the earliest day possible.' He drew her arm through his, and we parted.

The Monday fortnight was a glorious morning; one of those rare November days when the sky and the air are soft and bright as in April. 'What a beautiful day for Hannah!' was the first exclamation of the breakfast table. 'Did she tell you where they should dine?' 'No, ma'am; I forgot to ask.' 'I can tell you,' said the master of the house, with somewhat of good-humoured importance in his air, somewhat of the look of a man who, having kept a secret as long as it was necessary, is not sorry to get rid of the burthen. 'I can tell you: in London.' 'In London?' 'Yes. Your little favourite has been in high luck. She has married the only son of one of the best and richest men in B——, Mr. Smith the great hatter. It is quite a romance,' continued he. 'William Smith walked over one Sunday evening to see a match at cricket. He saw our pretty Hannah, and forgot to look at the cricketers. After having gazed his fill, he approached to address her, and the little damsel was off like a bird. William did not like her the less for that, and thought of her the more. He came again and again; and at last contrived to tame this wild dove, and even to get the *entrée* of the cottage. Hearing Hannah talk is not the way to fall out of love with her. So William, at last finding his case serious, laid the matter before his father, and requested his consent to the marriage. Mr. Smith was at first a little startled: but William is an only son, and an excellent son; and, after talking with me, and looking at Hannah (I believe her sweet face was the more eloquent advocate of the two), he relented; and having a spice of his son's romance, finding that he had not mentioned his situation in life, he made a point of its being kept secret till the wedding day. We have managed the business of settlements; and William, having discovered that his fair bride has some curiosity to see London (a curiosity, by the by, which I suspect she owes to you or poor Lucy), intends taking her thither for a fortnight. He will then bring her home to one of the best houses in B——, a fine garden, fine furniture, fine clothes, fine servants, and more money than she will know what to do with. Really, the surprise of Lord E——'s farmer's daughter, when, thinking she had married his steward, he brought her to Burleigh, and installed her as its mistress, could hardly have been greater. I hope the shock will not kill Hannah though, as is said to have been the case with that poor lady.' 'Oh, no! Hannah loves her husband too well. Anywhere with him!'

And I was right. Hannah has survived the shock. She is returned to B——, and I have been to call on her. I never saw anything so delicate and bridelike as she looked in her white gown and her lace mob, in a room light and simple, and tasteful and elegant, with nothing fine except some beautiful greenhouse plants. Her reception was a charming mixture of sweetness and modesty, a little more respectful than usual, and far more shamefaced! Poor thing! her cheeks must have pained her! But this was the only difference. In everything else she is still the same Hannah, and has lost none of her old habits of kindness and gratitude. She was making a handsome matronly cap, evidently for her mother, and spoke, even with tears, of her new father's goodness to her and to Susan. She would fetch the cake and wine herself, and would gather, in spite of all remonstrance, some of her choicest flowers as a parting nosegay. She did, indeed, just hint at her troubles with visitors and servants—how strange and sad it was! seemed distressed at ringing the bell, and visibly shrank from the sound of a double knock. But, in spite of these calamities, Hannah is a happy woman. The double rap was her husband's: and the glow on her cheek, and the smile of her lips and eyes when he appeared, spoke more plainly than ever: 'Anywhere with him!'

CHAPTER III

FROST AND THAW

January 23rd. At noon to-day I and my white greyhound, Mayflower, set out for a walk into a very beautiful world—a sort of silent fairyland—a creation of that matchless magician the hoar-frost. There had been just snow enough to cover the earth and all its colours with one sheet of pure and uniform white, and just time enough since the snow had fallen to allow the hedges to be freed of their fleecy load, and clothed with a delicate coating of rime. The atmosphere was deliciously calm; soft, even mild, in spite of the thermometer; no perceptible air, but a stillness that might almost be felt; the sky, rather grey than blue, throwing out in bold relief the snow-covered roofs of our village, and the rimy trees that rise above them, and the sun shining dimly as through a veil, giving a pale fair light, like the moon, only brighter. There was a silence, too, that might become the moon, as we stood at our little gate looking up the quiet street; a sabbath-like pause of work and play, rare on a workday; nothing was audible but the pleasant hum of frost, that low monotonous sound, which is perhaps the nearest approach that life and nature can make to absolute silence. The very wagons, as they come down the hill along the beaten track of crisp yellowish frost-dust, glide along like shadows; even May's bounding footsteps, at her height of glee and of speed, fall like snow upon snow.

But we shall hear noise enough presently: May has stopped at Lizzy's door! and Lizzy, as she sat on the window-sill with her bright rosy face laughing through the casement, has seen her and disappeared. She is coming. No! The key is turning in the door, and sounds of evil omen issue through the keyhole—sturdy 'Let me outs,' and 'I will goes,' mixed with shrill cries on May and on me from Lizzy, piercing through a low continuous harangue, of which the prominent parts are apologies, chilblains, sliding, broken bones, lollipops, rods, and gingerbread, from Lizzy's careful mother. 'Don't scratch the door, May! Don't roar so, my Lizzy! We'll call for you as we come back.' 'I'll go now! Let me out! I will go!' are the last words of Miss Lizzy. Mem.—Not to spoil that child—if I can help it. But I do think her mother might have let the poor little soul walk with us to-day. Nothing worse for children than coddling. Nothing better for chilblains than exercise. Besides, I don't believe she has any—and as to breaking her bones in sliding, I don't suppose there's a slide on the common. These murmuring cogitations have brought us up the hill, and half-way across the light and airy common, with its bright expanse of snow and its clusters of cottages, whose turf fires send such wreaths of smoke sailing up the air, and diffuse such aromatic fragrance around. And now comes the delightful sound of childish voices, ringing with glee and merriment almost from beneath our feet. Ah, Lizzy, your mother was right! They are shouting from that deep irregular pool, all glass now, where, on two long, smooth, liny slides, half a dozen ragged urchins are slipping along in tottering triumph. Half a dozen steps bring us to the bank right above them. May can hardly resist the temptation of joining her friends, for most of the varlets are of her acquaintance, especially the rogue who leads the slide— he with the brimless hat,whose bronzed complexion and white flaxen hair, reversing the usual lights and shadows of the human countenance, give so strange and foreign a look to his flat and comic features. This hobgoblin, Jack Rapley by name, is May's great crony; and she stands on the brink of the steep irregular descent, her black eyes fixed full upon him, as if she intended him the favour of jumping on his head. She does: she is down, and upon him; but Jack Rapley is not easily to be knocked off his feet. He saw her coming, and in the moment of her leap sprang dexterously off the slide on the rough ice, steadying himself by the shoulder of the next in the file, which unlucky follower, thus unexpectedly checked in his career, fell plump backwards, knocking down the rest of the line like a nest of card-houses. There is no harm done; but there they lie, roaring, kicking, sprawling, in every attitude of comic distress, whilst Jack Rapley and Mayflower, sole authors of this calamity, stand

apart from the throng, fondling, and coquetting, and compli-
menting each other, and very visibly laughing, May in her
black eyes, Jack in his wide close-shut mouth and his whole
monkey-face, at their comrades' mischances. I think, Miss
May, you may as well come up again, and leave Master
Rapley to fight your battles. He'll get out of the scrape.
He is a rustic wit, a sort of Robin Goodfellow, the sauciest,
idlest, cleverest, best-natured boy in the parish; always foremost in mischief, and always ready to do a good turn. The
sages of our village predict sad things of Jack Rapley, so
that I am sometimes a little ashamed to confess, before wise
people, that I have a lurking predilection for him (in common with other naughty ones), and that I like to hear him
talk to May, almost as well as she does. 'Come, May!' and
up she springs, as light as a bird. The road is gay now:
carts and post-chaises, and girls in red cloaks, and, afar off,
looking almost like a toy, the coach. It meets us fast and
soon. How much happier the walkers look than the riders
—especially the frost-bitten gentleman, and the shivering lady with the invisible face, sole passengers of that
commodious machine! Hooded, veiled, and bonneted as
she is, one sees from her attitude how miserable she would
look uncovered.

Another pond, and another noise of children. More
sliding? Oh, no! This is a sport of higher pretension.
Our good neighbour, the lieutenant, skating, and his own
pretty little boys, and two or three other four-year-old elves,
standing on the brink in an ecstasy of joy and wonder.
Oh, what happy spectators! And what a happy performer!
They admiring, he admired, with an ardour and sincerity
never excited by all the quadrilles and the spread-eagles
of the Seine and the Serpentine. He really skates well
though, and I am glad I came this way; for, with all the
father's feelings sitting gaily at his heart, it must still
gratify the pride of skill to have one spectator at that
solitary pond who has seen skating before.

Now we have reached the trees—the beautiful trees!
never so beautiful as to-day. Imagine the effect of a
straight and regular double avenue of oaks, nearly a mile
long, arching overhead, and closing into perspective like
the roof and columns of a cathedral, every tree and branch

encrusted with the bright and delicate congelation of hoar-frost, white and pure as snow, delicate and defined as carved ivory. How beautiful it is, how uniform, how various, how filling, how satiating to the eye and to the mind—above all, how melancholy! There is a thrilling awfulness, an intense feeling of simple power in that naked and colourless beauty, which falls on the earth like the thoughts of death—death pure, and glorious, and smiling—but still death. Sculpture has always the same effect on my imagination, and painting never. Colour is life. We are now at the end of this magnificent avenue, and at the top of a steep eminence commanding a wide view over four counties—a landscape of snow. A deep lane leads abruptly down the hill; a mere narrow cart-track, sinking between high banks clothed with fern, and furze, and low broom, crowned with luxuriant hedgerows, and famous for their summer smell of thyme. How lovely these banks are now—the tall weeds and the gorse fixed and stiffened in the hoar-frost, which fringes round the bright prickly holly, the pendent foliage of the bramble, and the deep orange leaves of the pollard oaks! Oh, this is rime in its loveliest form! And there is still a berry here and there on the holly, 'blushing in its natural coral' through the delicate tracery, still a stray hip or haw for the birds, who abound here always. The poor birds, how tame they are, how sadly tame! There is the beautiful and rare crested wren, 'that shadow of a bird,' as White of Selborne calls it, perched in the middle of the hedge, nestling as it were amongst the cold bare boughs, seeking, poor pretty thing, for the warmth it will not find. And there, farther on just under the bank, by the slender runlet, which still trickles between its transparent fantastic margin of thin ice, as if it were a thing of life—there, with a swift, scudding motion, flits, in short low flights, the gorgeous kingfisher, its magnificent plumage of scarlet and blue flashing in the sun, like the glories of some tropical bird. He is come for water to this little spring by the hill-side—water which even his long bill and slender head can hardly reach, so nearly do the fantastic forms of those garland-like icy margins meet over the tiny stream beneath. It is rarely that one sees the shy beauty so close or so long: and it is pleasant to see him in the grace and beauty of his natural liberty, the only way to look at a bird. We used, before we lived in a street, to fix a little board outside the parlour window, and cover it with bread-crumbs in the hard weather. It was quite delightful to see the pretty things come and feed, to conquer their shyness, and do away their mistrust. First came the more social tribes, 'the robin redbreast and the wren,' cautiously, suspiciously, picking up a crumb on the wing, with the little keen bright eye fixed on the window; then they would stop for two pecks; then stay till they were satisfied. The shyer birds, tamed by their example, came next; and at last one saucy fellow of a blackbird—a sad glutton, he would clear the board in two minutes—used to tap his yellow bill against the window for more. How we loved the fearless confidence of that fine frank-hearted creature! And surely he loved us. I wonder the practice is not more general. 'May! May! naughty May!' She has frightened away the kingfisher; and now, in her coaxing penitence, she is covering me with snow. 'Come, pretty May! it is time to go home.'

January 28th. We have had rain, and snow, and frost, and rain again; four days of absolute confinement. Now it is a thaw and a flood; but our light gravelly soil, and country boots, and country hardihood, will carry us through. What a dripping comfortless day it is! just like the last days of November: no sun, no sky, grey or blue; one low, overhanging, dark, dismal cloud, like London smoke: Mayflower is out coursing, too, and Lizzy gone to school. Never mind. Up the hill again! Walk we must. Oh, what a watery world to look back upon! Thames, Kennet, Loddon—all overflowed; our famous town, inland once, turned into a sort of Venice; C—— Park converted into an island; and the long range of meadows, from B—— to W——, one huge unnatural lake, with trees growing out of it. Oh, what a watery world! I will look at it no longer. I will walk on. The road is alive again. Noise is reborn. Wagons creak, horses splash, carts rattle, and pattens paddle through the dirt with more than their usual clink. The common has its old fine tints of green and brown, and its old variety of inhabitants—horses, cows, sheep, pigs, and donkeys. The ponds are unfrozen, except where some melancholy piece of melting ice floats sullenly on the water; and cackling geese and gabbling ducks have replaced the lieutenant and Jack Rapley. The avenue is chill and dark, the hedges are dripping, the lanes knee-deep, and all nature is in a state of 'dissolution and thaw.'

CHAPTER IV

A GREAT FARM-HOUSE

THESE are bad times for farmers. I am sorry for it. Independently of all questions of policy, as a mere matter of taste and of old association, it was a fine thing to witness the hearty hospitality and to think of the social happiness of a great farm-house. No situation in life seemed so richly privileged; none had so much power for good and so little for evil; it seemed a place where pride could not live, and poverty could not enter. These thoughts pressed on my mind the other day, in passing the green sheltered lane, overhung with trees like an avenue, that leads to the great farm at M——, where, ten or twelve years ago, I used to spend so many pleasant days. I could not help advancing a few paces up the lane, and then turning to lean over the gate, seemingly gazing on the rich undulating valley, crowned with woody hills, which, as I stood under the dark and shady arch, lay bathed in the sunshine before me, but really absorbed in thoughts of other times, in recollections of the old delights of that delightful place, and of the admirable qualities of its owners. How often I had opened the gate, and how gaily—certain of meeting a smiling welcome —and what a picture of comfort it was!

Passing up the lane, we used first to encounter a thick solid suburb of ricks, of all sorts, shapes, and dimensions. Then came the farm, like a town; a magnificent series of buildings, stables, cart-houses, cow-houses, granaries, and barns, that might hold half the corn of the parish, placed at all angles towards each other, and mixed with smaller habitations for pigs, dogs, and poultry. They formed, together with the old substantial farm-house, a sort of amphitheatre, looking over a beautiful meadow, which swept greenly and abruptly down into fertile enclosures, richly set with hedgerow timber, oak, and ash, and elm. Both the meadow and the farm-yard swarmed with inhabitants of the earth and of the air: horses, oxen, cows, calves, heifers, sheep, and pigs; beautiful greyhounds, all manner of poultry, a tame goat, and a pet donkey.

The master of this land of plenty was well fitted to preside over it: a thick, stout man, of middle height, and middle-aged, with a healthy, ruddy, square face, all alive with intelligence and good humour. There was a lurking jest in his eye, and a smile about the corners of his firmly closed lips, that gave assurance of good fellowship. His voice was loud enough to have hailed a ship at sea without the assistance of a speaking-trumpet, wonderfully rich and round in its tones, and harmonizing admirably with his bluff, jovial visage. He wore his dark shining hair combed straight over his forehead, and had a trick, when particularly merry, of stroking it down with his hand. The moment his hand approached his head, out flew a jest.

Besides his own great farm, the business of which seemed to go on like machinery, always regular, prosperous, and unfailing—besides this and two or three constant steward-ships, and a perpetual succession of arbitrations, in which, such was the influence of his acuteness, his temper, and his sturdy justice, that he was often named by both parties, and left to decide alone—in addition to these occupations, he was a sort of standing overseer and churchwarden; he ruled his own hamlet like a despotic monarch, and took a prime minister's share in the government of the large parish to which it was attached; and one of the gentlemen whose estates he managed being the independent member for an independent borough, he had every now and then a contested election on his shoulders. Even that did not discompose him. He had always leisure to receive his friends at home, or to visit them abroad; to take journeys to London, or make excursions to the seaside; was as punctual in pleasure as in business, and thought being happy and making happy as much the purpose of his life as getting rich. His great amusement was coursing. He kept several brace of capital greyhounds, so high-blooded that I remember when five of them were confined in five different kennels on account of their ferocity. The greatest of living painters once called a greyhound 'the line of beauty in perpetual motion.' Our friend's large dogs were a fine illustration of this remark. His old dog, Hector, for instance, for whom he refused a hundred guineas—what a superb dog was Hector!—a model of grace and symmetry, necked and crested like an Arabian, and bearing himself with a stateliness and gallantry which showed some 'conscience of his worth.' He was the largest dog I ever saw: but so finely proportioned that the most determined fault-finder could call him neither too long nor too heavy. There was not an inch too much of him. His colour was the purest white, entirely unspotted, except that his head was very regularly and richly marked with black. Hector was certainly a perfect beauty. But the little bitches, on which his master piqued himself still more, were not in my poor judgment so admirable. They were pretty little round, graceful things, sleek and glossy, and for the most part milk-white, with the smallest heads and the most dove-like eyes that were ever seen. There was a peculiar sort of innocent beauty about them, like that of a roly-poly child. They were as gentle as lambs, too; all the evil spirit of the family evaporated in the gentlemen. But, to my thinking, these pretty creatures were fitter for the parlour than the field. They were strong, certainly, excellently loined, cat-footed, and chested like a war-horse; but there was a want of length about them—a want of room, as the coursers say; something a little, a very little inclining to the clumsy: a dumpiness, a pointer look. They went off like an arrow from a bow; for the first hundred yards nothing could stand against them; then they began to flag, to find their weight too much for their speed, and to lose ground from the shortness of the stroke. Uphill, however, they were capital. There their compactness told. They turned with the hare and lost neither wind nor way in the sharpest ascent. I shall never forget one single-handed course of our good friend's favourite little bitch Helen, on W—— Hill. All the coursers were in the valley below, looking up to the hill-side as on a moving picture. I suppose she turned the hare twenty times on a piece of greensward not much bigger than an acre, and as steep as the roof of a house. It was an old hare, a famous hare, one that had baffled half the dogs in the country; but she killed him; and then, though almost as large as herself, took it up in her mouth, brought it to her master, and laid it down at his feet. Oh, how pleased he was! and what a pleasure it was to see his triumph! He did not always find W—— Hill so fortunate. It is a high steep hill, of a conical shape, encircled by a mountain road winding up to the summit like a corkscrew—a deep road dug out of the chalk, and fenced by high mounds on either side. The hares always make for this hollow way, as it is called, because it is too wide for a leap, and the dogs lose much time in mounting and descending the sharp acclivities. Very eager dogs, however, will sometimes dare the leap, and two of our good friend's favourite greyhounds perished in the attempt in two following years. They were found dead in the hollow way. After this he took a dislike to distant coursing meetings, and sported chiefly on his own beautiful farm.

His wife was like her husband, with a difference, as they say in heraldry. Like him in looks, only thinner and paler; like him in voice and phrase, only not so loud; like him in merriment and good humour; like him in her talent of welcoming and making happy, and being kind; like him in cherishing an abundance of pets, and in getting through with marvellous facility an astounding quantity of business and pleasure. Perhaps the quality in which they resembled each other most completely was the happy ease and serenity of behaviour so seldom found amongst people of the middle rank, who have usually a best manner and a worst, and whose best (that is, the studied, the company manner) is so very much the worst. She was frankness itself; entirely free from prickly defiance, or bristling self-love. She never took offence or gave it; never thought of herself or of what others would think of her; had never been afflicted with the besetting sins of her station, a dread of the vulgar, or an aspiration after the genteel. Those 'words of fear' had never disturbed her delightful heartiness.

Her pets were her cows, her poultry, her bees, and her flowers; chiefly her poultry, almost as numerous as the bees, and as various as the flowers. The farmyard swarmed with peacocks, turkeys, geese, tame and wild ducks, fowls, guinea-hens, and pigeons; besides a brood or two of favourite bantams in the green court before the door, with a little ridiculous strutter of a cock at their head, who imitated the magnificent demeanour of the great Tom of the barnyard, just as Tom in his turn copied the fierce bearing of that warlike and terrible biped the he-turkey. I am the least in the world afraid of a turkey-cock, and used to steer clear of the turkey as often as I could. Commend me to the peaceable vanity of that jewel of a bird the peacock, sweeping his gorgeous tail along the grass, or dropping it gracefully from some low-boughed tree, whilst he turns round his crested head with the air of a birthday belle, to see who admires him. What a glorious creature it is! How thoroughly content with himself and with all the world!

Next to her poultry our good farmer's wife loved her flower garden; and indeed it was of the very first water, the only thing about the place that was fine. She was a real, genuine florist: valued pinks, tulips, and auriculas for certain qualities of shape and colour, with which beauty has nothing to do; preferred black ranunculuses, and gave in to all those obliquities of a triple-refined taste by which the professed florist contrives to keep pace with the vagaries of the bibliomaniac. Of all odd fashions, that of dark, gloomy, dingy flowers appears to me the oddest. Your true connoisseurs now shall prefer a deep puce hollyhock to the gay pink blossoms which cluster round that splendid plant like a pyramid of roses. So did she. The nomenclature of her garden was more distressing still. One is never thoroughly sociable with flowers till they are naturalized, as it were, christened, provided with decent, homely, well-wearing English names. Now her plants had all sorts of heathenish appellations, which—no offence to her learning —always sounded wrong. I liked the bees' garden best, the plot of ground immediately round their hives, filled with common flowers for their use, and literally 'redolent of sweets.' Bees are insects of great taste in every way, and seem often to select for beauty as much as for flavour. They have a better eye for colour than the florist. The butterfly is also a dilettante. Rover though he be, he generally prefers the blossoms that become him best. What a pretty picture it is, in a sunshiny autumn day, to see a bright spotted butterfly, made up of gold and purple and splendid brown, swinging on the rich flower of the china-aster!

To come back to our farm. Within doors everything

went as well as without. There were no fine misses sitting before the piano, and mixing the alloy of their new-fangled tinsel with the old sterling metal; nothing but an only son excellently brought up, a fair slim youth, whose extraordinary and somewhat pensive elegance of mind and manner was thrown into fine relief by his father's loud hilarity, and harmonized delightfully with the smiling kindness of his mother. His Spensers and Thomsons, too, looked well amongst the hyacinths and geraniums that filled the windows of the little snug room in which they usually sat; a sort of afterthought, built at an angle from the house, and looking into the farmyard. It was closely packed with favourite arm-chairs, favourite sofas, favourite tables, and a sideboard decorated with the prize cups and collars of the greyhounds, and generally loaded with substantial work-baskets, jars of flowers, great pyramids of home-made cakes, and sparkling bottles of gooseberry wine, famous all over the country. The walls were covered with portraits of half a dozen greyhounds, a brace of spaniels, as large as life, an old pony, and the master and mistress of the house in half-length. She as unlike as possible, prim, mincing, delicate, in lace and satin; he so staringly and ridiculously like, that when the picture fixed its good-humoured eyes upon you as you entered the room, you were almost tempted to say, How d' ye do? Alas! the portraits are now gone, and the originals. Death and distance have despoiled that pleasant home. The garden has lost its smiling mistress; the greyhounds their kind master; and new people, new manners, and new cares have taken possession of the old abode of peace and plenty—the great farm-house.

CHAPTER V

LUCY

ABOUT a twelvemonth ago we had the misfortune to lose a very faithful and favourite female servant, one who has spoiled us for all others. Nobody can expect to meet with two Lucys. We all loved Lucy—poor Lucy! She did not die—she only married; but we were so sorry to part with her, that her wedding, which was kept at our house, was almost as tragical as a funeral, and from pure regret and affection we sum up her merits, and bemoan our loss, just as if she had really departed this life.

Lucy's praise is a most fertile theme; she united the pleasant and amusing qualities of a French soubrette with the solid excellence of an Englishwoman of the old school, and was good by contraries. In the first place, she was exceedingly agreeable to look at; remarkably pretty. She lived in our family eleven years; but, having come to us very young, was still under thirty, just in full bloom, and a very brilliant bloom it was. Her figure was rather tall and rather large, with delicate hands and feet, and a remarkable ease and vigour in her motions: I never saw any woman walk so fast or so well. Her face was round and dimpled, with sparkling grey eyes, black eyebrows and eyelashes, a profusion of dark hair, very red lips, very white teeth, and a complexion that entirely took away the look of vulgarity which the breadth and flatness of her face might otherwise have given. Such a complexion, so pure, so finely grained, so healthily fair, with such a sweet rosiness, brightening and varying like her dancing eyes whenever she spoke or smiled! When silent, she was almost pale; but, to confess the truth, she was not often silent. Lucy liked talking, and everybody liked to hear her talk. There is always great freshness and originality in an uneducated and quick-witted person, who surprises one continually by unsuspected knowledge or amusing ignorance; and Lucy had a real talent for conversation. Her light and pleasant temper, her cleverness, her universal kindness, and the admirable address, or, rather, the excellent feeling, with which she contrived to unite the most perfect respect with the most cordial and affectionate interest, gave a singular charm to her prattle. No confidence or indulgence—and she was well tried with both—ever made her forget herself for a moment. All our friends used to loiter at the door or in the hall to speak to Lucy, and they miss her, and ask for her, as if she were really one of the family. She was not less liked by her equals. Her constant simplicity and right-mindedness kept her always in her place with them as with us; and her gaiety and good humour made her a most welcome visitor in every shop and cottage round. She had another qualification for village society—she was an incomparable gossip, had a rare genius for picking up news, and great liberality in its diffusion. Births, deaths, marriages, casualties, quarrels, battles, scandal—nothing came amiss to her. She could have furnished a weekly paper from her own stores of facts without once resorting for assistance to the courts of law or the two Houses of Parliament. She was a very charitable reporter too; threw her own sunshine into the shady places, and would hope and doubt as long as either was possible. Her fertility of intelligence was wonderful; and so early! Her news had always the bloom on it: there was no being beforehand with Lucy. It was a little mortifying when one came prepared with something very recent and surprising, something that should have made her start with astonishment, to find her fully acquainted with the story, and able to furnish you with twenty particulars that you had never heard of. But this evil had its peculiar compensation. By Lucy's aid I passed with everybody, but Lucy herself, for a woman of great information, an excellent authority, an undoubted reference in all matters of gossip. Now I lag miserably behind the time; I never hear of a death till after the funeral, nor of a wedding till I read it in the papers; and, when people talk of reports and rumours, they undo me. I should be obliged to run away from the tea-tables, if I had not taken the resolution to look wise and say nothing, and live on my old reputation. Indeed, even now, Lucy's fund is not entirely exhausted; things have not quite done happening. I know nothing new; but my knowledge of bygone passages is absolute; I can prophesy past events like a gipsy.

Scattered amongst her great merits, Lucy had a few small faults, as all persons should have. She had occasionally an aptness to take offence where none was intended, and then the whole house bore audible testimony to her displeasure: she used to scour through half a dozen doors in a minute, for the mere purpose of banging them after her. She had rather more fears than were quite convenient of ghosts and witches, and thunder, and earwigs, and various other real and unreal sights and sounds, and thought nothing of rousing half the family, in the middle of the night, at the first symptom of a thunderstorm, or an apparition. She had a terrible genius for music, and a tremendous, powerful, shrill, high voice. Oh, her door-clapping was nothing to her singing! it rang through one's head like the screams of a peacock. Lastly, she was a sad flirt; she had about twenty lovers whilst she lived with us, probably more, but upwards of twenty she acknowledged. Her master, who watched with great amusement this uninterrupted and intricate succession of favourites, had the habit of calling her by the name of the reigning beau—Mrs. Charles, Mrs. John, Mrs. Robert; so that she has answered in her time to as many masculine appellations as would serve to supply a large family with a 'commodity of good names.' Once he departed from this custom, and called her ' Jenny Dennison.' On her inquiring the reason, he showed her *Old Mortality*, and asked if she could not guess. 'Dear me!' said she; 'why, Jenny Dennison had only two!' Amongst Lucy's twenty were three one-eyed lovers, like the three one-eyed calenders in the *Arabian Nights*. They were much about the same period, nearly contemporaries, and one of them had nearly carried off the fair Helen. If he had had two eyes, his success would have been certain. She said yes and no, and yes again; he was a very nice young man—but that one eye—that unlucky one eye—and the being rallied on her three calenders! There was no getting over that one eye: she said no once more, and stood firm. And yet the pendulum might have continued to vibrate many times longer, had it not been fixed by the athletic charms of a gigantic London tailor, a superb man

really: black-haired, black-eyed, six feet high, and large in
proportion. He came to improve the country fashions,
and fixed his shop-board in a cottage so near us that his
garden was only divided from our lawn by a plantation full
of acacias and honeysuckles, where 'the air smelt wooingly.'
It followed, of course, that he should make love to Lucy,
and that Lucy should listen. All was speedily settled; as
soon as he should be established in a good business, which,
from his incomparable talent at cutting out, nobody could
doubt, they were to be married. But they had not calculated on the perversity of country taste; he was too good a
workman; his suits fitted over-well; his employers missed
certain accustomed awkwardnesses and redundancies which
passed for beauties; besides, the stiffness and tightness
which distinguished the new coat of the *ancien régime* were
wanting in the make of this daring innovator. The shears
of our Bond Street cutter were as powerful as the wooden
sword of Harlequin; he turned his clowns into gentlemen,
and their brother clodhoppers laughed at them, and they
were ashamed. So the poor tailor lost his customers and
his credit; and, just as he had obtained Lucy's consent to
the marriage, he walked off one fair morning, and was never
heard of more. Lucy's absorbing feeling on this catastrophe
was astonishment, pure unmixed astonishment! One would
have thought that she considered fickleness as a female
privilege, and had never heard of a man deserting a woman
in her life. For three days she could only wonder; then
came great indignation, and a little, a very little grief, which
showed itself not so much in her words, which were chiefly
such disclaimers as 'I don't care!' 'Very lucky!' 'Happy
escape!' and so on, as in her goings and doings, her aversion
to the poor acacia grove, and even to the sight and smell of
honeysuckles, her total loss of memory, and above all, in
the distaste she showed to new conquests. She paid her
faithless suitor the compliment of remaining loverless for
three weary months; and even when she relented a little,
she admitted no fresh adorer, nothing but an old hanger-on;
one not quite discarded during the tailor's reign; one who
had dangled after her during the long courtship of the three
calenders; one who was the handiest and most complaisant
of wooers, always ready to fill up any interval, like a book,

which can be laid aside when company comes in, and resumed a month afterwards at the very page and line where
the reader left off. I think it was an affair of amusement
and convenience on both sides. Lucy never intended to
marry this commodious stopper of love-gaps; and he,
though he courted her for ten mortal years, never made a
direct offer, till after the banns were published between her
and her present husband: then, indeed, he said he was sorry
—he had hoped—was it too late? and so forth. Ah! his
sorrow was nothing to ours, and, when it came to the point,
nothing to Lucy's. She cried every day for a fortnight, and
had not her successor in office, the new housemaid, arrived,
I do really believe that this lover would have shared the
fate of the many successors to the unfortunate tailor.

I hope that her choice has been fortunate: it is certainly
very different from what we all expected. The happy man
had been a neighbour (not on the side of the acacia-trees),
and on his removal to a greater distance the marriage took
place. Poor dear Lucy! her spouse is the greatest possible
contrast to herself; ten years younger at the very least:
well-looking, but with no expression good or bad—I don't
think he could smile if he would—assuredly he never tries;
well made, but as stiff as a poker; I dare say he never ran
three yards in his life; perfectly steady, sober, honest, and
industrious; but so young, so grave, so dull! one of your
'demure boys,' as Falstaff calls them, 'that never come to
proof.' You might guess a mile off that he was a schoolmaster, from the swelling pomposity of gait, the solemn
decorum of manner, the affectation of age and wisdom,
which contrast so oddly with his young unmeaning face.
The moment he speaks you are certain. Nobody but a
village pedagogue ever did or ever could talk like Mr.
Brown—ever displayed such elaborate politeness, such a
study of phrases, such choice words and long words, and
fine words and hard words! He speaks by the book—
the spelling-book, and is civil after the fashion of the *Polite
Letter-Writer*. He is so entirely without tact, that he
does not in the least understand the impression produced by
his wife's delightful manners, and interrupts her perpetually
to speechify and apologize, and explain and amend. He is
fond of her, nevertheless, in his own cold slow way, and

proud of her, and grateful to her friends, and a very good
kind of young man altogether; only that I cannot quite
forgive him for taking Lucy away in the first place, and
making her a schoolmistress in the second. She a schoolmistress, a keeper of silence, a maintainer of discipline,
a scolder, a punisher! Ah! she would rather be scolded
herself; it would be a far lighter punishment. Lucy likes
her vocation as little as I do. She has not the natural love
of children which would reconcile her to the evils they cause;
and she has a real passion for cleanliness, a fiery spirit of
dispatch, which cannot endure the dust and litter created
by the little troop on the one hand, or their tormenting
slowness and stupidity on the other. She was the quickest
and neatest of workwomen, piqued herself on completing a
shirt or a gown sooner and better than seemed possible,
and was scandalized at finding such talents degraded to the
ignoble occupations of tacking a quarter of a yard of hem-
ming for one, pinning half a seam for another, picking
out the crooked stitching of a third, and working over the
weak irregular burst-out buttonhole of a fourth. When
she first went to S—— she was strongly tempted to do all
the work herself. 'The children would have liked it,' said
she, 'and really I don't think the mothers would have
objected; they care for nothing but marking. There are
seven girls now in the school working samplers to be framed.
"Such a waste of silk, and time, and trouble!" I said to Mrs.
Smith, and Mrs. Smith said to me——' Then she recounted
the whole battle of the samplers, and her defeat; and then
she sent for one which, in spite of her declaration that
her girls never finished anything, was quite completed
(probably with a good deal of her assistance), and of which,
notwithstanding her rational objection to its uselessness,
Lucy was not a little proud. She held it up with great
delight, pointed out all the beauties, selected her own
favourite parts, especially a certain square rosebud, and
the landscape at the bottom; and finally pinned it against
the wall, to show the effect that it would have when framed.
Really, that sampler was a superb thing in its way. First
came a plain pink border; then a green border, zigzag; then
a crimson, wavy; then a brown, of a different and more
complicated zigzag; then the alphabet, great and small, in

every colour of the rainbow, followed by a row of figures
flanked on one side by a flower, name unknown, tulip,
poppy, lily—something orange or scarlet, or orange-scarlet;
on the other by the famous rosebud; then divers sentences,
religious and moral—Lucy was quite provoked with me for
not being able to read them; I dare say she thought in her
heart that I was as stupid as any of her scholars! but never
was MS. so illegible, not even my own, as the print-work
of that sampler; then, last and finest, the landscape, in all
its glory.   It occupied the whole narrow line at the bottom,
and was composed with great regularity.   In the centre was
a house of a bright scarlet, with yellow windows, a green
door and a blue roof: on one side, a man with a dog; on the
other, a woman with a cat—this is Lucy's information;
I should never have guessed that there was any difference,
except in colour, between the man and the woman, the dog
and the cat; they were in form, height, and size alike to a
thread; the man grey, the woman pink, his attendant white,
and hers black.   Next to these figures, on either side, rose
two fir-trees from two red flower-pots, nice little round
bushes of a bright green intermixed with brown stitches,
which Lucy explained, not to me: 'Don't you see the fir-
cones, sir?   Don't you remember how fond she used to be
of picking them up in her little basket at the dear old place?
Poor thing, I thought of her all the time that I was working
them!   Don't you like the fir-cones?'   After this, I looked
at the landscape almost as loving as Lucy herself.

With all her dislike to keeping school, the dear Lucy
seems happy.   In addition to the merciful spirit of conformity, which shapes the mind to the situation, whatever that
may be, she has many sources of vanity and comfort—
her house above all.   It is a very respectable dwelling,
finely placed on the edge of a large common, close to a
high road, with a pretty flower-court before it, shaded by
four horse-chestnuts cut into arches, a sashed window on
either side of the door, and on the door a brass knocker,
which, being securely nailed down, serves as a quiet, peaceable
handle for all goers, instead of the importunate and noisy
use for which it was designed.   Jutting out at one end of
the court is a small stable; retiring back at the other, a
large schoolroom, and behind, a yard for children, pigs,

and poultry, a garden and an arbour. The inside is full
of comfort; miraculously clean and orderly for a village
school, and with a little touch of very allowable finery, in the
gay window curtains, the cupboard full of pretty china, the
handsome chairs, the bright mahogany table, the shining
tea-urn and brilliant tea-tray, that decorate the parlour.
What a pleasure it is to see Lucy presiding in that parlour,
in all the glory of her honest affection and warm hospitality,
making tea for the three guests whom she loves best in the
world, vaunting with courteous pride her home-made bread
and her fresh butter, yet thinking nothing good enough for
the occasion; smiling and glowing, and looking the very
image of beautiful happiness—such a moment almost
consoles us for losing her.

Lucy's pleasure is in her house; mine is in its situation.
The common on which it stands is one of a series of heathy
hills, or rather a high table-land, pierced in one part by a
ravine of marshy ground filled with alder bushes, growing
larger and larger as the valley widens, and at last mixing
with the fine old oaks of the forest of P——. Nothing
can be more delightful than to sit on the steep brow of the
hill, amongst the fragrant heath flowers, the bluebells and
the wild thyme, and look upon the sea of trees spreading
out beneath us; the sluggish water just peeping from amid
the alders, giving brightly back the bright blue sky; and,
farther down, herds of rough ponies, and of small stunted
cows, the wealth of the poor, coming up from the forest.
I have sometimes seen two hundred of these cows together,
each belonging to a different person, and distinguishing and
obeying the call of its milker. All the boundaries of this
heath are beautiful. On one side is the hanging coppice,
where the lily of the valley grows so plentifully amongst
broken ridges and fox-earths, and the roots of pollard-trees.
On another are the immense fir plantations of Mr. B——,
whose balmy odour hangs heavily in the air, or comes
sailing on the breeze like smoke across the landscape.
Farther on, beyond the pretty parsonage-house, with its
short avenue, its fish-ponds, and the magnificent poplars,
which form a landmark for many miles round, rise the
rock-like walls of the old city of S——, one of the most
perfect Roman remains now existing in England. The

wall can be traced all round, rising sometimes to a height of twenty feet, over a deep narrow slip of meadow land, once the ditch, and still full of aquatic flowers. The ground within rises level with the top of the wall, which is of grey stone, crowned with the finest forest trees, whose roots seem interlaced with the old masonry, and covered with wreaths of ivy, brambles, and a hundred other trailing plants. Close by one of the openings which mark the site of the gates is a graduated terrace, called by antiquaries the Amphitheatre, which commands a rich and extensive view, and is backed by the village church, and an old farm-house—the sole buildings in that once populous city, whose streets are now traced only by the blighted and withered appearance of the ripening corn. Roman coins and urns are often ploughed up there, and it is a favourite haunt of the lovers of 'hoar antiquity.' But the beauty of the place is independent even of its noble associations. The very heart expands in the deep verdure and perfect loneliness of that narrow winding valley, fenced on one side by steep coppices or its own tall irregular hedge, on the other by the venerable crag-like wall, whose proud coronet of trees, its jutting ivy, its huge twisted thorns, its briery festoons, and the deep caves where the rabbits burrow, make the old bulwark seem no work of man, but a majestic piece of nature. As a picture it is exquisite. Nothing can be finer than the mixture of those varied greens, so crisp and life-like, with the crumbling grey stone; nothing more perfectly in harmony with the solemn beauty of the place than the deep cooings of the wood-pigeons, who abound in the walls. I know no pleasure so intense, so soothing, so apt to bring sweet tears into the eyes, or to awaken thoughts that 'lie too deep for tears,' as a walk round the old city on a fine summer evening. A ride to S—— was always delightful to me, even before it became the residence of Lucy; it is now my prime festival.

CHAPTER VI

THE FIRST PRIMROSE

March 6th. Fine March weather: boisterous, blustering, much wind and squalls of rain; and yet the sky, where the clouds are swept away, deliciously blue, with snatches of sunshine, bright, and clear, and healthful, and the roads, in spite of the slight glittering showers, crisply dry. Altogether the day is tempting, very tempting. It will not do for the dear common, that windmill of a walk; but the close sheltered lanes at the bottom of the hill which keep out just enough of the stormy air, and let in all the sun, will be delightful. Past our old house, and round by the winding lanes, and the workhouse, and across the Lea, and so into the turnpike road again—that is our route for to-day. Forth we set, Mayflower and I, rejoicing in the sunshine, and still more in the wind, which gives such an intense feeling of existence, and, co-operating with brisk motion, sets our blood and our spirits in a glow. For mere physical pleasure there is nothing perhaps equal to the enjoyment of being drawn, in a light carriage, against such a wind as this, by a blood horse at his height of speed. Walking comes next to it; but walking is not quite so luxurious or so spiritual, not quite so much what one fancies of flying or being carried above the clouds in a balloon.

Nevertheless, a walk is a good thing; especially under this southern hedgerow, where nature is just beginning to live again: the periwinkles, with their starry-blue flowers, and their shining myrtle-like leaves, garlanding the bushes; woodbines and elder-trees pushing out their small swelling buds; and grasses and mosses springing forth in every variety of brown and green. Here we are at the corner where four lanes meet, or rather where a passable road of stones and gravel crosses an impassable one of beautiful but treacherous turf, and where the small white farm-house, scarcely larger than a cottage, and the well-stocked rick-

yard behind, tell of comfort and order, but leave all un-
guessed the great riches of the master. How he became so
rich is almost a puzzle; for, though the farm be his own, it
is not large; and though prudent and frugal on ordinary
occasions, Farmer Barnard is no miser. His horses, dogs,
and pigs are the best kept in the parish. May herself,
although her beauty be injured by her fatness, half envies
the plight of his bitch Fly: his wife's gowns and shawls
cost as much again as any shawls or gowns in the
village; his dinner parties (to be sure they are not frequent)
display twice the ordinary quantity of good things—two
couples of ducks, two dishes of green peas, two turkey
poults, two gammons of bacon, two plum-puddings; moreover, he keeps a single-horse chaise, and has built and
endowed a Methodist chapel. Yet is he the richest man in
these parts. Everything prospers with him. Money drifts
about him like snow. He looks like a rich man. There is
a sturdy squareness of face and figure; a good-humoured
obstinacy; a civil importance. He never boasts of his
wealth, or gives himself undue airs; but nobody can meet
him at market or vestry without finding out immediately
that he is the richest man there. They have no child to
all this money; but there is an adopted nephew, a fine
spirited lad, who may, perhaps, some day or other, play
the part of a fountain to the reservoir.

Now turn up the wide road till we come to the open
common, with its park-like trees, its beautiful stream,
wandering and twisting along, and its rural bridge. Here
we turn again, past that other white farm-house, half
hidden by the magnificent elms which stand before it. Ah!
riches dwell not there; but there is found the next best
thing—an industrious and light-hearted poverty. Twenty
years ago, Rachel Hilton was the prettiest and merriest
lass in the country. Her father, an old gamekeeper, had
retired to a village ale-house, where his good beer, his social
humour, and his black-eyed daughter brought much custom.
She had lovers by the score; but Joseph White, the dashing
and lively son of an opulent farmer, carried off the fair
Rachel. They married and settled here, and here they live
still, as merrily as ever, with fourteen children of all ages
and sizes, from nineteen years to nineteen months, working

harder than any people in the parish, and enjoying themselves more. I would match them for labour and laughter
against any family in England. She is a blithe jolly dame,
whose beauty has amplified into comeliness: he is tall, and
thin, and bony, with sinews like whipcord, a strong lively
voice, a sharp weather-beaten face, and eyes and lips that
smile and brighten when he speaks into a most contagious
hilarity. They are very poor, and I often wish them
richer; but I don't know—perhaps it might put them out.

Quite close to Farmer White's is a little ruinous cottage,
whitewashed once, and now in a sad state of betweenity,
where dangling stockings and shirts, swelled by the wind,
drying in a neglected garden, give signal of a washerwoman.
There dwells, at present, in single blessedness, Betty Adams,
the wife of our sometimes gardener. I never saw any one
who so much reminded me in person of that lady whom
everybody knows, Mistress Meg Merrilies — as tall, as
grizzled, as stately, as dark, as gipsy-looking, bonneted
and gowned like her prototype, and almost as oracular.
Here the resemblance ceases. Mrs. Adams is a perfectly
honest, industrious, painstaking person, who earns a good
deal of money by washing and charring, and spends it in
other luxuries than tidiness—in green tea, and gin and snuff.
Her husband lives in a great family, ten miles off. He is
a capital gardener—or rather he would be so if he were
not too ambitious. He undertakes all things, and finishes
none. But a smooth tongue, a knowing look, and a great
capacity of labour, carry him through. Let him but like
his ale and his master, and he will do work enough for four.
Give him his own way, and his full quantum, and nothing
comes amiss to him.

Ah, May is bounding forward! Her silly heart leaps at
the sight of the old place—and so, in good truth, does mine.
What a pretty place it was—or rather, how pretty I thought
it! I suppose I should have thought any place so where I
had spent eighteen happy years. But it was really pretty.
A large, heavy, white house, in the simplest style, surrounded
by fine oaks and elms, and tall massy plantations shaded
down into a beautiful lawn by wild overgrown shrubs,
bowery acacias, ragged sweet-briers, promontories of dog-
wood, and Portugal laurel, and bays overhung by laburnum

and bird-cherry; a long piece of water letting light into the picture, and looking just like a natural stream, the banks as rude and wild as the shrubbery, interspersed with broom, and furze, and bramble, and pollard-oaks covered with ivy and honeysuckle: the whole enclosed by an old mossy park paling, and terminating in a series of rich meadows, richly planted. This is an exact description of the home which, three years ago, it nearly broke my heart to leave. What a tearing up by the root it was! I have pitied cabbage-plants and celery, and all transplantable things ever since; though, in common with them, and with other vegetables, the first agony of the transportation being over, I have taken such firm and tenacious hold of my new soil, that I would not for the world be pulled up again, even to be restored to the old beloved ground—not even if its beauty were undiminished, which is by no means the case; for in those three years it has thrice changed masters, and every successive possessor has brought the curse of improvement upon the place; so that between filling up the water to cure dampness, cutting down trees to let in prospects, planting to keep them out, shutting up windows to darken the inside of the house (by which means one end looks precisely as an eight of spades would do that should have the misfortune to lose one of his corner pips), and building colonnades to lighten the out, added to a general clearance of pollards, and brambles, and ivy, and honeysuckles, and park palings, and irregular shrubs, the poor place is so transmogrified, that if it had its old looking-glass, the water, back again, it would not know its own face. And yet I love to haunt round about it: so does May. Her particular attraction is a certain broken bank full of rabbit-burrows, into which she insinuates her long pliant head and neck, and tears her pretty feet by vain scratchings: mine is a warm sunny hedgerow, in the same remote field, famous for early flowers. Never was a spot more variously flowery; primroses yellow, lilac white, violets of either hue, cowslips, oxlips, arums, orchises, wild hyacinths, ground-ivy, pansies, strawberries, heartsease, formed a small part of the flora of that wild hedgerow. How profusely they covered the sunny open slope under the weeping birch, 'the lady of the woods'—and how often have I started to see the early

innocent brown snake, who loved the spot as well as I
did, winding along the young blossom, or rustling amongst
the fallen leaves! There are primrose leaves already, and
short green buds, but no flowers; not even in that furze
cradle so full of roots, where they used to blow as in a
basket. No, my May, no rabbits; no primroses! We may
as well get over the gate into the woody winding lane,
which will bring us home again.

Here we are, making the best of our way between the
old elms that arch so solemnly overhead, dark and sheltered
even now. They say that a spirit haunts this deep pool—
a white lady without a head. I cannot say that I have
seen her, often as I have paced this lane at deep midnight,
to hear the nightingales, and look at the glow-worms—
but there, better and rarer than a thousand ghosts, dearer
even than nightingales or glow-worms, there is a primrose,
the first of the year; a tuft of primroses, springing in yonder
sheltered nook, from the mossy roots of an old willow, and
living again in the clear bright pool. Oh, how beautiful
they are—three fully blown, and two bursting buds! How
glad I am I came this way! They are not to be reached.
Even Jack Rapley's love of the difficult and the unattainable
would fail him here: May herself could not stand on that
steep bank. So much the better. Who would wish to
disturb them? There they live in their innocent and
fragrant beauty, sheltered from the storms, and rejoicing in
the sunshine, and looking as if they could feel their happiness.
Who would disturb them? Oh, how glad I am I came this
way home!

CHAPTER VII

VIOLETING

March 27th. It is a dull grey morning, with a dewy feeling in the air; fresh, but not windy; cool, but not cold; the very day for a person newly arrived from the heat, the glare, the noise, and the fever of London, to plunge into the remotest labyrinths of the country, and regain the repose of mind, the calmness of heart, which has been lost in that great Babel. I must go violeting—it is a necessity—and I must go alone: the sound of a voice, even my Lizzy's, the touch of Mayflower's head, even the bounding of her elastic foot, would disturb the serenity of feeling which I am trying to recover. I shall go quite alone, with my little basket, twisted like a beehive, which I love so well, because *she* gave it to me, and kept sacred to violets and to those whom I love; and I shall get out of the high road the moment I can. I would not meet any one just now, even of those whom I best like to meet.

Ha! Is not that group—a gentleman on a blood horse, a lady keeping pace with him so gracefully and easily—see how prettily her veil waves in the wind created by her own rapid motion!—and that gay, gallant boy, on the gallant white Arabian, curvetting at their side, but ready to spring before them every instant—is not that chivalrous-looking party Mr. and Mrs. M—— and dear B——? No! the servant is in a different livery. It is some of the ducal family, and one of their young Etonians. I may go on. I shall meet no one now; for I have fairly left the road, and am crossing the Lea by one of those wandering paths, amidst the gorse, and the heath, and the low broom, which the sheep and lambs have made—a path turfy, elastic, thymy, and sweet, even at this season.

We have the good fortune to live in an unenclosed parish, and may thank the wise obstinacy of two or three sturdy farmers, and the lucky unpopularity of a ranting madcap lord of the manor, for preserving the delicious green patches, the islets of wilderness amidst cultivation, which form, perhaps, the peculiar beauty of English scenery. The common that I am passing now—the Lea, as it is called— is one of the loveliest of these favoured spots. It is a little sheltered scene, retiring, as it were, from the village; sunk amidst higher lands—hills would be almost too grand a word; edged on one side by one gay high road, and inter- sected by another; and surrounded by a most picturesque confusion of meadows, cottages, farms, and orchards; with a great pond in one corner, unusually bright and clear, giving a delightful cheerfulness and daylight to the picture. The swallows haunt that pond; so do the children. There is a merry group round it now; I have seldom seen it without one. Children love water, clear, bright, sparkling water; it excites and feeds their curiosity; it is motion and life.

The path that I am treading leads to a less lively spot, to that large heavy building on one side of the common, whose solid wings, jutting out far beyond the main body, occupy three sides of a square, and give a cold shadowy look to the court. On one side is a gloomy garden, with an old man digging in it, laid out in straight dark beds of vegetables—potatoes, cabbages, onions, beans; all earthy and mouldy as a newly dug grave. Not a flower or flower- ing shrub! Not a rose-tree or currant-bush! Nothing but for sober melancholy use. Oh, how different from the long irregular slips of the cottage gardens, with their gay bunches of polyanthuses and crocuses, their wallflowers sending sweet odours through the narrow casement, and their gooseberry-trees bursting into a brilliancy of leaf, whose vivid greenness has the effect of a blossom on the eye! Oh, how different! On the other side of this gloomy abode is a meadow of that deep intense emerald hue which denotes the presence of stagnant water, surrounded by willows at regular distances, and, like the garden, separated from the common by a wide moat-like ditch. That is the parish workhouse. All about it is solid, substantial, useful —but so dreary! so cold! so dark! There are children in the court, and yet all is silent. I always hurry past that place as if it were a prison. Restraint, sickness, age, extreme poverty, misery which I have no power to remove or alleviate—these are the ideas, the feelings, which the sight of those walls excites; yet, perhaps, if not certainly, they contain less of that extreme desolation than the morbid fancy is apt to paint. There will be found order, cleanliness, food, clothing, warmth, refuge for the homeless, medicine and attendance for the sick, rest and sufficiency for old age, and sympathy, the true and active sympathy which the poor show to the poor, for the unhappy. There may be worse places than a parish workhouse—and yet I hurry past it. The feeling, the prejudice, will not be controlled.

The end of the dreary garden edges off into a close sheltered lane, wandering and winding, like a rivulet, in gentle 'sinuosities' (to use a word once applied by Mr. Wilberforce to the Thames at Henley), amidst green meadows, all alive with cattle, sheep, and beautiful lambs, in the very spring and pride of their tottering prettiness; or fields of arable land, more lively still with troops of stooping bean-setters, women and children, in all varieties of costume and colour; and ploughs and harrows, with their whistling boys and steady carters, going through, with a slow and plodding industry, the main business of this busy season. What work bean-setting is! What a reverse of the position assigned to man to distinguish him from the beasts of the field! Only think of stooping for six, eight, ten hours a day, drilling holes in the earth with a little stick, and then dropping in the beans one by one! They are paid according to the quantity they plant: and some of the poor women used to be accused of clumping them—that is to say, of dropping more than one bean into a hole. It seems to me, considering the temptation, that not to clump is to be at the very pinnacle of human virtue.

Another turn in the lane, and we come to the old house standing amongst the high elms—the old farm-house, which always, I don't know why, carries back my imagination to Shakespeare's days. It is a long, low, irregular building, with one room, at an angle from the house, covered with ivy, fine white-veined ivy; the first floor of the main building projecting and supported by oaken beams, and one of the windows below, with its old casement and long narrow panes, forming the half of a shallow hexagon. A porch, with seats in it, surmounted by a pinnacle, pointed roofs, and clustered chimneys, complete the picture. Alas! it is little else but a picture! The very walls are crumbling to decay under a careless landlord and a ruined tenant.

Now a few yards farther, and I reach the bank. Ah! I smell them already—their exquisite perfume steams and lingers in this moist heavy air. Through this little gate, and along the green south bank of this green wheat-field, and they burst upon me, the lovely violets, in tenfold loveliness! The ground is covered with them, white and purple, enamelling the short dewy grass, looking but the more vividly coloured under the dull, leaden sky. There they lie by hundreds, by thousands. In former years I have been used to watch them from the tiny green bud, till one or two stole into bloom. They never came on me before in such a sudden and luxuriant glory of simple beauty—and I do really owe one pure and genuine pleasure to feverish London! How beautifully they are placed, too, on this sloping bank, with the palm branches waving over them, full of early bees, and mixing their honeyed scent with the more delicate violet odour! How transparent and smooth and lusty are the branches, full of sap and life! And there, just by the old mossy root, is a superb tuft of primroses, with a yellow butterfly hovering over them, like a flower floating on the air. What happiness to sit on this tufty knoll, and fill my basket with the blossoms! What a renewal of heart and mind! To inhabit such a scene of peace and sweetness is again to be fearless, gay, and gentle as a child. Then it is that thought becomes poetry, and feeling religion. Then it is that we are happy and good. Oh, that my whole life could pass so, floating on blissful and innocent sensation, enjoying in peace and gratitude the common blessings of Nature, thankful above all for the simple habits, the healthful temperament, which render them so dear! Alas! who may dare expect a life of such happiness? But I can at least snatch and prolong the fleeting pleasure, can fill my basket with pure flowers, and my heart with pure thoughts; can gladden my little home with their sweetness; can divide my treasures with one, a dear one, who cannot seek them; can see them when I shut my eyes; and dream of them when I fall asleep.

CHAPTER VIII

THE TALKING LADY

BEN JONSON has a play called *The Silent Woman*, who turns out, as might be expected, to be no woman at all—nothing, as Master Slender said, but 'a great lubberly boy'; thereby, as I apprehend, discourteously presuming that a silent woman is a nonentity. If the learned dramatist, thus happily prepared and predisposed, had happened to fall in with such a specimen of female loquacity as I have just parted with, he might, perhaps, have given us a pendant to his picture in *The Talking Lady*. Pity but he had! He would have done her justice, which I could not at any time, least of all now: I am too much stunned; too much like one escaped from a belfry on a coronation day. I am just resting from the fatigue of four days' hard listening—four snowy, sleety, rainy days—days of every variety of falling weather, all of them too bad to admit the possibility that any petticoated thing, were she as hardy as a Scotch fir, should stir out—four days chained by 'sad civility' to that fireside, once so quiet, and again—cheering thought!—again I trust to be so, when the echo of that visitor's incessant tongue shall have died away.

The visitor in question is a very excellent and respectable elderly lady, upright in mind and body, with a figure that does honour to her dancing-master, a face exceedingly well preserved, wrinkled and freckled but still fair, and an air of gentility over her whole person, which is not the least affected by her out-of-fashion garb. She could never be taken for anything but a woman of family, and perhaps she could as little pass for any other than an old maid. She took us in her way from London to the west of England: and being, as she wrote, 'not quite well, not equal to much company, prayed that no other guest might be admitted, so that she might have the pleasure of our conversation all to herself' (*ours!* as if it were possible for any of us to

slide in a word edgewise!) 'and especially enjoy the gratification of talking over old times with the master of the
house, her countryman.' Such was the promise of her
letter, and to the letter it has been kept. All the news
and scandal of a large county forty years ago, and a
hundred years before, and ever since, all the marriages,
deaths, births, elopements, lawsuits, and casualties of her
own times, her father's, grandfather's, great-grandfather's,
nephews' and grand-nephews', has she detailed with a
minuteness, an accuracy, a prodigality of learning, a pro-
fuseness of proper names, a pedantry of locality, which
would excite the envy of a county historian, a king-at-
arms, or even a Scotch novelist. Her knowledge is astonishing; but the most astonishing part of all is how she came by
that knowledge. It should seem, to listen to her, as if, at
some time of her life, she must have listened herself; and
yet her countryman declares that, in the forty years he has
known her, no such event has occurred; and she knows
new news too! It must be intuition.

The manner of her speech has little remarkable. It is
rather old-fashioned and provincial, but perfectly ladylike, low, and gentle, and not seeming so fast as it is; like
the great pedestrians, she clears her ground easily, and
never seems to use any exertion; yet 'I would my horse had
the speed of her tongue, and so good a continuer.' She will
talk you sixteen hours a day for twenty days together, and
not deduct one poor five minutes for halts and baiting-time.
Talking, sheer talking, is meat and drink and sleep to her.
She likes nothing else. Eating is a sad interruption. For
the tea-table she has some toleration; but dinner, with its
clatter of plates and jingle of knives and forks, dinner is
her abhorrence. Nor are the other common pursuits of
life more in her favour. Walking exhausts the breath that
might be better employed. Dancing is a noisy diversion,
and singing is worse; she cannot endure any music, except
the long, grand, dull concerto, which nobody thinks of
listening to. Reading and chess she classes together as
silent barbarisms, unworthy of a social and civilized people.
Cards, too, have their faults: there is a rivalry, a mute
eloquence in those four aces, that leads away the attention;
besides, partners will sometimes scold; so she never plays

at cards; and upon the strength of this abstinence had very
nearly passed for *serious*, till it was discovered that she
could not abide a long sermon. She always looks out for
the shortest preacher, and never went to above one Bible
meeting in her life. 'Such speeches!' quoth she: 'I thought
the men never meant to have done. People have great
need of patience.' Plays, of course, she abhors, and operas,
and mobs, and all things that will be heard, especially
children; though for babies, particularly when asleep, for
dogs and pictures, and such silent intelligences as serve to
talk of and to talk to, she has a considerable partiality;
and an agreeable and gracious flattery to the mammas and
other owners of these pretty dumb things is a very usual
introduction to her miscellaneous harangues. The matter
of these orations is inconceivably various. Perhaps the
local and genealogical anecdotes, the sort of supplement to
the history of ——shire, may be her strongest point; but
she shines almost as much in medicine and housewifery
Her medical dissertations savour a little of that particular
branch of the science called quackery. She has a specific
against almost every disease to which the human frame is
liable; and is terribly prosy and unmerciful in her symptoms.
Her cures kill. In housekeeping, her notions resemble
those of other verbal managers: full of economy and re-
trenchment, with a leaning towards reform, though she
loves so well to declaim on the abuses in the cook's department, that I am not sure that she would very heartily thank
any radical who should sweep them quite away. For the
rest, her system sounds very finely in theory, but rather
fails in practice. Her recipes would be capital, only that
some way or other they do not eat well; her preserves seldom
keep; and her sweet wines are sure to turn sour. These
are certainly her favourite topics; but any one will do.
Allude to some anecdote of the neighbourhood, and she
forthwith treats you with as many parallel passages as are
to be found in an air with variations. Take up a new
publication, and she is equally at home there; for though
she knows little of books, she has, in the course of an up-
and-down life, met with a good many authors, and teases
and provokes you by telling of them precisely what you do
not care to hear—the maiden names of their wives and the

Christian names of their daughters, and into what families
their sisters and cousins married, and in what towns they
have lived, what streets, and what numbers. Boswell himself never drew up the table of Dr. Johnson's Fleet Street
courts with greater care than she made out to me the
successive residences of P. P——, Esq., author of a tract on
the French Revolution, and a pamphlet on the Poor Laws.
The very weather is not a safe subject. Her memory is a
perpetual register of hard frosts, and long droughts, and
high winds, and terrible storms, with all the evils that
followed in their train, and all the personal events connected
with them, so that if you happen to remark that clouds are
come up, and you fear it may rain, she replies: 'Aye, it is
just such a morning as three-and-thirty years ago, when
my poor cousin was married—you remember my cousin
Barbara—she married So-and-so, the son of So-and-so';
and then comes the whole pedigree of the bridegroom; the
amount of the settlements, and the reading and signing
them overnight; a description of the wedding dresses,
in the style of *Sir Charles Grandison*, and how much the
bride's gown cost per yard; the names, residences, and a
short subsequent history of the bridesmaids and men, the
gentleman who gave the bride away, and the clergyman who
performed the ceremony, with a learned antiquarian digres-
sion relative to the church; then the setting out in procession; the marriage; the kissing; the crying; the breakfasting;
the drawing the cake through the ring; and finally, the
bridal excursion, which brings us back again at an hour's
end to the starting-post — the weather — and the whole
story of the sopping, the drying, the clothes-spoiling, the
cold-catching, and all the small evils of a summer shower.
By this time it rains, and she sits down to a pathetic see-
saw of conjectures on the chance of Mrs. Smith's having
set out for her daily walk, or the possibility that Dr. Brown
may have ventured to visit his patients in his gig, and the
certainty that Lady Green's new housemaid would come
from London on the outside of the coach.

With all this intolerable prosing, she is actually reckoned
a pleasant woman! Her acquaintance in the great manu-
facturing town where she usually resides is very large, which
may partly account for the misnomer. Her conversation is

of a sort to bear dividing. Besides, there is, in all large societies, an instinctive sympathy which directs each individual to the companion most congenial to his humour. Doubtless her associates deserve the old French compliment: 'Ils ont tous un grand talent pour le silence.' Parcelled out amongst some seventy or eighty, there may even be some savour in her talk. It is the *tête-à-tête* that kills, or the small fireside circle of three or four, where only one can speak, and all the rest must seem to listen—*seem!* did I say? must listen in good earnest. Hotspur's expedient in a similar situation of crying 'Hem! Go to,' and marking not a word, will not do here; compared to her, Owen Glendower was no conjurer. She has the eye of a hawk, and detects a wandering glance, an incipient yawn, the slightest movement of impatience; the very needle must be quiet; if a pair of scissors do but wag, she is affronted, draws herself up, breaks off in the middle of a story, of a sentence, of a word, and the unlucky culprit must, for civility's sake, summon a more than Spartan fortitude, and beg the torturer to resume her torments—'That, that is the unkindest cut of all!' I wonder, if she happened to have married, how many husbands she would have talked to death. It is certain that none of her relations are long-lived, after she comes to reside with them. Father, mother, uncle, sister, brother, two nephews, and one niece, all these have successively passed away, though a healthy race, and with no visible disorder—except—— But we must not be uncharitable. They might have died though she had been born dumb— 'It is an accident that happens every day.' Since the decease of her last nephew, she attempted to form an establishment with a widow lady, for the sake, as they both said, of the comfort of society. But—strange miscalculation!—she was a talker too! They parted in a week.

And we have also parted. I am just returned from escorting her to the coach, which is to convey her two hundred miles westward; and I have still the murmur of her adieux resounding in my ears, like the indistinct hum of the air on a frosty night. It was curious to see how, almost simultaneously, these mournful adieux shaded into cheerful salutations of her new comrades, the passengers in the mail. Poor souls! Little does the civil young lad who made way for her, or the fat lady, his mamma, who with pains and inconvenience made room for her, or the grumpy gentleman in the opposite corner, who, after some dispute, was at length won to admit her dressing-box—little do they suspect what is to befall them. Two hundred miles! and she never sleeps in a carriage! Well, patience be with them, and comfort and peace! A pleasant journey to them! And to her all happiness! She is a most kind and excellent person, one for whom I would do anything in my poor power—aye, even were it to listen to her another four days.

CHAPTER IX

THE COWSLIP BALL

May 16*th*. There are moments in life when, without any visible or immediate cause, the spirits sink and fail, as it were, under the mere pressure of existence: moments of unaccountable depression, when one is weary of one's very thoughts, haunted by images that will not depart—images many and various, but all painful; friends lost, or changed, or dead; hopes disappointed even in their accomplishment; fruitless regrets, powerless wishes, doubt and fear, and self-distrust, and self-disapprobation. They who have known these feelings (and who is there so happy as not to have known some of them?) will understand why Alfieri became powerless, and Froissart dull; and why even needlework, that most effectual sedative, that grand soother and composer of woman's distress, fails to comfort me to-day. I will go out into the air this cool pleasant afternoon, and try what that will do. I fancy that exercise, or exertion of any kind, is the true specific for nervousness. 'Fling but a stone, the giant dies.' I will go to the meadows, the beautiful meadows! and I will have my materials of happiness, Lizzy and May, and a basket for flowers, and we will make a cowslip ball. 'Did you ever see a cowslip ball, my Lizzy?' 'No.' 'Come away, then; make haste! run, Lizzy!'

And on we go, fast, fast! down the road, across the Lea, past the workhouse, along by the great pond, till we slide into the deep narrow lane, whose hedges seem to meet over the water, and win our way to the little farm-house at the end. 'Through the farmyard, Lizzy; over the gate; never mind the cows; they are quiet enough.' 'I don't mind 'em,' said Miss Lizzy, boldly and truly, and with a proud affronted air, displeased at being thought to mind anything, and showing by her attitude and manner some design of proving her courage by an attack on the largest of the herd, in the shape of a pull by the tail. 'I don't mind 'em.' 'I know you don't, Lizzy; but let them alone, and don't chase the turkey-cock. Come to me, my dear!' and, for a wonder, Lizzy came.

In the meantime, my other pet, Mayflower, had also gotten into a scrape. She had driven about a huge un-wieldy sow, till the animal's grunting had disturbed the repose of a still more enormous Newfoundland dog, the guardian of the yard. Out he sallied, growling, from the depth of his kennel, erecting his tail, and shaking his long chain. May's attention was instantly diverted from the sow to this new playmate, friend or foe, she cared not which; and he of the kennel, seeing his charge unhurt, and out of danger, was at leisure to observe the charms of his fair enemy, as she frolicked round him, always beyond the reach of his chain, yet always, with the natural instinctive coquetry of her sex, alluring him to the pursuit which she knew to be vain. I never saw a prettier flirtation. At last the noble animal, wearied out, retired to the inmost recesses of his habitation, and would not even approach her when she stood right before the entrance. 'You are properly served, May. Come along, Lizzy. Across this wheat-field, and now over the gate. Stop! let me lift you down. No jump-ing, no breaking of necks, Lizzy!' and here we are in the meadows, and out of the world. Robinson Crusoe, in his lonely island, had scarcely a more complete, or a more beautiful solitude.

These meadows consist of a double row of small enclosures of rich grassland, a mile or two in length, sloping down from high arable grounds on either side, to a little nameless brook that winds between them, with a course which, in its infinite variety, clearness, and rapidity, seems to emulate the bold rivers of the north, of whom, far more than of our lazy southern streams, our rivulet presents a miniature likeness. Never was water more exquisitely tricksy—now darting over the bright pebbles, sparkling and flashing in the light with a bubbling music, as sweet and wild as the song of the wood-lark; now stretching quietly along, giving back the rich tufts of the golden marsh-marigolds which grow on its margin; now sweeping round a fine reach of green grass, rising steeply into a high mound, a mimic promontory, whilst the other side sinks softly away, like some tiny bay, and the water flows between, so clear, so wide, so shallow, that Lizzy, longing for adventure, is sure she could cross unwetted; now dashing through two sand-banks, a torrent deep and narrow, which May clears at a bound; now sleeping, half-hidden, beneath the alders, and hawthorns, and wild roses, with which the banks are so profusely and variously fringed, whilst flags,[1] lilies, and other aquatic plants almost cover the surface of the stream. In good truth, it is a beautiful brook, and one that Walton himself might have sitten by and loved, for trout are there; we see them as they dart up the stream, and hear and start at the sudden plunge when they spring to the surface for the summer flies. Izaak Walton would have loved our brook and quiet meadows; they breathe the very spirit of his own peacefulness, a soothing quietude that sinks into the soul. There is no path through them, not one; we might wander a whole spring day and not see a trace of human habitation. They belong to a number of small proprietors, who allow each other access through their respective grounds, from pure kindness and neighbourly feeling; a privilege never abused: and the fields on the other side of the water are reached by a rough plank, or a tree thrown across, or some such homely bridge. We ourselves possess one of the most beautiful; so that the strange pleasure of property, that instinct which makes Lizzy delight in her broken doll, and May in the bare bone which she has pilfered from the kennel of her recreant admirer of Newfoundland, is added to the other charms of this en-chanting scenery; a strange pleasure it is, when one so poor as I can feel it! Perhaps it is felt most by the poor; with

[1] Walking along these meadows one bright sunny afternoon a year or two back, and rather later in the season, I had an opportunity of noticing a curious circumstance in natural history. Standing close to the edge of the stream, I remarked a singular appearance on a large tuft of flags. It looked like bunches of flowers, the leaves of which seemed dark, yet transparent, intermingled with brilliant tubes of bright blue or shining green. On ex-amining this phenomenon more closely, it turned out to be several clusters of dragon-flies, just emerged from their deformed chrysalis state, and still torpid and motionless from the wetness of their filmy wings. Half an hour later we returned to the spot, and they were gone. We had seen them at the very moment when beauty was complete and animation dormant. I have since found nearly a similar account of this curious process in Mr. Bingley's very entertaining work, called *Animal Biography*.

the rich it may be less intense—too much diffused and spread
out, becoming thin by expansion, like leaf-gold; the little
of the poor may be not only more precious, but more
pleasant to them: certain that bit of grassy and blossomy
earth, with its green knolls and tufted bushes, its old pollards
wreathed with ivy, and its bright and babbling waters, is
very dear to me. But I must always have loved these
meadows, so fresh and cool, and delicious to the eye and to
the tread, full of cowslips, and of all vernal flowers: Shakespeare's song of spring bursts irrepressibly from our lips as
we step on them:

> When daisies pied, and violets blue,
>   And lady-smocks all silver-white,
> And cuckoo-buds of yellow hue,
>   Do paint the meadows with delight,
> The cuckoo then, on every tree——

'Cuckoo! cuckoo!' cried Lizzy, breaking in with her clear
childish voice; and immediately, as if at her call, the real
bird, from a neighbouring tree (for these meadows are dotted
with timber like a park), began to echo my lovely little
girl: 'Cuckoo! cuckoo!' I have a prejudice very unpastoral
and unpoetical (but I cannot help it, I have many such)
against this harbinger of spring. His note is so monotonous,
so melancholy; and then the boys mimic him; one hears
'Cuckoo! cuckoo!' in dirty streets, amongst smoky houses,
and the bird is hated for faults not his own. But prejudices
of taste, likings and dislikings, are not always vanquishable
by reason; so, to escape the serenade from the tree, which
promised to be of considerable duration (when once that
eternal song begins, on it goes ticking like a clock)—to
escape that noise, I determined to excite another, and
challenged Lizzy to a cowslip-gathering: a trial of skill and
speed, to see which should soonest fill her basket. My
stratagem succeeded completely. What scrambling, what
shouting, what glee from Lizzy! Twenty cuckoos might
have sung unheard whilst she was pulling her own flowers,
and stealing mine, and laughing, screaming, and talking
through all.

At last the baskets were filled, and Lizzy declared victor;
and down we sat, on the brink of the stream, under a
spreading hawthorn, just disclosing its own pearly buds,

and surrounded with the rich and enamelled flowers of the wild hyacinth, blue and white, to make our cowslip ball. Every one knows the process: to nip off the tuft of flowerets just below the top of the stalk, and hang each cluster nicely balanced across a ribbon, till you have a long string like a garland; then to press them closely together, and tie them tightly up. We went on very prosperously, *considering*— as people say of a young lady's drawing, or a Frenchman's English, or a woman's tragedy, or the poor little dwarf who works without fingers, or the ingenious sailor who writes with his toes, or generally of any performance which is accomplished by means seemingly inadequate to its production. To be sure we met with a few accidents. First, Lizzy spoiled nearly all her cowslips by snapping them off too short; so there was a fresh gathering; in the next place, May overset my full basket, and sent the blossoms floating, like so many fairy favours, down the brook; then, when we were going on pretty steadily, just as we had made a superb wreath, and were thinking of tying it together, Lizzy, who held the ribbon, caught a glimpse of a gorgeous butterfly, all brown and red and purple, and skipping off to pursue the new object, let go her hold: so all our treasures were abroad again. At last, however, by dint of taking a branch of alder as a substitute for Lizzy, and hanging the basket in a pollard-ash, out of sight of May, the cowslip ball was finished. What a concentration of fragrance and beauty it was! golden and sweet to satiety! rich to sight, and touch, and smell! Lizzy was enchanted, and ran off with her prize, hiding amongst the trees in the very coyness of ecstasy, as if any human eye, even mine, would be a restraint on her innocent raptures.

In the meanwhile I sat listening, not to my enemy the cuckoo, but to a whole concert of nightingales, scarcely interrupted by any meaner bird, answering and vying with each other in those short delicious strains which are to the ear as roses to the eye: those snatches of lovely sound which come across us as airs from heaven. Pleasant thoughts, delightful associations, awoke as I listened; and almost unconsciously I repeated to myself the beautiful story of the Lutist and the Nightingale, from Ford's *Lover's Melancholy*. Here it is. Is there in English poetry anything finer?

Passing from Italy to Greece, the tales
Which poets of an elder time have feign'd,
To glorify their Tempe, bred in me
Desire of visiting [that] Paradise.
To Thessaly I came, and living private,
Without acquaintance of more sweet companions
Than the old inmates to my love, my thoughts,
I day by day frequented silent groves
And solitary walks.   One morning early
This accident encounter'd me: I heard
The sweetest and most ravishing contention
That art and nature ever were at strife in.
A sound of music touch'd mine ears, or rather
Indeed entranced my soul; as I stole nearer,
Invited by the melody, I saw
This youth, this fair-faced youth, upon his lute
With strains of strange variety and harmony
Proclaiming, as it seem'd, so bold a challenge
To the clear choristers of the woods, the birds,
That as they flock'd about him, all stood silent,
Wondering at what they heard.   I wonder'd too.
A nightingale,
Nature's best skill'd musician, undertakes
The challenge; and for every several strain
The well-shaped youth could touch, she sang him down.
He could not run divisions with more art
Upon his quaking instrument than she,
The nightingale, did with her various notes
Reply to.
Some time thus spent, the young man grew at last
Into a pretty anger, that a bird,
Whom art had never taught clefs, moods, or notes,
Should vie with him for mastery, whose study
Had busied many hours to perfect practice.
To end the controversy, in a rapture
Upon his instrument he plays so swiftly,
So many voluntaries, and so quick,
That there was curiosity and cunning,
Concord in discord, lines of differing method
Meeting in one full centre of delight.
The bird (ordain'd to be
Music's first martyr) strove to imitate
These several sounds; which when her warbling throat
Fail'd in, for grief down dropt she on his lute,
And brake her heart.   It was the quaintest sadness
To see the conqueror upon her hearse
To weep a funeral elegy of tears.
He look'd upon the trophies of his art,
Then sigh'd, then wip'd his eyes; then sigh'd and cry'd:
'Alas! poor creature, I will soon avenge
This cruelty upon the author of it.

Henceforth this lute, guilty of innocent blood,
Shall never more betray a harmless peace
To an untimely end!' and in that sorrow,
As he was pashing it against a tree,
I suddenly stept in.

When I had finished the recitation of this exquisite passage, the sky, which had been all the afternoon dull and heavy, began to look more and more threatening; darker clouds, like wreaths of black smoke, flew across the dead leaden tint; a cooler, damper air blew over the meadows, and a few large heavy drops splashed in the water. 'We shall have a storm. Lizzy! May! where are ye? Quick, quick, my Lizzy! run, run! faster, faster!'

And off we ran; Lizzy not at all displeased at the thoughts of a wetting, to which indeed she is almost as familiar as a duck; May, on the other hand, peering up at the weather, and shaking her pretty ears with manifest dismay. Of all animals, next to a cat, a greyhound dreads rain. She might have escaped it; her light feet would have borne her home long before the shower; but May is too faithful for that, too true a comrade, understands too well the laws of good-fellowship; so she waited for us. She did, to be sure, gallop on before, and then stop and look back, and beckon as it were, with some scorn in her black eyes at the slowness of our progress. We in the meanwhile got on as fast as we could, encouraging and reproaching each other. 'Faster, my Lizzy! Oh, what a bad runner!' 'Faster, faster! Oh, what a bad runner!' echoed my sauce-box. 'You are so fat, Lizzy, you make no way!' 'Ah! who else is fat?' retorted the darling. Certainly her mother is right; I do spoil that child.

By this time we were thoroughly soaked, all three. It was a pelting shower, that drove through our thin summer clothing and poor May's short glossy coat in a moment. And then, when we were wet to the skin, the sun came out, actually the sun, as if to laugh at our plight; and then, more provoking still, when the sun was shining, and the shower over, came a maid and a boy to look after us, loaded with cloaks and umbrellas enough to fence us against a whole day's rain. Never mind! on we go, faster and faster; Lizzy obliged to be most ignobly carried, having had the misfortune to lose a shoe in the mud, which we left the boy to look after.

Here we are at home—dripping; but glowing and laughing, and bearing our calamity most manfully. May, a dog of excellent sense, went instantly to bed in the stable, and is at this moment over head and ears in straw; Lizzy is gone to bed too, coaxed into that wise measure by a promise of tea and toast, and of not going home till to-morrow, and the story of Little Red Riding Hood; and I am enjoying the luxury of dry clothing by a good fire. Really, getting wet through now and then is no bad thing, finery apart; for one should not like spoiling a new pelisse, or a handsome plume; but when there is nothing in question but a white gown and a straw bonnet, as was the case to-day, it is rather pleasant than not. The little chill refreshes, and our enjoyment of the subsequent warmth and dryness is positive and absolute. Besides, the stimulus and exertion do good to the mind as well as body. How melancholy I was all the morning! how cheerful I am now! Nothing like a shower-bath—a real shower-bath, such as Lizzy and May and I have undergone, to cure low spirits. Try it, my dear readers, if ever ye be nervous—I will answer for its success.

CHAPTER X

A COUNTRY CRICKET MATCH

I DOUBT if there be any scene in the world more animating or delightful than a cricket match—I do not mean a set match at Lord's ground for money, hard money, between a certain number of gentlemen and players, as they are called—people who make a trade of that noble sport, and degrade it into an affair of bettings, and hedgings, and cheatings, it may be, like boxing or horse-racing; nor do I mean a pretty fête in a gentleman's park, where one club of cricketing dandies encounters another such club, and where they show off in graceful costume to a gay marquee of admiring belles, who condescend so to purchase admiration, and while away a long summer morning in partaking cold collations, conversing occasionally, and seeming to understand the game—the whole being conducted according to ball-room etiquette, so as to be exceedingly elegant and exceedingly dull. No! the cricket that I mean is a real solid old-fashioned match between neighbouring parishes, where each attacks the other for honour and a supper, glory and half a crown a man. If there be any gentlemen amongst them, it is well—if not, it is so much the better. Your gentleman cricketer is in general rather an anomalous character. Elderly gentlemen are obviously good for nothing; and young beaux are, for the most part, hampered and trammelled by dress and habit: the stiff cravat, the pinched-in waist, the dandy-walk—oh, they will never do for cricket! Now, our country lads, accustomed to the flail or the hammer (your blacksmiths are capital hitters), have the free use of their arms; they know how to move their shoulders; and they can move their feet too—they can run; then they are so much better made, so much more athletic, and yet so much lissomer—to use a Hampshire phrase, which deserves at least to be good English. Here and there, indeed, one meets with an old

Etonian, who retains his boyish love for that game which formed so considerable a branch of his education: some even preserve their boyish proficiency, but in general it wears away like the Greek, quite as certainly, and almost as fast; a few years of Oxford, or Cambridge, or the Continent, are sufficient to annihilate both the power and the inclination. No! a village match is the thing—where our highest officer, our conductor (to borrow a musical term), is but a little farmer's second son; where a day-labourer is our bowler, and a blacksmith our long-stop; where the spectators consist of the retired cricketers, the veterans of the green, the careful mothers, the girls, and all the boys of two parishes, together with a few amateurs, little above them in rank, and not at all in pretension; where laughing and shouting, and the very ecstasy of merriment and good humour, prevail: such a match, in short, as I attended yesterday, at the expense of getting twice wet through; and as I would attend to-morrow at the certainty of having that ducking doubled.

For the last three weeks our village has been in a state of great excitement, occasioned by a challenge from our north-western neighbours, the men of B——, to contend with us at cricket. Now we have not been much in the habit of playing matches. Three or four years ago, indeed, we encountered the men of S——, our neighbours south-by-east, with a sort of doubtful success, beating them on our own ground, whilst in the second match returned the compliment on theirs. This discouraged us. Then an unnatural coalition between a high-church curate and an evangelical gentleman farmer drove our lads from the Sunday-evening practice, which, as it did not begin before both services were concluded, and as it tended to keep the young men from the ale-house, our magistrates had winked at, if not encouraged. The sport therefore had languished until the present season, when under another change of circumstances the spirit began to revive. Half a dozen fine active lads, of influence amongst their comrades, grew into men and yearned for cricket: an enterprising publican gave a set of ribbons: his rival, mine host of the ' Rose,' an outdoer by profession, gave two; and the clergyman and his lay ally, both well-disposed and good-natured men, gratified by the submission to their authority, and finding, perhaps, that no great good resulted from the substitution of public-houses for out-of-doors diversions, relaxed. In short the practice recommenced, and the hill was again alive with men and boys, and innocent merriment; but farther than the ribbon matches amongst ourselves nobody dreamed of going, till this challenge—we were modest, and doubted our own strength. The B—— people, on the other hand, must have been braggers born, a whole parish of gasconaders. Never was such boasting! such crowing! such ostentatious display of practice! such mutual compliments from man to man—bowler to batter, batter to bowler! It was a wonder they did not challenge all England! It must be confessed that we were a little astounded; yet we firmly resolved not to decline the combat; and one of the most spirited of the new growth, William Grey by name, took up the glove in a style of manly courtesy, that would have done honour to a knight in the days of chivalry. 'We were not professed players,' he said, 'being little better than schoolboys, and scarcely older; but, since they had done us the honour to challenge us, we would try our strength. It would be no discredit to be beaten by such a field.'

Having accepted the wager of battle, our champion began forthwith to collect his forces. William Grey is himself one of the finest youths that one shall see—tall, active, slender and yet strong, with a piercing eye full of sagacity, and a smile full of good humour, a farmer's son by station, and used to hard work as farmers' sons are now, liked by everybody, and admitted to be an excellent cricketer. He immediately set forth to muster his men, remembering with great complacency that Samuel Long, a bowler *comme il y en a peu*, the very man who had knocked down nine wickets, had beaten us, bowled us out at the fatal return match some years ago at S——, had luckily, in a remove of a quarter of a mile last Lady Day, crossed the boundaries of his old parish, and actually belonged to us. Here was a stroke of good fortune! Our captain applied to him instantly, and he agreed at a word. Indeed Samuel Long is a very civilized person. He is a middle-aged man who looks rather old amongst our young lads, and whose thickness and breadth give no token of remarkable activity; but he is very active, and so steady a player! so safe! We had half gained the match when we had secured him. He is a man of substance, too, in every way; owns one cow, two donkeys, six pigs, and geese and ducks beyond count; dresses like a farmer, and owes no man a shilling—and all this from pure industry, sheer day-labour. Note that your good cricketer is commonly the most industrious man in the parish; the habits that make him such are precisely those which make a good workman—steadiness, sobriety, and activity; Samuel Long might pass for the beau-ideal of the two characters. Happy were we to possess him! Then we had another piece of good luck. James Brown, a journeyman blacksmith and a native, who, being of a rambling disposition, had roamed from place to place for half a dozen years, had just returned to settle with his brother at another corner of our village, bringing with him a prodigious reputation in cricket and in gallantry—the gay Lothario of the neighbourhood. He is said to have made more conquests in love and in cricket than any blacksmith in the county. To him also went the indefatigable William Grey, and he also consented to play. No end to our good fortune! Another celebrated batter, called Joseph Hearne, had likewise recently married into the parish. He worked, it is true, at the A—— mills, but slept at the house of his wife's father in our territories. He also was sought and found by our leader. But he was grand and shy; made an immense favour of the thing; courted courting and then hung back: 'Did not know that he could be spared; had partly resolved not to play again—at least not this season; thought it rash to accept the challenge; thought they might do without him——' 'Truly I think so too,' said our spirited champion; 'we will not trouble you, Mr. Hearne.'

Having thus secured two powerful auxiliaries, and rejected a third, we began to reckon and select the regular native forces. Thus ran our list: William Grey, 1. Samuel Long, 2. James Brown, 3. George and John Simmons, one capital, the other so-so, an uncertain hitter, but a good fieldsman, 5. Joel Brent, excellent, 6. Ben Appleton—here was a little pause; Ben's abilities at cricket were not completely ascertained; but then he was so good a fellow, so full of fun and waggery; no doing without Ben. So he figured in the list, 7. George Harris—a short halt there too! Slowish—slow but sure. I think the proverb brought him in, 8. Tom Coper—oh, beyond the world, Tom Coper! the red-headed gardening lad, whose left-handed strokes send *her* (a cricket ball, like that other moving thing a ship, is always of the feminine gender)—send her spinning a mile, 9. Harry Willis, another blacksmith, 10.

We had now ten of our eleven, but the choice of the last occasioned some demur. Three young Martins, rich farmers of the neighbourhood, successively presented themselves, and were all rejected by our independent and impartial general for want of merit—*cricketal* merit. 'Not good enough,' was his pithy answer. Then our worthy neighbour, the half-pay lieutenant, offered his services; he, too, though with some hesitation and modesty, was refused—'Not quite young enough,' was his sentence. John Strong, the exceeding long son of our dwarfish mason, was the next candidate; a nice youth—everybody likes John Strong—and a willing, but so tall and so limp, bent in the middle—a thread-paper, six feet high! We were all afraid that, in spite of his name, his strength would never hold out. 'Wait till next year, John,' quoth William Grey, with all the dignified seniority of twenty speaking to eighteen. 'Coper's a year younger,' said John; 'Coper's a foot shorter,' replied William: so John retired; and the eleventh man remained unchosen, almost to the eleventh hour. The eve of the match arrived, and the post was still vacant, when a little boy of fifteen, David Willis, brother to Harry, admitted by accident to the last practice, saw eight of them out, and was voted in by acclamation.

That Sunday evening's practice (for Monday was the important day) was a period of great anxiety, and, to say the truth, of great pleasure. There is something strangely delightful in the innocent spirit of party. To be one of a numerous body, to be authorized to say *we*, to have a rightful interest in triumph or defeat, is gratifying at once to social feeling and to personal pride. There was not a ten-years-old urchin, or a septuagenary woman in the parish, who did not feel an additional importance, a reflected

consequence, in speaking of 'our side.' An election interests
in the same way; but that feeling is less pure. Money is
there, and hatred, and politics, and lies. Oh, to be a voter,
or a voter's wife, comes nothing near the genuine and hearty
sympathy of belonging to a parish, breathing the same air,
looking on the same trees, listening to the same nightingales! Talk of a patriotic elector! Give me a parochial
patriot, a man who loves his parish! Even we, the female
partisans, may partake the common ardour. I am sure I did.
I never, though tolerably eager and enthusiastic at all times
remember being in a more delicious state of excitation than
on the eve of that battle. Our hopes waxed stronger and
stronger. Those of our players who were present were
excellent. William Grey got forty notches off his own bat;
and that brilliant hitter, Tom Coper, gained eight from two
successive balls. As the evening advanced, too, we had
encouragement of another sort. A spy, who had been
dispatched to reconnoitre the enemy's quarters, returned
from their practising ground with a most consolatory
report. 'Really,' said Charles Grover, our intelligencer—
a fine old steady judge, one who had played well in his
day—'they are no better than so many old women. Any
five of ours would beat their eleven.' This sent us to bed
in high spirits.

Morning dawned less favourably. The sky promised a
series of deluging showers, and kept its word, as English
skies are wont to do on such occasions; and a lamentable
message arrived at the headquarters from our trusty comrade Joel Brent. His master, a great farmer, had begun
the hay harvest that very morning, and Joel, being as
eminent in one field as in another, could not be spared.
Imagine Joel's plight! the most ardent of all our eleven!
a knight held back from the tourney! a soldier from the
battle! The poor swain was inconsolable. At last, one
who is always ready to do a good-natured action, great or
little, set forth to back his petition; and, by dint of appealing
to the public spirit of our worthy neighbour and the state
of the barometer, talking alternately of the parish honour
and thunder-showers, of lost matches and sopped hay, he
carried his point, and returned triumphantly with the
delighted Joel.

In the meantime we became sensible of another defalcation. On calling over our roll, Brown was missing; and the spy of the preceding night, Charles Grover—the universal scout and messenger of the village, a man who will run half a dozen miles for a pint of beer, who does errands for the very love of the trade, who, if he had been a lord, would have been an ambassador—was instantly dispatched to summon the truant. His report spread general consternation. Brown had set off at four o'clock in the morning to play in a cricket match at M——, a little town twelve miles off, which had been his last residence. Here was desertion! Here was treachery! Here was treachery against that goodly state, our parish! To send James Brown to Coventry was the immediate resolution; but even that seemed too light a punishment for such delinquency. Then how we cried him down! At ten on Sunday night (for the rascal had actually practised with us, and never said a word of his intended disloyalty) he was our faithful mate, and the best player (take him for all in all) of the eleven. At ten in the morning he had run away, and we were well rid of him; he was no batter compared with William Grey or Tom Coper; not fit to wipe the shoes of Samuel Long as a bowler; nothing of a scout to John Simmons; the boy David Willis was worth fifty of him—

> I trust we have within our realm
> Five hundred good as he,

was the universal sentiment. So we took tall John Strong, who, with an incurable hankering after the honour of being admitted, had kept constantly with the players, to take the chance of some such accident—we took John for our *pis aller*. I never saw any one prouder than the good-humoured lad was of this not very flattering piece of preferment.

John Strong was elected, and Brown sent to Coventry; and when I first heard of his delinquency, I thought the punishment only too mild for the crime. But I have since learned the secret history of the offence (if we could know the secret histories of all offences, how much better the world would seem than it does now!), and really my wrath is much abated. It was a piece of gallantry, of devotion to the sex, or rather a chivalrous obedience to one chosen fair.

I must tell my readers the story. Mary Allen, the prettiest
girl of M——, had, it seems, revenged upon our blacksmith
the numberless inconstancies of which he stood accused.
He was in love over head and ears, but the nymph was
cruel. She said no, and no, and no, and poor Brown, three
times rejected, at last resolved to leave the place, partly
in despair, and partly in that hope which often mingles
strangely with a lover's despair, the hope that when he was
gone he should be missed. He came home to his brother's
accordingly; but for five weeks he heard nothing from or of
the inexorable Mary, and was glad to beguile his own 'vexing
thoughts' by endeavouring to create in his mind an artificial
and factitious interest in our cricket match—all unimport-
ant as such a trifle must have seemed to a man in love.
Poor James, however, is a social and warm-hearted person,
not likely to resist a contagious sympathy. As the time for
the play advanced, the interest which he had at first affected
became genuine and sincere: and he was really, when he left
the ground on Sunday night, almost as enthusiastically
absorbed in the event of the next day as Joel Brent himself.
He little foresaw the new and delightful interest which
awaited him at home, where, on the moment of his arrival,
his sister-in-law and confidante presented him with a billet
from the lady of his heart. It had, with the usual delay of
letters sent by private hands in that rank of life, loitered on
the road, in a degree inconceivable to those who are accustomed to the punctual speed of the post, and had taken ten
days for its twelve miles' journey. Have my readers any
wish to see this *billet-doux*? I can show them (but in
strict confidence) a literal copy. It was addressed,

> 'For mistur jem browne
>   'blaxmith by
>   'S——.'

The inside ran thus: 'Mistur browne this is to Inform
yew that oure parish plays bramley men next monday is a
week, i think we shall lose without yew. from your humbell
servant to command
>   'MARY ALLEN.'

Was there ever a prettier relenting? a summons more
flattering, more delicate, more irresistible? The precious

epistle was undated; but, having ascertained who brought it, and found, by cross-examining the messenger, that the Monday in question was the very next day, we were not surprised to find that *Mistur browne* forgot his engagement to us, forgot all but Mary and Mary's letter, and set off at four o'clock the next morning to walk twelve miles, and play for her parish, and in her sight. Really we must not send James Brown to Coventry—must we? Though if, as his sister-in-law tells our damsel Harriet he hopes to do, he should bring the fair Mary home as his bride, he will not greatly care how little we say to him. But he must not be sent to Coventry—true-love forbid!

At last we were all assembled, and marched down to H—— Common, the appointed ground, which, though in our dominions, according to the map, was the constant practising place of our opponents, and *terra incognita* to us. We found our adversaries on the ground as we expected, for our various delays had hindered us from taking the field so early as we wished; and, as soon as we had settled all preliminaries, the match began.

But, aias! I have been so long settling my preliminaries that I have left myself no room for the detail of our victory, and must squeeze the account of our grand achievements into as little compass as Cowley, when he crammed the names of eleven of his mistresses into the narrow space of four eight-syllable lines. *They* began the warfare—these boastful men of B——. And what think you, gentle reader, was the amount of their innings? These challengers —the famous eleven—how many did they get? Think! imagine! guess! You cannot? Well! they got twenty-two, or rather, they got twenty; for two of theirs were short notches, and would never have been allowed, only that, seeing what they were made of, we and our umpires were not particular. They should have had twenty more, if they had chosen to claim them. Oh, how well we fielded! and how well we bowled! Our good play had quite as much to do with their miserable failure as their bad. Samuel Long is a slow bowler, George Simmons a fast one, and the change from Long's lobbing to Simmons's fast balls posed them completely. Poor simpletons! they were always wrong, expecting the slow for the quick, and the quick for

the slow. Well, we went in. And what were our innings?
Guess again!—guess! A hundred and sixty-nine! In spite
of soaking showers, and wretched ground, where the ball
would not run a yard, we headed them by a hundred and
forty-seven; and then they gave in, as well they might.
William Grey pressed them much to try another innings.
'There was so much chance,' as he courteously observed,
'in cricket, that, advantageous as our position seemed, we
might, very possibly, be overtaken. The B—— men had
better try.' But they were beaten sulky, and would not
move—to my great disappointment; I wanted to prolong
the pleasure of success. What a glorious sensation it is to
be for five hours together winning — winning — winning!
always feeling what a whist-player feels when he takes up
four honours, seven trumps! Who would think that a little
bit of leather and two pieces of wood had such a delightful
and delighting power?

The only drawback on my enjoyment was the failure of
the pretty boy, David Willis, who, injudiciously put in first,
and playing for the first time in a match amongst men and
strangers, who talked to him, and stared at him, was seized
with such a fit of shamefaced shyness that he could scarcely
hold his bat, and was bowled out without a stroke, from
actual nervousness. 'He will come off that,' Tom Coper
says. I am afraid he will. I wonder whether Tom had
ever any modesty to lose. Our other modest lad, John
Strong, did very well; his length told in fielding, and he got
good fame. Joel Brent, the rescued mower, got into a
scrape, and out of it again; his fortune for the day. He
ran out his mate, Samuel Long, who, I do believe, but for
the excess of Joel's eagerness, would have stayed in till this
time; by which exploit he got into sad disgrace; and then he
himself got thirty-seven runs, which redeemed his reputation.
William Grey made a hit which actually lost the cricket ball.
We think she lodged in a hedge a quarter of a mile off, but
nobody could find her. And George Simmons had nearly
lost his shoe, which he tossed away in a passion for having
been caught out owing to the ball glancing against it. These,
together with a very complete somerset of Ben Appleton,
our long-stop, who floundered about in the mud, making
faces and attitudes as laughable as Grimaldi, none could

tell whether by accident or design, were the chief incidents of the scene of action. Amongst the spectators nothing remarkable occurred, beyond the general calamity of two or three drenchings, except that a form, placed by the side of a hedge, under a very insufficient shelter, was knocked into the ditch, in a sudden rush of the cricketers to escape a pelting shower, by which means all parties shared the fate of Ben Appleton, some on land and some by water; and that, amidst the scramble, a saucy gipsy of a girl contrived to steal from the knee of the demure and well-apparelled Samuel Long a smart handkerchief, which his careful dame had tied around it, to preserve his new (what is the mincing feminine word?)—his new—inexpressibles; thus reversing the story of Desdemona, and causing the new Othello to call aloud for his handkerchief, to the great diversion of the company. And so we parted; the players retired to their supper, and we to our homes; all wet through, all good-humoured, and all happy—except the losers.

To-day we are happy too. Hats, with ribbons in them, go glancing up and down; and William Grey says, with a proud humility: 'We do not challenge any parish; but if we be challenged, we are ready.'

CHAPTER XI

TOM CORDERY

THERE are certain things and persons that look as if they could never die: things of such vigour and hardiness that they seem constituted for an interminable duration, a sort of immortality. An old pollard-oak of my acquaintance used to give me this impression. Never was tree so gnarled, so knotted, so full of crooked life. Garlanded with ivy and woodbine, almost bending under the weight of its own rich leaves and acorns, tough, vigorous, lusty, concentrating as it were the very spirit of vitality into its own curtailed proportions—could that tree ever die? I have asked myself twenty times, as I stood looking on the deep water over which it hung, and in which it seemed to live again—would that strong dwarf ever fall? Alas! the question is answered. Walking by the spot to-day—this very day—there it lay prostrate; the ivy still clinging about it, the twigs swelling with sap, and putting forth already the early buds. There it lay, a victim to the taste and skill of some admirer of British woods, who, with the tact of Ugo Foscolo (that prince of amateurs), has discovered in the knots and gnarls of the exterior coat the leopard-like beauty which is concealed within the trunk. There it lies, a type of sylvan instability, fallen like an emperor. Another piece of strong nature in a human form used to convey to me exactly the same feeling—and he is gone too! Tom Cordery is dead. The bell is tolling for him at this very moment. Tom Cordery dead! the words seem almost a contradiction. One is tempted to send for the sexton and the undertaker, to undig the grave, to force open the coffin-lid—there must be some mistake. But, alas! it is too true; the typhus fever, that axe which levels the strong as the weak, has hewed him down at a blow. Poor Tom Cordery!

This human oak grew on the wild north-of-Hampshire country, of which I have before made honourable mention;

a country of heath, and hill, and forest, partly reclaimed,
enclosed, and planted by some of the greater proprietors,
but for the most part uncultivated and uncivilized; a
proper refuge for wild animals of every species. Of these
the most notable was my friend Tom Cordery, who presented
in his own person no unfit emblem of the district in which
he lived—the gentlest of savages, the wildest of civilized
men. He was by calling rat - catcher, hare - finder, and
broom-maker; a triad of trades which he had substituted
for the one grand profession of poaching, which he followed
in his younger days with unrivalled talent and success, and
would, undoubtedly, have pursued till his death, had not
the bursting of an overloaded gun unluckily shot off his left
hand. As it was, he still contrived to mingle a little of his
old unlawful occupation with his honest callings; was a
reference of high authority amongst the young aspirants,
an adviser of undoubted honour and secrecy—suspected,
and more than suspected, as being one 'who, though he
played no more, o'erlooked the cards.' Yet he kept to
windward of the law, and indeed contrived to be on such
terms of social and even friendly intercourse with the
guardians of the game on M—— Common as may be said
to prevail between reputed thieves and the myrmidons
of justice in the neighbourhood of Bow Street. Indeed,
his especial crony, the head keeper, used sometimes to hint,
when Tom, elevated by ale, had provoked him by over-
crowing, 'that a stump was no bad shield, and that to shoot
off a hand and a bit of an arm for a blind would be nothing
to so daring a chap as Tom Cordery.' This conjecture,
never broached till the keeper was warm with wrath and
liquor, and Tom fairly out of hearing, seemed always to me
a little super-subtle; but it is certain that Tom's new professions did bear rather a suspicious analogy to the old, and
the ferrets, and terriers, and mongrels by whom he was
surrounded 'did really look,' as the worthy keeper observed,
'fitter to find Christian hares and pheasants than rats and
such vermin.' So in good truth did Tom himself. Never
did any human being look more like that sort of sportsman
commonly called a poacher. He was a tall, finely-built man,
with a prodigious stride that cleared the ground like a
horse, and a power of continuing his slow and steady speed

that seemed nothing less than miraculous. Neither man, nor horse, nor dog could out-tire him. He had a bold, undaunted presence, and an evident strength and power of bone and muscle. You might see by looking at him that he did not know what fear meant. In his youth he had fought more battles than any man in the forest. He was as if born without nerves, totally insensible to the recoils and disgusts of humanity. I have known him take up a huge adder, cut off its head, and then deposit the living and writhing body in his brimless hat, and walk with it coiling and wreathing about his head, like another Medusa, till the sport of the day was over, and he carried it home to secure the fat. With all this iron stubbornness of nature, he was of a most mild and gentle demeanour, had a fine placidity of countenance, and a quick blue eye beaming with good humour. His face was sunburnt into one general pale vermilion hue that overspread all his features; his very hair was sunburnt too. His costume was generally a smock-frock of no doubtful complexion, dirt-coloured, which hung round him in tatters like fringe, rather augmenting than diminishing the freedom, and, if I may so say, the gallantry of his bearing. This frock was furnished with a huge inside pocket, in which to deposit the game killed by his patrons—for of his three employments, that which consisted of finding hares for the great farmers and small gentry, who were wont to course on the common, was by far the most profitable and most pleasing to him, and to them. Everybody liked Tom Cordery. He had himself an aptness to like, which is certain to be repaid in kind—the very dogs knew him, and loved him, and would beat for him almost as soon as for their master. Even May, the most sagacious of greyhounds, appreciated his talents, and would as soon listen to Tom sohoing as to old Tray giving tongue.

Nor was his conversation less agreeable to the other part of the company. Servants and masters were equally desirous to secure Tom. Besides his general and professional familiarity with beasts and birds, their ways and doings, a knowledge so minute and accurate that it might have put to shame many a professed naturalist, he had no small acquaintance with the goings-on of that unfeathered biped called man; in short, he was, next after Lucy, who

recognized his rivalry by hating, decrying, and under-
valuing him, by far the best news-gatherer of the country-
side. His news he of course picked up on the civilized side
of the parish (there is no gossiping in the forest), partly at
that well-frequented inn the 'Red Lion'—of which Tom was
a regular and noted supporter—partly amongst his several
employers, and partly by his own sagacity. In the matter
of marriages (pairings, he was wont to call them) he relied
chiefly on his own skill in noting certain preliminary indications; and certainly for a guesser by profession, and a very
bold one, he was astonishingly often right. At the ale-house
especially he was of the first authority. An air of mild importance, a diplomatic reserve on some points, great smooth-
ness of speech, and that gentleness which is so often the
result of conscious power, made him there an absolute ruler.
Perhaps the effect of these causes might be a little aided by
the latent dread which that power inspired in others. Many
an exploit had proved that Tom Cordery's one arm was
fairly worth any two on the common. The pommelling of
Bob Arlott, and the levelling of Jem Serle to the earth by
one swing of a huge old hare (which unusual weapon was,
by the way, the first-slain of Mayflower, on its way home to
us in that walking cupboard, his pocket, when the unlucky
rencontre with Jem Serle broke two heads, the dead and the
living)—arguments such as these might have some cogency
at the 'Red Lion.'

But he managed everybody, as your gentle-mannered
person is apt to do. Even the rude squires and rough
farmers, his temporary masters, he managed, particularly
as far as concerned the beat, and was sure to bring them
round to his own peculiar fancies or prejudices, however
strongly their own wishes might turn them aside from the
direction indicated, and however often Tom's sagacity in
that instance might have been found at fault. Two spots
in the large wild enclosures into which the heath had been
divided were his especial favourites. The Hundred Acres,
alias the Poor Allotment, alias the Burnt Common (do any
or all of these titles convey any notion of the real destination
of that many-named place?—a piece of moorland portioned
out to serve for fuel to the poor of the parish)—this was one.
Oh, the barrenness of this miserable moor! Flat, marshy,

dingy, bare. Here that piece of green treachery, a bog;
there parched, and pared, and shrivelled, and black with
smoke and ashes; utterly desolate and wretched everywhere, except where amidst the desolation blossomed, as
in mockery, the enamelled gentianella. No hares ever
came there; they had too much taste. Yet thither would
Tom lead his unwary employers; thither, however warned,
or cautioned, or experienced, would he by reasoning, or
induction, or gentle persuasion, or actual fraud, entice the
hapless gentlemen; and then to see him with his rabble of
finders pacing up and down this precious 'sitting-ground'
(for so was Tom, thriftless liar, wont to call it), pretending to
look for game, counterfeiting a meuse; forging a form; and
telling a story some ten years old of a famous hare once
killed on that spot by his honour's favourite bitch, Marigold.
I never could thoroughly understand whether it were
design, a fear that too many hares might be killed, or a real
and honest mistake, a genuine prejudice in favour of the
place, that influenced Tom Cordery in this point. Half the
one, perhaps, and half the other. Mixed motives, let Pope
and his disciples say what they will, are by far the commonest in this parti-coloured world. Or he had shared the fate
of greater men, and lied till he believed—a coursing Cromwell, beginning in hypocrisy and ending in fanaticism.
Another pet spot was the Gallows Piece, an enclosure about
as large as the Hundred Acres, where a gibbet had once
borne the bodies of two murderers, with the chains and
bones, even in my remembrance, clanking and creaking in
the wind. The gibbet was gone now; but the name remained, and the feeling, deep, sad, and shuddering. The
place, too, was wild, awful, fearful; a heathy, furzy spot,
sinking into broken hollows, where murderers might lurk;
a few withered pines at the upper end, and amongst them,
half-hidden by the brambles, the stone in which the gallows
had been fixed—the bones must have been mouldering
beneath. All Tom's eloquence, seconded by two capital
courses, failed to drag me thither a second time.

Tom was not, however, without that strong sense of
natural beauty which they who live amongst the wild-
nesses and fastnesses of nature so often exhibit. One spot,
where the common trenches on the civilized world, was

scarcely less his admiration than mine. It is a high hill, half-covered with furze, and heath, and broom, and sinking abruptly down to a large pond, almost a lake, covered with wild water-fowl. The ground, richly clothed with wood—oak, and beech, and elm—rises on the other side with equal abruptness, as if shutting in those glassy waters from all but the sky, which shines so brightly in their clear bosom; just in the bottom peeps a small sheltered farm, whose wreaths of light smoke and the white glancing wings of the wild ducks as they flit across the lake are all that give token of motion or of life. I have stood there in utter oblivion of greyhound or of hare, till moments have swelled to minutes, and minutes to hours; and so has Tom, conveying, by his exclamation of delight at its 'pleasantness,' exactly the same feeling which a poet or a painter (for it breathes the very spirit of calm and sunshiny beauty that a master painter loves) would express by different but not truer praise. He called his own home 'pleasant,' too; and there, though one loves to hear any home so called—there, I must confess, that favourite phrase, which I like almost as well as they who have no other, did seem rather misapplied. And yet it was finely placed, very finely. It stood in a sort of defile, where a road almost perpendicular wound from the top of a steep, abrupt hill, crowned with a tuft of old Scottish firs, into a dingle of fern and wild brushwood. A shallow, sullen stream oozed from the bank on one side, and, after forming a rude channel across the road, sank into a dark, deep pool, half-hidden amongst the sallows. Behind these sallows, in a nook between them and the hill, rose the uncouth and shapeless cottage of Tom Cordery. It is a scene which hangs upon the eye and the memory, striking, grand, almost sublime, and, above all, eminently foreign. No English painter would choose such a subject for an English landscape; no one in a picture would take it for English. It might pass for one of those scenes which have furnished models to Salvator Rosa. Tom's cottage was, however, very thoroughly national and characteristic: a low, ruinous hovel, the door of which was fastened with a sedulous attention to security, that contrasted strangely with the tattered thatch of the roof, and the half-broken windows. No garden, no pigsty, no pens for geese, none of the usual signs of cottage habitation—yet the house was covered with nondescript dwellings, and the very walls were animate with their extraordinary tenants: pheasants, partridges, rabbits, tame wild ducks, half-tame hares, and their enemies by nature and education, the ferrets, terriers, and mongrels, of whom his retinue consisted. Great ingenuity had been evinced in keeping separate these jarring elements; and by dint of hutches, cages, fences, kennels, and half a dozen little hurdled enclosures, resembling the sort of courts which children are apt to build round their card-houses, peace was in general tolerably well preserved. Frequent sounds, however, of fear or of anger, as their several instincts were aroused, gave tokens that it was but a forced and hollow truce, and at such times the clamour was prodigious. Tom had the remarkable tenderness for animals, when domesticated, which is so often found in those whose sole vocation seems to be their destruction in the field; and the one long, straggling, unceiled, barn-like room, which served for kitchen, bed-chamber, and hall, was cumbered with bipeds and quadrupeds of all kinds and descriptions—the sick, the delicate, the newly caught, the lying-in. In the midst of this menagerie sat Tom's wife (for he was married, though without a family—married to a woman lame of a leg as he himself was minus an arm), now trying to quiet her noisy inmates, now to outscold them. How long his friend the keeper would have continued to wink at this den of live game, none can say; the roof fairly fell in during the deep snow of last winter, killing, as poor Tom observed, two as fine litters of rabbits as ever were kittened. Remotely, I have no doubt that he himself fell a sacrifice to this misadventure. The overseer, to whom he applied to reinstate his beloved habitation, decided that the walls would never bear another roof, and removed him and his wife, as an especial favour, to a tidy, snug, comfortable room in the workhouse. The workhouse! From that hour poor Tom visibly altered. He lost his hilarity and independence. It was a change such as he had himself often inflicted, a complete change of habits, a transition from the wild to the tame. No labour was demanded of him; he went about as before, finding hares, killing rats, selling brooms, but the spirit of the man was departed. He talked of the quiet of his old abode, and the noise of the new; complained of children and other bad company; and looked down on his neighbours with the sort of contempt with which a cock pheasant might regard a barn-door fowl. Most of all did he, braced into a gipsy-like defiance of wet and cold, grumble at the warmth and dryness of his apartment. He used to foretell that it would kill him, and assuredly it did so. Never could the typhus fever have found out that wild hill-side, or have lurked under that broken roof. The free touch of the air would have chased the demon. Alas, poor Tom! warmth, and snugness, and comfort, whole windows, and an entire ceiling, were the death of him. Alas, poor Tom!

CHAPTER XII

AN OLD BACHELOR

THERE is no effect of the subtle operation of the association of ideas more universal and more curious than the manner in which the most trivial circumstances recall particular persons to our memory. Sometimes these glances of recollection are purely pleasurable. Thus I have a double liking for May Day, as being the birthday of a dear friend whose fair idea bursts upon me with the first sunbeam of that glad morning; and I can never hear certain airs of Mozart and Handel without seeming to catch an echo of that sweetest voice in which I first learnt to love them. Pretty often, however, the point of association is less elegant, and occasionally it is tolerably ludicrous. We happened to-day to have for dinner a couple of wild ducks, the first of the season; and as the master of the house, who is so little of an epicure that I am sure he would never while he lived, out of its feathers, know a wild duck from a tame—whilst he, with a little affectation of science, was squeezing the lemon and mixing Cayenne pepper with the gravy, two of us exclaimed in a breath: 'Poor Mr. Sidney!' 'Aye,' rejoined the squeezer of lemons, 'poor Sidney! I think he would have allowed that these ducks were done even to half a turn.' And then he told the story more elaborately to a young visitor, to whom Mr. Sidney was unknown—how, after eating the best parts of a couple of wild ducks, which all the company pronounced to be the finest and best dressed wild ducks ever brought to table, that judicious critic in the gastronomic art limited the too sweeping praise by gravely asserting that the birds were certainly excellent, and that the cookery would have been excellent also, had they not been roasted half a turn too much. Mr. Sidney has been dead these fifteen years; but no wild ducks have ever appeared on our homely board without recalling that observation. It is his memorable saying; his one good thing.

Mr. Sidney was, as might be conjectured, an epicure; he was also an old bachelor, a clergyman, and senior fellow of —— College, a post which he had long filled, being, although only a second son, so well provided for that he could afford to reject living after living in expectation of one favourite rectory, to which he had taken an early fancy from the pleasantness of the situation and the imputed salubrity of the air. Of the latter quality, indeed, he used to give an instance, which, however satisfactory as confirming his prepossession, could hardly have been quite agreeable, as preventing him from gratifying it — namely, the extraordinary and provoking longevity of the incumbent, who at upwards of ninety gave no sign of decay, and bade fair to emulate the age of old Parr.

Whilst waiting for the expected living, Mr. Sidney, who disliked a college residence, built himself a very pretty house in our neighbourhood, which he called his home; and where he lived, as much as a love of Bath and Brighton and London and lords would let him. He counted many noble families amongst his near connections, and passed a good deal of his time at their country seats—a life for which he was by character and habit peculiarly fitted.

In person he was a tall, stout, gentlemanly man, 'about fifty, or by 'r lady inclining to threescore,' with fine features, a composed gravity of countenance and demeanour, a bald head most accurately powdered, and a very graceful bow—quite the pattern of an elderly man of fashion. His conversation was in excellent keeping with the calm imperturbability of his countenance and the sedate gravity of his manner—smooth, dull, commonplace, exceedingly safe, and somewhat imposing. He spoke so little that people really fell into the mistake of imagining that he thought; and the tone of decision with which he would advance some second-hand opinion was well calculated to confirm the mistake. Gravity was certainly his chief characteristic, and yet it was not a clerical gravity either. He had none of the generic marks of his profession. Although perfectly decorous in life and word and thought, no stranger ever took Mr. Sidney for a clergyman. He never did any duty anywhere, that ever I heard of, except the agreeable duty of saying grace before dinner; and even that was often performed by some lay host, in pure forgetfulness of his guest's ordination. Indeed, but for the direction of his letters, and an eye to —— Rectory, I am persuaded that the circumstance might have slipped out of his own recollection.

His quality of old bachelor was more perceptible. There lurked under all his polish, well covered, but not concealed, the quiet selfishness, the little whims, the precise habits, the primness and priggishness of that disconsolate condition. His man Andrews, for instance, valet, groom, and body-servant abroad; butler, cook, caterer, and major-domo at home; tall, portly, powdered, and black-coated as his master, and like him in all things but the knowing pigtail which stuck out horizontally above his shirt collar, giving a ludicrous dignity to his appearance — Andrews, who, constant as the dial pointed nine, carried up his chocolate and shaving water, and regular as 'the chimes at midnight,' prepared his white - wine whey; who never forgot his gouty shoe in travelling (once for two days he had a slight touch of that gentlemanly disorder), and never gave him the newspaper unaired—to whom could this jewel of a valet, this matchless piece of clockwork belong, but an old bachelor? And his little dog Viper, unparagoned of terriers, black, sleek, sharp, and shrewish; who would beg and sneeze and fetch and carry like a Christian; eat olives and sweetmeats and mustard, drink coffee and wine and liqueurs—who but an old bachelor could have taught Viper his multifarious accomplishments?

Little Viper was a most useful person in his way; for although Mr. Sidney was a very creditable acquaintance to meet on the king's highway (your dull man, if he rides well, should never think of dismounting), or even on the level ground of a carpet, in the crowd of a large party, yet, when he happened to drop in to take a family dinner—a pretty frequent habit of his when in the country—then Viper's talents were inestimable in relieving the ennui occasioned by that grave piece of gentility his master, 'not only *dull* in himself, but the cause of *dullness* in others.' Anything to pass away the heavy hours, till whist or piquet relieved the female world from his intolerable silence.

In other respects these visits were sufficiently perplexing.

Every housewife can tell what a formidable guest is an epicure who comes to take pot-luck—how sure it is to be bad luck, especially when the unfortunate hostess lives five miles from a market town. Mr. Sidney always came unseasonably, on washing-day or Saturday, or the day before a great party. So sure as we had a scrap dinner, so sure came he. My dear mother, who, with true benevolence and hospitality, cared much for her guest's comfort, and nothing for her own pride, used to grieve over his discomfiture, and try all that could be done by potted meats and omelets, and little things tossed up on a sudden, to amend the bill of fare. But cookery is an obstinate art, and will have its time—however you may force the component parts, there is no forcing a dinner. Mr. Sidney had the evil habit of arriving just as the last bell rang; and in spite of all the hurry-scurry in the kitchen department, the new niceties and the old homely dishes were sure to disagree. There was a total want of keeping. The kickshaws were half-raw, the solids were mere rags; the vegetables were cold; the soup was scalding; no shallots to the rump steaks; no mushrooms with the broiled chicken; no fish; no oysters; no ice; no pine-apple. Poor Mr. Sidney! He must have had a great regard for us to put up with our bad dinners.

Perhaps the chance of a rubber had something to do with his visits to our house. If there be such a thing as a ruling passion, the love of whist was his. Cards were not merely the amusement but the business of his life. I do not mean as a money-making speculation; for although he belonged to a fashionable club in London, and to every card-meeting of decent gentility within reach of his country home, he never went beyond a regular moderate stake, and could not be induced to bet even by the rashest defier of calculation, or the most provoking undervaluer of his play. It always seemed to me that he regarded whist as far too important and scientific a pursuit to be degraded into an affair of gambling. It had in his eyes all the dignity of a study; an acquirement equally gentlemanly and clerical. It was undoubtedly his test of ability. He had the value of a man of family and a man of the world for rank, and wealth, and station, and dignities of all sorts. No human being entertained a higher respect for a king, a prince, a prime minister, a duke, a bishop, or a lord. But these were conventional feelings. His genuine and unfeigned veneration was reserved for him who played a good rubber, a praise he did not easily give. He was a capital player himself, and held all his country competitors, except one, in supreme and undisguised contempt, which they endured to admiration. I wonder they did not send him to Coventry. He was the most disagreeable partner in the world, and nearly as unpleasant an adversary; for he not only enforced the Pythagorean law of science, which makes one hate whist so, but used to distribute quite impartially to every one at table little disagreeable observations on every card they played. It was not scolding, or grumbling, or fretting; one has a sympathy with those expressions of feeling, and at the worst can scold again; it was a smooth, polite commentary on the errors of the party, delivered in the calm tone of undoubted superiority with which a great critic will sometimes take a small poet, or a batch of poets, to task in a review. How the people could bear it!—but the world is a good-natured world, and does not like a man the less for treating it scornfully.

So passed six evenings out of the seven with Mr. Sidney; for it was pretty well known that, on the rare occurrence of his spending a day at home without company, his factotum Andrews used to have the honour of being beaten by his master in a snug game at double dummy; but what he did with himself on Sunday occasioned me some speculation. Never in my life did I see him take up a book, although he sometimes talked of Shakespeare and Milton, and Johnson and Burke, in a manner which proved that he had heard of such things; and as to the newspaper, which he did read, that was generally conned over long before night; besides, he never exhibited spectacles, and I have a notion that he could not read newspaper type at night without them. How he could possibly get through the after-coffee hours on a Sunday puzzled me long. Chance solved the problem. He came to call on us after church, and agreed to dine and sleep at our house. The moment tea was over, without the slightest apology or attempt at conversation, he drew his chair to the fire, set his feet on the fender, and fell fast asleep in the most comfortable and orderly manner possible.

It was evidently a weekly habit. Every sense and limb seemed composed to it. Viper looked up in his face, curled himself round on the hearthrug, and went to sleep too; and Andrews, just as the clock struck twelve, came in to wake him, that he might go to bed. It was clearly an invariable custom; a settled thing.

His house and grounds were kept in the neatest manner possible. There was something even disagreeable in the excessive nicety, the Dutch preciseness of the shining gravel walks, the smooth-shaven turf of the lawn, and the fine-sifted mould of the shrubberies. A few dead leaves or scattered flowers, even a weed or two, anything to take away from the artificial toy-like look of the place, would have been an improvement. Mr. Sidney, however, did not think so. He actually caused his gardener to remove those littering plants called roses and gum cistuses. Other flowers fared little better. No sooner were they in bloom than he pulled them up for fear they should drop. Indoors, matters were still worse. The rooms and furniture were very handsome, abounding in the luxurious Turkey carpets, the sofas, easy chairs, and ottomans which his habits required: and yet I never in my life saw any house which looked less comfortable. Everything was so constantly in its place, so provokingly in order, so full of naked nicety, so thoroughly old-bachelorish. No work! no books! no music! no flowers! But for those two things of life, Viper and a sparkling fire, one might have thought the place uninhabited. Once a year, indeed, it gave signs of animation, in the shape of a Christmas party. That was Mr. Sidney's shining time. Nothing could exceed the smiling hospitality of the host, or the lavish profusion of the entertainment. It breathed the very spirit of a welcome splendidly liberal: and little Viper frisked and bounded, and Andrews's tail vibrated (I was going to say wagged) with cordiality and pleasure. Andrews, on these occasions, laid aside his 'customary black' in favour of a blue coat and a white silk court waistcoat, with a light running pattern of embroidery and silver spangles, assumed to do honour to his master and the company. How much he enjoyed the applause which the wines and the cookery elicited from the gentlemen; and how anxiously he would direct the ladies' attention to a MS. collection of riddles, the compilation of some deceased countess, laid on the drawing-room table for their amusement between dinner and tea! Once, I remember, he carried his attention so far as to produce a gone-by toy, called a bandalore, for the recreation of myself and another little girl, admitted by virtue of the Christmas holidays to this annual festival. Poor Andrews! I am convinced that he considered the entertainment of the visitors quite as much his affair as his master's; and certainly they both succeeded. Never did parties pass more pleasantly. On those evenings Mr. Sidney even forgot to find fault at whist.

At last, towards the end of a severe winter, during which he had suffered much from repeated colds, the rectory of —— became vacant, and our worthy neighbour hastened to take possession. The day before his journey he called on us in the highest spirits, anticipating a renewal of health and youth in this favourite spot, and approaching nearer than I had ever heard him to a jest on the subject of looking out for a wife. Married or single, he made us promise to visit him during the ensuing summer. Alas! long before the summer arrived our poor friend was dead. He had waited for this living thirty years; he did not enjoy it thirty days.

CHAPTER XIII

THE HARD SUMMER

August 15th. Cold, cloudy, windy, wet. Here we are, in the midst of the dog-days, clustering merrily round the warm hearth, like so many crickets, instead of chirruping in the green fields like that other merry insect the grasshopper; shivering under the influence of the Jupiter Pluvius of England, the watery St. Swithin; peering at that scarce personage the sun, when he happens to make his appearance, as intently as astronomers look after a comet, or the common people stare at a balloon; exclaiming against the cold weather, just as we used to exclaim against the warm. 'What a change from last year!' is the first sentence you hear, go where you may. Everybody remarks it, and everybody complains of it; and yet in my mind it has its advantages, or at least its compensations, as everything in nature has, if we would only take the trouble to seek for them.

Last year, in spite of the love which we are now pleased to profess towards that ardent luminary, not one of the sun's numerous admirers had courage to look him in the face: there was no bearing the world till he had said 'Good night' to it. Then we might stir; then we began to wake and to live. All day long we languished under his influence in a strange dreaminess, too hot to work, too hot to read, too hot to write, too hot even to talk; sitting hour after hour in a green arbour, embowered in leafiness, letting thought and fancy float as they would. Those day-dreams were pretty things in their way; there is no denying that. But then, if one half of the world were to dream through a whole summer, like the sleeping beauty in the wood, what would become of the other?

The only office requiring the slightest exertion, which I performed in that warm weather, was watering my flowers. Common sympathy called for that labour. The poor things withered, and faded, and pined away; they almost, so to say, panted for drought. Moreover, if I had not watered them myself, I suspect that no one else would; for water last year was nearly as precious hereabout as wine. Our land springs were dried up; our wells were exhausted; our deep ponds were dwindling into mud; and geese, and ducks, and pigs, and laundresses used to look with a jealous and suspicious eye on the few and scanty half-buckets of that impure element which my trusty lackey was fain to filch for my poor geraniums and campanulas and tuberoses. We were forced to smuggle them in through my faithful adherent's territories, the stable, to avoid lectures within doors; and at last even that resource failed; my garden, my blooming garden, the joy of my eyes, was forced to go waterless like its neighbours, and became shrivelled, scorched, and sunburnt, like them. It really went to my heart to look at it.

On the other side of the house matters were still worse. What a dusty world it was, when about sunset we became cool enough to creep into it! Flowers in the court looking fit for a *hortus siccus*; mummies of plants, dried as in an oven; hollyhocks, once pink, turned into Quakers; cloves smelling of dust. Oh, dusty world! May herself looked of that complexion; so did Lizzy; so did all the houses, windows, chickens, children, trees, and pigs in the village; so above all did the shoes. No foot could make three plunges into that abyss of pulverized gravel, which had the impudence to call itself a hard road, without being clothed with a coat a quarter of an inch thick. Woe to white gowns! woe to black! Drab was your only wear.

Then, when we were out of the street, what a toil it was to mount the hill, climbing with weary steps and slow, upon the brown turf by the wayside, slippery, hot, and hard as a rock! And then if we happened to meet a carriage coming along the middle of the road—the bottomless middle— what a sandy whirlwind it was! What choking! what suffocation! No state could be more pitiable, except indeed that of the travellers who carried this misery about with them. I shall never forget the plight in which we met the coach one evening in last August, full an hour after its time, steeds and driver, carriage and passengers, all one dust. The outsides, and the horses, and the coachman, seemed reduced to a torpid quietness, the resignation of despair.

They had left off trying to better their condition, and taken refuge in a wise and patient hopelessness, bent to endure in silence the extremity of ill. The six insides, on the contrary, were still fighting against their fate, vainly struggling to ameliorate their hapless destiny. They were visibly grumbling at the weather, scolding at the dust, and heating themselves like a furnace, by striving against the heat. How well I remember the fat gentleman without his coat, who was wiping his forehead, heaving up his wig, and certainly uttering that English ejaculation which, to our national reproach, is the phrase of our language best known on the Continent! And that poor boy, red-hot, all in a flame, whose mamma, having divested her own person of all superfluous apparel, was trying to relieve his sufferings by the removal of his neckerchief—an operation which he resisted with all his might. How perfectly I remember him, as well as the pale girl who sat opposite, fanning herself with her bonnet into an absolute fever! They vanished after a while into their own dust; but I have them all before my eyes at this moment, a companion picture to Hogarth's 'Afternoon,' a standing lesson to the grumblers at cold summers.

For my part, I really like this wet season. It keeps us within, to be sure, rather more than is quite agreeable; but then we are at least awake and alive there, and the world out of doors is so much the pleasanter when we can get abroad. Everything does well, except those fastidious bipeds, men and women; corn ripens, grass grows, fruit is plentiful; there is no lack of birds to eat it, and there has not been such a wasp season these dozen years. My garden wants no watering, and is more beautiful than ever, beating my old rival in that primitive art, the pretty wife of the little mason, out and out. Measured with mine, her flowers are naught. Look at those hollyhocks, like pyramids of roses; those garlands of the *Convolvulus major* of all colours, hanging around that tall pole, like the wreathy hop-bine; those magnificent dusky cloves, breathing of the Spice Islands; those flaunting double dahlias; those splendid scarlet geraniums and those fierce and warlike flowers, the tiger lilies. Oh, how beautiful they are! Besides, the weather clears sometimes—it has cleared this evening; and here are we, after a merry walk up the hill, almost as quick as in the winter, bounding lightly along the bright green turf of the pleasant common, enticed by the gay shouts of a dozen clear young voices to linger awhile, and see the boys play at cricket.

I plead guilty to a strong partiality towards that unpopular class of beings, country boys: I have a large acquaintance amongst them, and I can almost say that I know good of many and harm of none. In general they are an open, spirited, good-humoured race, with a proneness to embrace the pleasures and eschew the evils of their condition, a capacity for happiness quite unmatched in man, or woman, or girl. They are patient, too, and bear their fate as scapegoats (for all sins whatsoever are laid, as matters of course, to their door), whether at home or abroad, with amazing resignation; and, considering the many lies of which they are the objects, they tell wonderfully few in return. The worst that can be said of them is, that they seldom, when grown to man's estate, keep the promise of their boyhood; but that is a fault to come—a fault that may not come, and ought not to be anticipated. It is astonishing how sensible they are to notice from their betters, or those whom they think such. I do not speak of money, or gifts, or praise, or the more coarse and common briberies — they are more delicate courtiers; a word, a nod, a smile, or the mere calling of them by their names, is enough to ensure their hearts and their services. Half a dozen of them, poor urchins, have run away now to bring us chairs from their several homes. 'Thank you, Joe Kirby!—you are always first. Yes, that is just the place. I shall see everything there. Have you been in yet, Joe?' 'No, ma'am! I go in next.' 'Ah, I am glad of that—and now's the time. Really that was a pretty ball of Jem Eusden's!—I was sure it would go to the wicket. Run, Joe! They are waiting for you.' There was small need to bid Joe Kirby make haste; I think he is, next to a race-horse, or a greyhound, or a deer, the fastest creature that runs—the most completely alert and active. Joe is mine especial friend, and leader of the 'tender juveniles,' as Joel Brent is of the adults. In both instances this post of honour was gained by merit, even more remarkably so in Joe's case than in Joel's; for Joe is a less boy than many of his companions (some of whom are fifteeners and

sixteeners, quite as tall and nearly as old as Tom Coper),
and a poorer than all, as may be conjectured from the
lamentable state of that patched round frock, and the
ragged condition of those unpatched shoes, which would
encumber, if anything could, the light feet that wear them.
But why should I lament the poverty that never troubles
him? Joe is the merriest and happiest creature that ever
lived twelve years in this wicked world. Care cannot come
near him. He hath a perpetual smile on his round ruddy
face, and a laugh in his hazel eye that drives the witch
away. He works at yonder farm on the top of the hill,
where he is in such repute for intelligence and good humour
that he has the honour of performing all the errands of the
house, of helping the maid, the mistress, and the master,
in addition to his own stated office of carter's boy. There he
works hard from five till seven, and then he comes here to
work still harder, under the name of play—batting, bowling,
and fielding as if for life, filling the place of four boys; being,
at a pinch, a whole eleven. The late Mr. Knyvett, the
king's organist, who used in his own person to sing twenty
parts at once of the 'Hallelujah Chorus,' so that you would
have thought he had a nest of nightingales in his throat, was
but a type of Joe Kirby. There is a sort of ubiquity about
him; he thinks nothing of being in two places at once, and
for pitching a ball, William Grey himself is nothing to him.
It goes straight to the mark like a bullet. He is king of
the cricketers from eight to sixteen, both inclusive, and
an excellent ruler he makes. Nevertheless, in the best-
ordered states there will be grumblers, and we have an
opposition here in the shape of Jem Eusden.

Jem Eusden is a stunted lad of thirteen, or thereabout,
lean, small, and short, yet strong and active. His face is
of an extraordinary ugliness, colourless, withered, haggard,
with a look of extreme age, much increased by hair so light
that it might rather pass for white than flaxen. He is
constantly arrayed in the blue cap and old-fashioned coat,
the costume of an endowed school to which he belongs;
where he sits still all day, and rushes into the field at night,
fresh, untired, and ripe for action, to scold, and brawl, and
storm, and bluster. He hates Joe Kirby, whose immovable good humour, broad smiles, and knowing nods, must

certainly be very provoking to so fierce and turbulent a
spirit; and he has himself (being, except by rare accident,
no great player) the preposterous ambition of wishing to be
manager of the sports. In short, he is a demagogue in
embryo, with every quality necessary to a splendid success
in that vocation—a strong voice, a fluent utterance, an
incessant iteration, and a frontless impudence. He is
a great 'scholar,' too, to use the country phrase; his
'piece,' as our village schoolmaster terms a fine sheet of
flourishing writing, something between a valentine and a
sampler, enclosed within a border of little coloured prints—
his last, I remember, was encircled by an engraved history
of Moses, beginning at the finding in the bulrushes, with
Pharaoh's daughter, dressed in a rose-coloured gown and
blue feathers—his piece is not only the admiration of the
school, but of the parish, and is sent triumphantly round
from house to house at Christmas, to extort halfpence and
sixpences from all encouragers of learning — Montem in
miniature. The Mosaic history was so successful that the
produce enabled Jem to purchase a bat and ball, which,
besides adding to his natural arrogance (for the little
pedant actually began to mutter against being eclipsed by a
dunce, and went so far as to challenge Joe Kirby to a trial in
Practice or the Rule of Three), gave him, when compared
with the general poverty, a most unnatural preponderance
in the cricket state. He had the ways and means in his
hands (for, alas! the hard winter had made sad havoc
among the bats, and the best ball was a bad one)—he had
the ways and means, could withhold the supplies, and his
party was beginning to wax strong, when Joe received a
present of two bats and a ball for the youngsters in general,
and himself in particular—and Jem's adherents left him on
the spot; they ratted, to a man, that very evening. Notwithstanding this desertion, their forsaken leader has in
nothing relaxed from his pretensions or his ill humour. He
still quarrels and brawls as if he had a faction to back him,
and thinks nothing of contending with both sides, the ins
and the outs, secure of out-talking the whole field. He has
been squabbling these ten minutes, and is just marching
off now with his own bat (he has never deigned to use one of
Joe's) in his hand. What an ill-conditioned hobgoblin it is!

And yet there is something bold and sturdy about him too.
I should miss Jem Eusden.

Ah, there is another deserter from the party! my friend
the little hussar—I do not know his name, and call him after
his cap and jacket.   He is a very remarkable person, about
the age of eight years, the youngest piece of gravity and
dignity I ever encountered; short, and square, and upright,
and slow, with a fine bronzed flat visage, resembling those
convertible signs the 'Broad Face' and the 'Saracen's Head,'
which, happening to be next-door neighbours in the town of
B——, I never know apart, resembling, indeed, any face that
is open-eyed and immovable, the very sign of a boy!   He
stalks about with his hands in his breeches pockets, like a
piece of machinery; sits leisurely down when he ought to field,
and never gets farther in batting than to stop the ball.   His
is the only voice never heard in the mêlée; I doubt, indeed,
if he have one, which may be partly the reason of a circumstance that I record to his honour, his fidelity to Jem Eusden,
to whom he has adhered, through every change of fortune,
with a tenacity proceeding perhaps from an instinctive
consciousness that the loquacious leader talks enough for
two.   He is the only thing resembling a follower that our
demagogue possesses, and is cherished by him accordingly.
Jem quarrels for him, scolds for him, pushes for him; and but
for Joe Kirby's invincible good-humour, and a just discrimi-
nation of the innocent from the guilty, the activity of Jem's
friendship would get the poor hussar ten drubbings a day.

But it is growing late.   The sun has set a long time.
Only see what a gorgeous colouring has spread itself over
those parting masses of clouds in the west—what a train of
rosy light!   We shall have a fine sunshiny day to-morrow—a
blessing not to be undervalued, in spite of my late vitu-
peration of heat.   Shall we go home now?   And shall we
take the longest but prettiest road, that by the green lanes?
This way to the left, round the corner of the common, past
Mr. Welles's cottage, and our path lays straight before us.
How snug and comfortable that cottage looks!   Its little
yard all alive with the cow, and the mare, and the colt almost
as large as the mare, and the young foal, and the great
yard dog, all so fat!   Fenced in with hay-rick, and wheat-
rick, and bean-stack, and backed by the long garden, the

spacious drying-ground, the fine orchard, and that large field quartered into four different crops. How comfortable this cottage looks, and how well the owners earn their comforts! They are the most prosperous pair in the parish —she a laundress, with twenty times more work than she can do, unrivalled in flounces and shirt-frills, and such delicacies of the craft; he, partly a farmer, partly a farmer's man, tilling his own ground, and then tilling other people's —affording a proof, even in this declining age, when the circumstances of so many worthy members of the community seem to have 'an alacrity in sinking,' that it is possible to amend them by sheer industry. He, who was born in the workhouse, and bred up as a parish boy, has now, by mere manual labour, risen to the rank of a landowner, pays rates and taxes, grumbles at the times, and is called Master Welles—the title next to Mister—that by which Shakespeare was called; what would man have more? His wife, besides being the best laundress in the county, is a comely woman still. There she stands at the spring, dipping up water for to-morrow—the clear, deep, silent spring, which sleeps so peacefully under its high flowery bank, red with the tall spiral stalks of the foxglove and their rich pendent bells, blue with the beautiful forget-me-not, that gem-like blossom which looks like a living jewel of turquoise and topaz. It is almost too late to see its beauty; and here is the pleasant shady lane, where the high elms will shut out the little twilight that remains. Ah, but we shall have the fairies' lamps to guide us, the stars of the earth, the glow-worms! Here they are, three almost together. Do you not see them? One seems tremulous, vibrating, as if on the extremity of a leaf of grass; the others are deeper in the edge, in some green cell on which their light falls with an emerald lustre. I hope my friends the cricketers will not come this way home. I would not have the pretty creatures removed for more than I care to say, and in this matter I would hardly trust Joe Kirby—boys so love to stick them in their hats. But this lane is quite deserted. It is only a road from field to field. No one comes here at this hour. They are quite safe; and I shall walk here to-morrow and visit them again. And now, good night! beautiful insects, lamps of the fairies, good night!

CHAPTER XIV

NUTTING

September 26th. One of those delicious autumnal days,
when the air, the sky, and the earth seem lulled into an
universal calm, softer and milder even than May. We
sallied forth for a walk, in a mood congenial to the weather
and the season, avoiding by mutual consent the bright and
sunny common and the gay high road, and stealing through
shady unfrequented lanes, where we were not likely to meet
any one—not even the pretty family procession which in
other years we used to contemplate with so much interest—
the father, mother, and children returning from the wheat-
field, the little ones laden with bristling, close-tied bunches
of wheat-ears, their own gleanings, or a bottle and a basket
which had contained their frugal dinner, whilst the mother
would carry her babe, hushing and lulling it, and the father
and an elder child trudged after with the cradle, all seeming
weary, and all happy. We shall not see such a procession
as this to-day; for the harvest is nearly over, the fields
are deserted, the silence may almost be felt. Except the
wintry notes of the redbreast, Nature herself is mute. But
how beautiful, how gentle, how harmonious, how rich!
The rain has preserved to the herbage all the freshness and
verdure of spring, and the world of leaves has lost nothing of
its midsummer brightness, and the harebell is on the banks,
and the woodbine in the hedges, and the low furze, which
the lambs cropped in the spring, has burst again into its
golden blossoms.

All is beautiful that the eye can see, perhaps the more
beautiful for being shut in with a forest-like closeness. We
have no prospect in this labyrinth of lanes, cross-roads,
mere cartways, leading to the innumerable little farms into
which this part of the parish is divided. Uphill or down,
these quiet woody lanes scarcely give us a peep at the world,
except when, leaning over a gate, we look into one of the

small enclosures, hemmed in with hedgerows, so closely
set with growing timber, that the meady opening looks almost like a glade in a wood; or when some cottage, planted
at a corner of one of the little greens formed by the meeting
of these crossways, almost startles us by the unexpected
sight of the dwellings of men in such a solitude. But that
we have more of hill and dale, and that our cross-roads are
excellent in their kind, this side of our parish would resemble
the description given of La Vendée in Madame Laroche-
Jacquelin's most interesting book.[1] I am sure if wood can
entitle a country to be called Le Bocage, none can have a
better right to the name. Even this pretty snug farm-
house on the hill-side, with its front covered with the rich
vine, which goes wreathing up to the very top of the clustered
chimney, and its sloping orchard full of fruit—even this
pretty quiet nest can hardly peep out of its leaves. Ah!
they are gathering in the orchard harvest. Look at that
young rogue in the old mossy apple-tree—that great tree,
bending with the weight of its golden rennets—see how he
pelts his little sister beneath with apples as red and as
round as her own cheeks, while she, with her outstretched
frock, is trying to catch them, and laughing and offering to
pelt again as often as one bobs against her; and look at that
still younger imp, who, as grave as a judge, is creeping on
hands and knees under the tree, picking up the apples as
they fall so deedily,[2] and depositing them so honestly in the
great basket on the grass, already fixed so firmly and opened
so widely, and filled almost to overflowing by the brown
rough fruitage of the golden rennet's next neighbour the
russeting; and see that smallest urchin of all, seated apart in
infantine state on the turfy bank, with that toothsome piece
of deformity, a crumpling, in each hand, now biting from
one sweet, hard, juicy morsel, and now from another. Is not

---

[1] An almost equally interesting account of that very peculiar and interesting scenery may be found in *The Maid of La Vendée*, an English novel,
remarkable for its simplicity and truth of painting, written by Mrs. Le Noir,
the daughter of Christopher Smart, and inheritrix of much of his talent.
Her works deserve to be better known.

[2] 'Deedily'—I am not quite sure that this word is good English; but it is
genuine Hampshire, and is used by the most correct of female writers, Miss
Austen. It means (and it is no small merit that it has no exact synonym)
anything done with a profound and plodding attention, an action which
engrosses all the powers of mind and body.

that a pretty English picture? And then, farther up the
orchard, that bold hardy lad, the eldest-born, who has scaled
(Heaven knows how!) the tall straight upper branch of
that great pear-tree, and is sitting there as securely and as
fearlessly, in as much real safety and apparent danger, as a
sailor on the top-mast. Now he shakes the tree with a
mighty swing that brings down a pelting shower of stony
bergamots, which the father gathers rapidly up, whilst the
mother can hardly assist for her motherly fear—a fear which
only spurs the spirited boy to bolder ventures. Is not that
a pretty picture? And they are such a handsome family
too, the Brookers. I do not know that there is any gipsy
blood, but there is the true gipsy complexion, richly brown,
with cheeks and lips so deeply red, black hair curling close
to their heads in short crisp rings, white shining teeth—and
such eyes! That sort of beauty entirely eclipses your mere
roses and lilies. Even Lizzy, the prettiest of fair children,
would look poor and watery by the side of Willy Brooker,
the sober little personage who is picking up the apples with
his small chubby hands, and filling the basket so orderly,
next to his father the most useful man in the field. 'Willy!
He hears without seeing; for we are quite hidden by the
high bank, and a spreading hawthorn bush that overtops it,
though between the lower branches and the grass we have
found a convenient peep-hole. 'Willy!' The voice sounds
to him like some fairy dream, and the black eyes are raised
from the ground with sudden wonder, the long silky eyelashes thrown back till they rest on the delicate brow, and
a deeper blush is burning on those dark cheeks, and a smile is
dimpling about those scarlet lips. But the voice is silent
now, and the little quiet boy, after a moment's pause, is
gone coolly to work again. He is indeed a most lovely
child. I think some day or other he must marry Lizzy; I
shall propose the match to their respective mammas. At
present the parties are rather too young for a wedding—the
intended bridegroom being, as I should judge, six, or thereabout, and the fair bride barely five—but at least we might
have a betrothment after the royal fashion; there could be
no harm in that. Miss Lizzy, I have no doubt, would be
as demure and coquettish as if ten winters more had gone
over her head, and poor Willy would open his innocent

black eyes, and wonder what was going forward. They would be the very Oberon and Titania of the village, the fairy king and queen.

Ah! here is the hedge along which the periwinkle wreathes and twines so profusely, with its ever-green leaves shining like the myrtle, and its starry blue flowers. It is seldom found wild in this part of England; but when we do meet with it, it is so abundant and so welcome, the very robin redbreast of flowers, a winter friend.   Unless in those unfrequent frosts which destroy all vegetation, it blossoms from September to June, surviving the last lingering crane's-bill, forerunning the earliest primrose, hardier even than the mountain daisy—peeping out from beneath the snow, looking at itself in the ice, smiling through the tempests of life, and yet welcoming and enjoying the sunbeams.   Oh, to be like that flower!

The little spring that has been bubbling under the hedge all along the hill-side, begins, now that we have mounted the eminence and are imperceptibly descending, to deviate into a capricious variety of clear deep pools and channels, so narrow and so choked with weeds that a child might overstep them.   The hedge has also changed its character. It is no longer the close compact vegetable wall of hawthorn, and maple, and brier-roses, intertwined with bramble and woodbine, and crowned with large elms or thickly set saplings.   No! the pretty meadow which rises high above us, backed and almost surrounded by a tall coppice, needs no defence on our side but its own steep bank, garnished with tufts of broom, with pollard-oaks wreathed with ivy, and here and there with long patches of hazel overhanging the water. 'Ah, there are still nuts on that bough!' and in an instant my dear companion, active and eager and delighted as a boy, has hooked down with his walking-stick one of the lissom hazel stalks, and cleared it of its tawny clusters, and in another moment he has mounted the bank, and is in the midst of the nuttery, now transferring the spoil from the lower branches into that vast variety of pockets which gentlemen carry about them, now bending the tall tops into the lane, holding them down by main force, so that I might reach them and enjoy the pleasure of collecting some of the plunder myself. A very great pleasure he knew it would be. I doffed my shawl, tucked up my flounces, turned my straw bonnet into a basket, and began gathering and scrambling—for, manage it how you may, nutting is scrambling work; those boughs, however tightly you may grasp them by the young fragrant twigs and the bright green leaves, will recoil and burst away; but there is a pleasure even in that; so on we go, scrambling and gathering with all our might and all our glee. Oh, what an enjoyment! All my life long I have had a passion for that sort of seeking which implies finding (the secret, I believe, of the love of field sports, which is in man's mind a natural impulse) — therefore I love violeting; therefore, when we had a fine garden, I used to love to gather strawberries, and cut asparagus, and, above all, to collect the filberts from the shrubberies; but this hedgerow nutting beats that sport all to nothing. That was a make-believe thing compared with this; there was no surprise, no suspense, no unexpectedness —it was as inferior to this wild nutting as the turning out of a bag-fox is to unearthing the fellow, in the eyes of a staunch fox-hunter.

Oh, what an enjoyment this nut-gathering is! They are in such abundance that it seems as if there were not a boy in the parish, nor a young man, nor a young woman—for a basket of nuts is the universal tribute of country gallantry; our pretty damsel Harriet has had at least half a dozen this season; but no one has found out these. And they are so full, too, we lose half of them from over-ripeness; they drop from the socket at the slightest motion. If we lose, there is one who finds. May is as fond of nuts as a squirrel, and cracks the shell and extracts the kernel with equal dexterity. Her white glossy head is upturned now to watch them as they fall. See how her neck is thrown back like that of a swan, and how beautifully her folded ears quiver with expectation, and how her quick eye follows the rustling noise, and her light feet dance and pat the ground, and leap up with eagerness, seeming almost sustained in the air, just as I have seen her when Brush is beating a hedgerow, and she knows from his questing that there is a hare afoot. See, she has caught that nut just before it touched the water; but the water would have been no defence—she fishes them from the bottom, she delves after them amongst the matted grass; even my bonnet, how beggingly she looks at that! 'Oh, what a pleasure nutting is! Is it not, May? But the pockets are almost full, and so is the basket-bonnet, and that bright watch the sun says it is late; and after all it is wrong to rob the poor boys—is it not, May? May shakes her graceful head denyingly, as if she understood the question. 'And we must go home now—must we not? But we will come nutting again some time or other—shall we not, my May?'

CHAPTER XV

THE VISIT

October 27th. A lovely autumnal day; the air soft, balmy, genial; the sky of that softened and delicate blue upon which the eye loves to rest—the blue which gives such relief to the rich beauty of the earth, all around glowing in the ripe and mellow tints of the most gorgeous of the seasons. Really such an autumn may well compensate our English climate for the fine spring of the south, that spring of which the poets talk, but which we so seldom enjoy. Such an autumn glows upon us like a splendid evening; it is the very sunset of the year; and I have been tempted forth into a wider range of enjoyment than usual. This *walk* (if I may use the Irish figure of speech called a bull) will be a *ride.* A very dear friend has beguiled me into accompanying her in her pretty equipage to her beautiful home, four miles off; and having sent forward in the style of a running footman the servant who had driven her, she assumes the reins, and off we set.

My fair companion is a person whom nature and fortune would have spoiled if they could. She is one of those striking women whom a stranger cannot pass without turning to look again: tall and finely proportioned, with a bold Roman contour of figure and feature, a delicate English complexion, and an air of distinction altogether her own. Her beauty is duchess - like. She seems born to wear feathers and diamonds, and to form the grace and ornament of a court; and the noble frankness and simplicity of her countenance and manner confirm the impression. Destiny has, however, dealt more kindly by her. She is the wife of a rich country gentleman of high descent and higher attainments, to whom she is most devotedly attached; the mother of a little girl as lovely as herself, and the delight of all who have the happiness of her acquaintance, to whom she is endeared not merely by her remarkable sweetness of temper, and kindness of heart, but by the singular ingenuousness and openness of character which communicate an indescribable charm to her conversation. She is as transparent as water. You may see every colour, every shade of a mind as lofty and beautiful as her person. Talking with her is like being in the Palace of Truth described by Madame de Genlis; and yet so kindly are her feelings, so great her indulgence to the little failings and foibles of our common nature, so intense her sympathy with the wants, the wishes, the sorrows, and the happiness of her fellow-creatures, that, with all her frank speaking, I never knew her make an enemy or lose a friend.

But we must get on. What would she say if she knew I was putting her into print? We must get on up the hill. Ah, that is precisely what we are not likely to do! This horse, this beautiful and high-bred horse, well fed, and fat and glossy, who stood prancing at our gate like an Arabian, has suddenly turned sulky. He does not indeed stand quite still, but his way of moving is little better—the slowest and most sullen of all walks. Even they who ply the hearse at funerals, sad-looking beasts who totter under black feathers, go faster. It is of no use to admonish him by whip, or rein, or word. The rogue has found out that it is a weak and tender hand that guides him now. Oh, for one pull, one stroke of his old driver the groom! How he would fly! But there is the groom half a mile before us, out of earshot, clearing the ground at a capital rate, beating us hollow. He has just turned the top of the hill, and in a moment—aye, *now* he is out of sight, and will undoubtedly so continue till he meets us at the lawn gate. Well, there is no great harm. It is only prolonging the pleasure of enjoying together this charming scenery in this fine weather. If once we make up our minds not to care how slowly our steed goes, not to fret ourselves by vain exertions, it is no matter what his pace may be. There is little doubt of his getting home by sunset, and that will content us. He is, after all, a fine noble animal; and perhaps when he finds that we are determined to give him his way, he may relent and give us ours. All his sex are sticklers for dominion; though, when it is undisputed, some of them are generous enough to abandon it. Two or three of the most discreet

wives of my acquaintance contrive to manage their husbands sufficiently with no better secret than this seeming
submission, and in our case the example has the more weight
since we have no possible way of helping ourselves.

Thus philosophizing, we reached the top of the hill, and
viewed with 'reverted eyes' the beautiful prospect that lay
bathed in golden sunshine behind us. Cowper says, with
that boldness of expressing in poetry the commonest and
simplest feelings, which is perhaps one great secret of his
originality:

> Scenes must be beautiful, which, daily seen,
> Please daily, and whose novelty survives
> Long knowledge and the scrutiny of years.

Every day I walk up this hill—every day I pause at the
top to admire the broad winding road with the green waste
on each side, uniting it with the thickly timbered hedgerows;
the two pretty cottages at unequal distances, placed so as to
mark the bends; the village beyond, with its mass of roofs
and clustered chimneys peeping through the trees; and the
rich distance, where cottages, mansions, churches, towns,
seem embowered in some wide forest, and shut in by blue
shadowy hills. Every day I admire this most beautiful
landscape; yet never did it seem to me so fine or so glowing
as now. All the tints of the glorious autumn, orange, tawny,
yellow, red, are poured in profusion amongst the bright
greens of the meadows and turnip-fields, till the eyes are
satiated with colour; and then before us we have the
common with its picturesque roughness of surface tufted
with cottages, dappled with water, edging off on one side
into fields and farms and orchards, and terminated on the
other by the princely oak avenue. What a richness and
variety the wild broken ground gives to the luxuriant
cultivation of the rest of the landscape! Cowper has
described it for me. How perpetually, as we walk in the
country, his vivid pictures recur to the memory! Here is
his common and mine:

> The common overgrown with fern, and rough
> With prickly gorse, that, shapeless and deform'd
> And dangerous to the touch, has yet its bloom,
> And decks itself with ornaments of gold . . .

> . . . there the turf
> Smells fresh, and, rich in odoriferous herbs
> And fungous fruits of earth, regales the sense
> With luxury of unexpected sweets.

The description is exact. There, too, to the left is my cricket ground (Cowper's common wanted that finishing grace); and there stands one solitary urchin, as if in contemplation of its past and future glories; for, alas! cricket is over for the season. Ah! it is Ben Kirby, next brother to Joe, king of the youngsters, and probably his successor— for this Michaelmas has cost us Joe. He is promoted from the farm to the mansion house, two miles off; there he cleans shoes, rubs knives, and runs on errands, and is, as his mother expresses it, 'a sort of 'prentice to the footman.' I should not wonder if Joe, some day or other, should overtop the footman, and rise to be butler; and his splendid prospects must be our consolation for the loss of this great favourite. In the meantime we have Ben.

Ben Kirby is a year younger than Joe, and the school-fellow and rival of Jem Eusden. To be sure his abilities lie in rather a different line: Jem is a scholar, Ben is a wag; Jem is great in figures and writing, Ben in faces and mischief. His master says of him, that if there were two such in the school he must resign his office; and as far as my observation goes, the worthy pedagogue is right. Ben is, it must be confessed, a great corrupter of gravity. He hath an exceeding aversion to authority and decorum, and a wonderful boldness and dexterity in overthrowing the one and puzzling the other. His contortions of visage are astounding. His 'power over his own muscles and those of other people' is almost equal to that of Liston; and indeed the original face, flat and square and Chinese in its shape, of a fine tan complexion, with a snub nose, and a slit for a mouth, is nearly as comical as that matchless performer's. When aided by Ben's singular mobility of feature, his knowing winks and grins and shrugs and nods, together with a certain dry shrewdness, a habit of saying sharp things, and a marvellous gift of impudence, it forms as fine a specimen as possible of a humorous country boy, an oddity in embryo. Everybody likes Ben, except his butts (which may perhaps comprise half his acquaintance); and of them no one so thoroughly hates and dreads him as our parish schoolmaster, a most worthy King Log,. whom Ben dumb-founds twenty times a day. He is a great ornament of the cricket ground, has a real genius for the game, and displays it after a very original manner, under the disguise of awkwardness—as the clown shows off his agility in a panto-mime. Nothing comes amiss to him. By the by, he would have been the very lad for us in our present dilemma; not a horse in England could master Ben Kirby. But we are too far from him now—and perhaps it is as well that we are so. I believe the rogue has a kindness for me, in remembrance of certain apples and nuts which my usual companion, who delights in his wit, is accustomed to dole out to him. But it is a Robin Goodfellow nevertheless, a perfect Puck, that loves nothing on earth so well as mis-chief. Perhaps the horse may be the safer conductor of the two.

The avenue is quite alive to-day. Old women are picking up twigs and acorns, and pigs of all sizes doing their utmost to spare them the latter part of the trouble; boys and girls groping for beech-nuts under yonder clump; and a group of younger elves collecting as many dead leaves as they can find to feed the bonfire which is smoking away so briskly amongst the trees—a sort of rehearsal of the grand bonfire nine days hence; of the loyal conflagration of the arch-traitor Guy Fawkes, which is annually solemnized in the avenue, accompanied with as much of squibbery and crackery as our boys can beg or borrow—not to say steal. Ben Kirby is a great man on the 5th November. All the savings of a month, the hoarded halfpence, the new farthings, the very luck-penny, go off *in fumo* on that night. For my part, I like this daylight mockery better. There is no gunpowder—odious gunpowder!—no noise but the merry shouts of the small fry, so shrill and happy, and the cawing of the rooks, who are wheeling in large circles overhead, and wondering what is going forward in their territory, seeming in their loud clamour to ask what that light smoke may mean that curls so prettily amongst their old oaks, towering as if to meet the clouds. There is something very intelligent in the ways of that black people the rooks, particularly in their wonder. I suppose it results from their numbers and their unity of purpose, a sort of collective and corporate wisdom. Yet geese congregate also; and geese never by any chance look wise. But then geese are a domestic fowl; we have spoiled them; and rooks are free commoners of nature, who use the habitations we provide for them, tenant our groves and our avenues, but never dream of becoming our subjects.

What a labyrinth of a road this is! I do think there are four turnings in the short half-mile between the avenue and the mill. And what a pity, as my companion observes— not that our good and jolly miller, the very representative of the old English yeomanry, should be so rich, but that one consequence of his riches should be the pulling down of the prettiest old mill that ever looked at itself in the Loddon, with the picturesque, low-browed, irregular cottage, which stood with its light-pointed roof, its clustered chimneys, and its ever-open door, looking like the real abode of comfort and hospitality, to build this huge, staring, frightful, red-brick mill, as ugly as a manufactory, and this great square house, ugly and red to match, just behind. The old buildings always used to remind me of Woollett's beautiful engraving of a scene in the *Maid of the Mill*. It will be long before any artist will make a drawing of this. Only think of this redness in a picture! this boiled lobster of a house! Falstaff's description of Bardolph's nose would look pale in the comparison.

Here is that monstrous machine of a tilted wagon, with its load of flour, and its four fat horses. I wonder whether our horse will have the decency to get out of the way. If he does not, I am sure we cannot make him; and that enormous ship upon wheels, that ark on dry land, would roll over us like the car of Juggernaut. Really—oh no! there is no danger now. I should have remembered that it is my friend Samuel Long who drives the mill team. He will take care of us. 'Thank you, Samuel!' And Samuel has put us on our way, steered us safely past his wagon, escorted us over the bridge; and now, having seen us through our immediate difficulties, has parted from us with a very civil bow and good-humoured smile, as one who is always civil and good-humoured, but with a certain triumphant, masterful look in his eyes, which I have noted in men, even

the best of them, when a woman gets into straits by attempting manly employments. He has done us great good,
though, and may be allowed his little feeling of superiority.
The parting salute he bestowed on our steed, in the shape of
an astounding crack of his huge whip, has put that refractory
animal on his mettle. On we go! past the glazier's pretty
house, with its porch and its filbert walk; along the narrow
lane bordered with elms, whose fallen leaves have made
the road one yellow; past that little farm-house with the
horse-chestnut trees before, glowing like oranges; past the
whitewashed school on the other side, gay with October
roses; past the park, and the lodge, and the mansion, where
once dwelt the great Earl of Clarendon—and now the
rascal has begun to discover that Samuel Long and his whip
are a mile off, and that his mistress is driving him, and he
slackens his pace accordingly. Perhaps he feels the beauty
of the road just here, and goes slowly to enjoy it. Very
beautiful it certainly is. The park paling forms the boundary on one side, with fine clumps of oak, and deer in all
attitudes; the water, tufted with alders, flowing along on
the other. Another turn, and the water winds away,
succeeded by a low hedge, and a sweep of green meadows:
whilst the park and its paling are replaced by a steep bank,
on which stands a small, quiet, village ale-house; and higher
up, embosomed in wood, is the little country church with
its sloping churchyard and its low white steeple, peeping
out from amongst magnificent yew-trees:

> Huge trunks! and each particular trunk a growth
> Of intertwisted fibres serpentine
> Up-coiling, and inveterately convolved.
>
> WORDSWORTH.

No village church was ever more happily placed. It is the
very image of the peace and humbleness inculcated within
its walls.

Ah, here is a higher hill rising before us, almost like a
mountain! How grandly the view opens as we ascend over
that wild bank, overgrown with fern, and heath, and gorse,
and between those tall hollies, glowing with their coral
berries! What an expanse! But we have little time to
gaze at present; for that piece of perversity, our horse, who
has walked over so much level ground, has now, inspired,

I presume, by a desire to revisit his stable, taken it into that unaccountable noddle of his to trot up this, the very steepest hill in the county. Here we are on the top; and in five minutes we have reached the lawn gate, and are in the very midst of that beautiful piece of art or nature (I do not know to which class it belongs), the pleasure ground of F—— Hill. Never was the 'prophetic eye of taste' exerted with more magical skill than in these plantations. Thirty years ago this place had no existence; it was a mere undistinguished tract of field and meadow and common land; now it is a mimic forest, delighting the eye with the finest combinations of trees and shrubs, the rarest effects of form and foliage, and bewildering the mind with its green glades, and impervious recesses, and apparently interminable extent. It is the triumph of landscape gardening, and never more beautiful than in this autumn sunset, lighting up the ruddy beech and the spotted sycamore, and gilding the shining fir-cones that hang so thickly amongst the dark pines. The robins are singing around us, as if they too felt the magic of the hour. How gracefully the road winds through the leafy labyrinth, leading imperceptibly to the more orna-mented sweep! Here we are at the door amidst geraniums, and carnations, and jasmines, still in flower. Ah, here is a flower sweeter than all, a bird gayer than the robin, the little bird that chirps to the tune of 'Mamma! mamma!' the bright-faced fairy, whose tiny feet come pattering along, making a merry music, mamma's own Frances! And following her guidance, here we are in the dear round room time enough to catch the last rays of the sun, as they light the noble landscape which lies like a panorama around us, lingering longest on that long island of old thorns and stunted oaks, the oasis of B—— Heath, and then vanishing in a succession of gorgeous clouds.

October 28th. Another soft and brilliant morning. But the pleasures of to-day must be written in shorthand. I have left myself no room for notes of admiration.

First we drove about the coppice: an extensive wood of oak, and elm, and beech, chiefly the former, which adjoins the park paling of F—— Hill, of which demesne, indeed, it forms one of the most delightful parts. The roads through the coppice are studiously wild: so that they have the appearance of mere cart tracks; and the manner in which the ground is tumbled about, the steep declivities, the sunny slopes, the sudden swells and falls, now a close narrow valley, then a sharp ascent to an eminence commanding an immense extent of prospect, have a striking air of natural beauty, developed and heightened by the perfection of art. All this, indeed, was familiar to me; the colouring only was new. I had been there in early spring, when the fragrant palms were on the willow, and the yellow tassels on the hazel, and every twig was swelling with renewed life; and I had been there again and again in the green leafiness of midsummer; but never as now, when the dark verdure of the fir-plantations, hanging over the picturesque and unequal paling, partly covered with moss and ivy, contrasts so remarkably with the shining orange leaves of the beech, already half fallen, the pale yellow of the scattering elm, the deeper and richer tints of the oak, and the glossy stems of the 'lady of the woods,' the delicate weeping birch. The underwood is no less picturesque. The red spotted leaves and redder berries of the old thorns, the scarlet festoons of the bramble, the tall fern of every hue, seem to vie with the brilliant mosaic of the ground, now covered with dead leaves, and strewn with fir-cones, now, where a little glade intervenes, gay with various mosses and splendid fungi. How beautiful is this coppice to-day! especially where the little spring, as clear as crystal, comes bubbling out from the 'old fantastic' beech root, and trickles over the grass, bright and silent as the dew in a May morning. The wood-pigeons (who are just returned from their summer migration, and are cropping the ivy berries) add their low cooings, the very note of love, to the slight fluttering of the falling leaves in the quiet air, giving a voice to the sunshine and the beauty. This coppice is a place to live and die in. But we must go. And how fine is the ascent which leads us again into the world, past those cottages hidden as in a pit, and by that hanging orchard and that rough heathy bank! The scenery in this one spot has a wildness, and abruptness of rise and fall, rare in any part of England, rare above all in this rich and lovely but monotonous county. It is Switzerland in miniature.

And now we cross the hill to pay a morning visit to the family at the great house—another fine place, commanding another fine sweep of country. The park, studded with old trees, and sinking gently into a valley, rich in wood and water, is in the best style of ornamental landscape, though more according to the common routine of gentlemen's seats than the singularly original place which we have just left. There is, however, one distinctive beauty in the grounds of the great house—the magnificent firs which shade the terraces and surround the sweep, giving out in summer odours really Sabaean, and now in this low autumn sun producing an effect almost magical, as the huge red trunks, garlanded with ivy, stand out from the deep shadows like an army of giants. Indoors—oh, I must not take my readers indoors, or we shall never get away!—indoors the sunshine is brighter still; for there, in a lofty lightsome room, sat a damsel fair and arch and piquant, one whom Titian or Velazquez should be born again to paint, leaning over an instrument [1] as sparkling and fanciful as herself, singing pretty French romances, and Scottish Jacobite songs, and all sorts of graceful and airy drolleries picked up I know not where—an English improvisatrice! a gayer Annot Lyle!—whilst her sister, of a higher order of beauty, and with an earnest kindness in her smile that deepens its power, lends to the piano, as her father to the violin, an expression, a sensibility, a spirit, an eloquence, almost superhuman—almost divine! Oh, to hear these two instruments accompanying my dear companion (I forgot to say that she is a singer worthy to be so accompanied) in Haydn's exquisite canzonet, *She never told her Love*—to hear her voice, with all its power, its sweetness, its gush of sound, so sustained and assisted by modulations that rivalled its intensity of expression; to hear at once such poetry, such music, such execution, is a pleasure never to be forgotten, or mixed with meaner things! I seem to hear it still.

> As in the bursting springtime o'er the eye
> Of one who haunts the fields fair visions creep
> Beneath the closed lids (afore dull sleep
> Dims the quick fancy) of sweet flowers that lie
> On grassy banks, oxlip of orient dye,

[1] The dital harp.

And palest primrose and blue violet,
All in their fresh and dewy beauty set,
Pictur'd within the sense, and will not fly:
So in mine ear resounds and lives again
One mingled melody—a voice, a pair
Of instruments most voice-like!   Of the air
Rather than of the earth seems that high strain,
A spirit's song, and worthy of the train
That sooth'd old Prospero with music rare.

CHAPTER XVI

A PARTING GLANCE AT OUR VILLAGE

It is now eighteen months since our village first sat for its picture, and I cannot say farewell to my courteous readers without giving them some little intelligence of our goings-on, a sort of parting glance at us and our condition. In outward appearance it hath, I suppose, undergone less alteration than any place of its inches in the kingdom. There it stands, the same long straggling street of pretty cottages, divided by pretty gardens, wholly unchanged in size or appearance, unincreased and undiminished by a single brick. To be sure, yesterday evening a slight misfortune happened to our goodly tenement, occasioned by the unlucky diligence mentioned in my first notice, which, under the conduct of a sleepy coachman and a restive horse, contrived to knock down and demolish the wall of our court, and fairly to drive through the front garden, thereby destroying sundry curious stocks, carnations, and geraniums. It is a mercy that the unruly steed was content with battering the wall; for the messuage itself would come about our ears at the touch of a finger, and really there is one little end parlour, an afterthought of the original builder, which stands so temptingly in the way that I wonder the sagacious quadruped missed it. There was quite din enough without that addition. The three insides (ladies) squalling from the interior of that commodious vehicle; the outsides (gentlemen) swearing on the roof; the coachman, still half-asleep, but unconsciously blowing his horn; we in the house screaming and scolding; the passers - by shouting and halloing; and May, who little brooked such an invasion of her territories, barking in her tremendous lion-note, and putting down the other noises like a clap of thunder. But passengers, coachman, horses, and spectators, all righted at last; and there is no harm done but to my flowers and to the wall. May, however, stands bewailing the ruins, for that low wall

was her favourite haunt; she used to parade backwards and
forwards on the top of it, as if to show herself, just after the
manner of a peacock on the top of a house; and would sit or
lie for hours on the corner next the gate, basking in the
sunshine like a marble statue.   Really she has quite the air
of one who laments the destruction of personal property;
but the wall is to be rebuilt to-morrow with old weather-
stained bricks—no patchwork!—and exactly in the same
form; May herself will not find the difference; so that in the
way of alteration this little misfortune will pass for nothing.
Neither have we any improvements worth calling such:
except that the wheeler's green door hath been re-touched,
out of the same pot, as I judge from the tint, with which
he furbished up our new-old pony-chaise; that the shop
window of our neighbour, the universal dealer, hath
been beautified, and his name and calling splendidly set
forth in yellow letters on a black ground; and that our
landlord of the 'Rose' hath hoisted a new sign of unparalleled
splendour; one side consisting of a full-faced damask rose,
of the size and hue of a peony, the other of a maiden-blush
in profile, which looks exactly like a carnation, so that
both flowers are considerably indebted to the modesty of
the 'out-of-door artist,' who has warily written 'The Rose'
under each—except these trifling ornaments, which nothing
but the jealous eye of a lover could detect, the dear place is
altogether unchanged.

The only real improvement with which we have been
visited for our sins (I hate all innovation, whether for
better or worse, as if I was a furious Tory, or a woman of
threescore and ten)—the only misfortune of that sort which
has befallen us, is underfoot.   The road has been adjusted
on the plan of Mr. Macadam: and a tremendous operation
it is.   I do not know what good may ensue; but, for the
last six months, some part or other of the highway has been
impassable for any feet, except such as are shod by the
blacksmith; and even the four-footed people who wear
iron shoes make wry faces, poor things! at those stones,
enemies to man and beast.   However, the business is
nearly done now; we are covered with sharp flints every
inch of us, except a 'bad step' up the hill, which, indeed,
looks like a bit cut out of the deserts of Arabia, fitter for

camels and caravans than for Christian horses and coaches;
a point which, in spite of my dislike of alteration, I was
forced to acknowledge to our surveyor, a portly gentleman,
who in a smart gig, drawn by a prancing steed, was kicking
up a prodigious dust at that very moment. He and I
ought to be great enemies; for, besides the macadamite
enormity of the stony road, he hath actually been guilty
of tree murder, having been accessory before the fact in the
death of three limes along the rope-walk—dear sweet innocent limes, that did no harm on earth except shading the
path! I never should have forgiven that offence had not
their removal, by opening a beautiful view from the village
up the hill, reconciled even my tree-loving eye to their
abstraction. And, to say the truth, though we have had
twenty little squabbles, there is no bearing malice with our
surveyor; he is so civil and good-humoured, has such a
bustling and happy self-importance, such an honest earnestness in his vocation (which is gratuitous, by the by), and
such an intense conviction that the state of the turnpike
road between B—— and K—— is the principal affair of
this life, that I would not undeceive him for the world.
How often have I seen him on a cold winter morning, with
a face all frost and business, greatcoated up to the eyes,
driving from post to post, from one gang of labourers to
another, praising, scolding, ordering; cheated, laughed at,
and liked by them all! Well, when once the hill is finished
we shall have done with him for ever, as he used to tell me
by way of consolation when I shook my head at him, as he
went jolting along over his dear new roads, at the imminent
risk of his springs and his bones—we shall see no more of
him; for the macadam ways are warranted not to wear out.
So be it; I never wish to see a road-mender again.

But if the form of outward things be all unchanged
around us, if the dwellings of man remain the same to the
sight and the touch, the little world within hath undergone
its usual mutations—the hive is the same, but of the bees
some are dead and some are flown away, and some that
we left insects in the shell are already putting forth their
young wings. Children in our village really sprout up like
mushrooms; the air is so promotive of growth that the
rogues spring into men and women as if touched by Harle-

quin's wand, and are quite offended if one happens to say or do anything which has a reference to their previous condition. My father grievously affronted Sally L——, only yesterday, by bestowing upon her a great lump of gingerbread, with which he had stuffed his pockets at a fair. She immediately, as she said, gave it to the 'children.' Now Sally cannot be above twelve, to my certain knowledge, though taller than I am. Lizzy herself is growing womanly. I actually caught that little lady stuck on a chest of drawers, contemplating herself in the glass, and striving with all her might to gather the rich curls that hung about her neck and turn them under a comb. Well! if Sally and Lizzy live to be old maids, they may probably make the *amende honorable* to time, and wish to be thought young again. In the meanwhile, shall we walk up the street?

The first cottage is that of Mr. H——, the patriot, the illuminator, the independent and sturdy yet friendly member of our little state, who, stout and comely, with a handsome chaise-cart, a strong mare, and a neat garden, might have passed for a portrait of that enviable class of Englishmen who, after a youth of frugal industry, sit down in some retired place to 'live upon their means.' He and his wife seemed the happiest couple on earth: except a little too much leisure, I never suspected that they had one trouble or one care. But Care, the witch, will come everywhere, even to that happiest station and this prettiest place. She came in one of her most terrific forms—blindness, or (which is perhaps still more tremendous) the faint glimmering light and gradual darkness which precede the total eclipse. For a long time we had missed the pleasant bustling officiousness, the little services, the voluntary tasks, which our good neighbour loved so well. Fruit-trees were blighted, and escaped his grand specific, fumigation; wasps multiplied, and their nests remained untraced; the cheerful modest knock with which, just at the very hour when he knew it could be spared, he presented himself to ask for the newspaper, was heard no more; he no longer hung over his gate to waylay passengers, and entice them into chat; at last he even left off driving his little chaise, and was only seen moping up and down the garden-walk or stealing gropingly from the wood-pile to the house. He evidently shunned conversation or questions, forbade his wife to tell what ailed him, and even when he put a green shade over his darkened eyes, fled from human sympathy with a stern pride that seemed almost ashamed of the humbling infirmity. That strange (but to a vigorous and healthy man perhaps natural) feeling soon softened. The disease increased hourly, and he became dependent on his excellent wife for every comfort and relief. She had many willing assistants in her labour of love; all his neighbours strove to return, according to their several means, the kindness which all had received from him in some shape or other. The country boys, to whose service he had devoted so much time, in shaping bats, constructing bows and arrows, and other quips and trickeries of the same nature, vied with each other in performing little offices about the yard and stable; and John Evans, the half-witted gardener, to whom he had been a constant friend, repaid his goodness by the most unwearied attention. Gratitude even seemed to sharpen poor John's perception and faculties. There is an old man in our parish workhouse who occasionally walks through the street, led by a little boy holding the end of a long stick. The idea of this man, who had lived in utter blindness for thirty years, was always singularly distressing to Mr. H——. I shall never forget the address with which our simple gardener used to try to divert his attention from this miserable fellow-sufferer. He would get between them to prevent the possibility of recognition by the dim and uncertain vision; would talk loudly to drown the peculiar noise, the sort of duet of feet, caused by the quick short steps of the child and the slow irregular tread of the old man; and, if anyone ventured to allude to blind Robert, he would turn the conversation with an adroitness and acuteness which might put to shame the proudest intellect. So passed many months. At last Mr. H—— was persuaded to consult a celebrated oculist, and the result was most comforting. The disease was ascertained to be a cataract; and now with the increase of darkness came an increase of hope. The film spread, thickened, ripened, speedily and healthily; and to-day the requisite operation has been performed with equal skill and success. You may still see some of the country boys lingering round the gate with looks of strong and wondering interest; poor John is going to and fro, he knows not for what, unable to rest a moment; Mrs. H——, too, is walking in the garden, shedding tears of thankfulness; and he who came to support their spirit, the stout strong-hearted farmer A——, seems trembling and overcome. The most tranquil person in the house is probably the patient: he bore the operation with resolute firmness, and *he has seen again*. Think of the bliss bound up in those four words! He is in darkness now, and must remain so for some weeks; but he has seen, and he will see; and that humble cottage is again a happy dwelling.

Next we come to the shoemaker's abode. All is unchanged there, except that its master becomes more industrious and more pale-faced, and that his fair daughter is a notable exemplification of the development which I have already noticed amongst our young things. But she is in the real transition state, just emerging from the chrysalis, and the eighteen months between fourteen and a half and sixteen would metamorphose a child into a woman all the world over. She is still pretty, but not so elegant as when she wore frocks and pinafores, and, unconsciously classical, parted her long brown locks in the middle of her forehead, and twisted them up in a knot behind, giving to her finely shaped head and throat the air of a Grecian statue. Then she was stirring all day in her small housewifery, or her busy idleness, delving and digging in her flower border, tossing and dandling every infant that came within her reach, feeding pigs and poultry, playing with May, and prattling with an open-hearted frankness to the country lads, who assembled at evening in the shop to enjoy a little gentle gossiping; for be it known to my London readers that the shoemaker's in a country village is now what (according to tradition, and the old novels) the barber's used to be, the resort of all the male newsmongers, especially the young. Then she talked to these visitors gaily and openly, sang and laughed, and ran in and out, and took no more thought of a young man than of a gosling. Then she was only fourteen. Now she wears gowns and aprons —puts her hair in paper—has left off singing, talks—has left off running, walks—nurses the infants with a grave solemn grace — has entirely cut her former playmate

Mayflower, who tosses her pretty head as much as to say, Who cares?—and has nearly renounced all acquaintance with the visitors of the shop, who are by no means disposed to take matters so quietly. There she stands on the threshold, shy and demure, just vouchsafing a formal nod or a faint smile as they pass, and if she in her turn be compelled to pass the open door of their news-room (for the working apartment is separate from the house), edging along as slyly and mincingly as if there were no such beings as young men in the world. Exquisite coquette! I think (she is my opposite neighbour, and I have a right to watch her doings—the right of retaliation) there is one youth particularly distinguished by her non-notice, one whom she never will see nor speak to, who stands a very fair chance to carry her off. He is called Jem Tanner, and is a fine lad, with an open ruddy countenance, a clear blue eye, and curling hair of that tint which the poets are pleased to denominate golden. Though not one of our eleven, he was a promising cricketer. We have missed him lately on the green at the Sunday evening game, and I find on inquiry that he now frequents a chapel about a mile off, where he is the best male singer, as our nymph of the shoe shop is incomparably the first female. I am not fond of betting; but I would venture the lowest stake of gentility, a silver threepence, that, before the winter ends, a wedding will be the result of these weekly meetings at the chapel. In the long dark evenings, when the father has enough to do in piloting the mother with conjugal gallantry through the dirty lanes, think of the opportunity that Jem will have to escort the daughter! A little difficulty he may have to encounter: the lass will be coy for a while; the mother will talk of their youth, the father of their finances; but the marriage, I doubt not, will ensue.

Next in order, on the other side of the street, is the blacksmith's house. Change has been busy here in a different and more awful form. Our sometime constable, the tipsiest of parish officers, of blacksmiths, and of men, is dead. Returning from a revel with a companion as full of beer as himself, one or the other, or both, contrived to overset the cart in a ditch (the living scapegrace is pleased to lay the blame of the mishap on the horse, but that is contrary to all probability, this respectable quadruped being a water-drinker); and inward bruises, acting on inflamed blood and an impaired constitution, carried him off in a very short time, leaving an ailing wife and eight children, the eldest of whom is only fourteen years of age. This sounds like a very tragical story; yet, perhaps because the loss of a drunken husband is not quite so great a calamity as the loss of a sober one, the effect of the event is not altogether so melancholy as might be expected. The widow, when she was a wife, had a complaining broken-spirited air, a peevish manner, a whining voice, a dismal countenance, and a person so neglected and slovenly, that it was difficult to believe that she had once been remarkably handsome. She is now quite another woman. The very first Sunday she put on her weeds, we all observed how tidy and comfortable she looked, how much her countenance, in spite of a decent show of tears, was improved, and how completely through all her sighings her tone had lost its peevishness. I have never seen her out of spirits or out of humour since. She talks and laughs and bustles about, managing her journeymen and scolding her children as notably as any dame in the parish. The very house looks more cheerful; she has cut down the old willow-trees that stood in the court, and let in the light; and now the sun glances brightly from the casement windows, and plays amidst the vine-leaves and the clusters of grapes which cover the walls; the door is newly painted, and shines like the face of its mistress; even the forge has lost half its dinginess. Everything smiles. She indeed talks by fits of 'poor George,' especially when any allusion to her old enemy, mine host of the 'Rose,' brings the deceased to her memory; then she bewails (as is proper) her dear husband and her desolate condition; calls herself a lone widow; sighs over her eight children; complains of the troubles of business, and tries to persuade herself and others that she is as wretched as a good wife ought to be. But this will not do. She is a happier woman than she has been any time these fifteen years, and she knows it. My dear village-husbands, if you have a mind that your wives should be really sorry when you die, whether by a fall from a cart or otherwise, keep from the ale-house!

Next comes the tall thin red house, that ought to boast

genteeler inmates than its short fat mistress, its children, its pigs, and its quantity of noise, happiness, and vulgarity. The din is greater than ever. The husband, a merry jolly tar, with a voice that sounds as if issuing from a speaking-trumpet, is returned from a voyage to India; and another little one, a chubby roaring boy, has added his lusty cries to the family concert.

This door, blockaded by huge bales of goods, and half-darkened by that moving mountain, the tilted wagon of the S—— Mill, which stands before it, belongs to the village shop. Increase has been here too in every shape. Within fourteen months two little pretty quiet girls have come into the world. Before Fanny could well manage to totter across the road to her good friend the nymph of the shoe shop, Margaret made her appearance; and poor Fanny, discarded at once from the maid's arms and her mother's knee, degraded from the rank and privileges of 'the baby' (for at that age precedence is strangely reversed), would have had a premature foretaste of the instability of human felicity had she not taken refuge with that best of nurses, a fond father. Everything thrives about the shop, from the rosy children to the neat maid and the smart apprentice. No room now for lodgers, and no need! The young mantua-making schoolmistress, the old inmates, are gone; one of them not very far. She grew tired of scolding little boys and girls about their A B C, and of being scolded in her turn by their sisters and mothers about pelisses and gowns; so she gave up both trades almost a year ago, and has been ever since our pretty Harriet. I do not think she has ever repented of the exchange, though it might not perhaps have been made so soon had not her elder sister, who had been long engaged to an attendant at one of the colleges of Oxford, thought herself on the point of marriage just as our housemaid left us. Poor Betsy! She had shared the fate of many a prouder maiden, wearing out her youth in expectation of the promotion that was to authorize her union with the man of her heart. Many a year had she waited in smiling constancy, fond of William in no common measure, and proud of him, as well she might be; for when the vacation so far lessened his duties as to render a short absence practicable, and he stole up here for a few days to enjoy her company, it was difficult to distinguish him in air and manner, as he sauntered about in elegant indolence with his fishing-rod and his flute, from the young Oxonians his masters. At last promotion came; and Betsy, apprised of it by an affectionate and congratulatory letter from his sister, prepared her wedding clothes, and looked hourly for the bridegroom. No bridegroom came. A second letter announced, with regret and indignation, that William had made another choice, and was to be married early in the ensuing month. Poor Betsy! We were alarmed for her health, almost for her life. She wept incessantly, took no food, wandered recklessly about from morning till night, lost her natural rest, her flesh, her colour; and in less than a week she was so altered that no one would have known her. Consolation and remonstrance were alike rejected, till at last Harriet happened to strike the right chord by telling her that 'she wondered at her want of spirit.' This was touching her on the point of honour; she had always been remarkably high-spirited, and could as little brook the imputation as a soldier or a gentleman. This lucky suggestion gave an immediate turn to her feelings; anger and scorn succeeded to grief: she wiped her eyes, 'hemmed away a sigh,' and began to scold most manfully. She did still better. She recalled an old admirer, who, in spite of repeated rejections, had remained constant in his attachment, and made such good speed that she was actually married the day before her faithless lover, and is now the happy wife of a very respectable tradesman.

Ah! the in-and-out cottage! the dear, dear home! No weddings there! No changes! Except that the white kitten, who sits purring at the window under the great myrtle, has succeeded to his lamented grandfather, our beautiful Persian cat, I cannot find one alteration to talk about. The wall of the court, indeed—but that will be mended to-morrow.

Here is the new sign, the well-frequented Rose Inn; plenty of changes there! Our landlord is always improving, if it be only a pigsty or a watering-trough—plenty of changes and one splendid wedding. Miss Phoebe is married, not to her old lover the recruiting sergeant (for he had one wife already, probably more), but to a patten-maker, as arrant a dandy as ever wore mustachios. How Phoebe could 'abase her eyes' from the stately sergeant to this youth, half a foot shorter than herself, whose 'waist would go into any alderman's thumb-ring,' might, if the final choice of a coquette had ever been matter of wonder, have occasioned some speculation. But our patten-maker is a man of spirit; and the wedding was of extraordinary splendour. Three gigs, each containing four persons, graced the procession, besides numerous carts and innumerable pedestrians. The bride was equipped in muslin and satin, and really looked very pretty, with her black sparkling eyes, her clear brown complexion, her blushes and her smiles; the bridemaidens were only less smart than the bride; and the bridegroom was 'point device in his accoutrements,' and as munificent as a nabob. Cakes flew about the village; plum-puddings were abundant; and strong beer, aye, even mine host's best double X, was profusely distributed. There was all manner of eating and drinking, with singing, fiddling, and dancing between; and in the evening, to crown all, there was Mr. Moon the conjurer. Think of that stroke of good fortune! Mr. Moon, the very pearl of all conjurers, who had the honour of puzzling and delighting their late Majesties with his 'wonderful and pleasing exhibition of thaumaturgics, tachygraphy, mathematical operations, and magical deceptions,' happened to arrive about an hour before dinner, and commenced his ingenious deceptions very unintentionally at our house. Calling to apply for permission to perform in the village, being equipped in a gay scarlet coat, and having something smart and sportsmanlike in his appearance, he was announced by Harriet as one of the gentlemen of the C—— Hunt, and taken (*mis*taken, I should have said) by the whole family for a certain captain newly arrived in the neighbourhood. That misunderstanding, which must, I think, have retaliated on Mr. Moon a little of the puzzlement that he inflicts on others, vanished of course at the production of his bill of fare; and the requested permission was instantly given. Never could he have arrived in a happier hour! Never were spectators more gratified or more scared. All the tricks prospered. The cock crew after his head was cut off, and half-crowns and sovereigns flew about as if winged; the very wedding ring could not escape Mr. Moon's incantations. We heard of nothing else for a week. From the bridegroom, *un esprit fort*, who defied all manner of conjuration and diablerie, down to my Lizzy, whose boundless faith swallows the *Arabian Tales*, all believed and trembled. So thoroughly were men, women, and children impressed with the idea of the worthy conjurer's dealings with the devil, that when he had occasion to go to B——, not a soul would give him a cart, from pure awe; and if it had not been for our pony-chaise, poor Mr. Moon must have walked. I hope he is really a prophet; for he foretold all happiness to the new-married pair.

So this pretty white house with the lime-trees before it, which has been under repair for these three years, is on the point of being finished. The vicar has taken it, as the vicarage house is not yet fit for his reception. He has sent before him a neat modest maidservant—whose respectable appearance gives a character to her master and mistress—a hamper full of flower-roots, sundry boxes of books, a pianoforte, and some simple and useful furniture. Well, we shall certainly have neighbours, and I have a presentiment that we shall find friends.

Lizzy, you may now come along with me round the corner and up the lane, just to the end of the wheeler's shop, and then we shall go home; it is high time. What is this *affiche* in the parlour window? 'Apartments to let—inquire within.' These are certainly the curate's lodgings—is he going away? Oh, I suppose the new vicar will do his own duty—yet, however well he may do it, rich and poor will regret the departure of Mr. B——. Well, I hope that he may soon get a good living. 'Lodgings to let'—who ever thought of seeing such a placard hereabout? The lodgings, indeed, are very convenient for 'a single gentleman, a man and his wife, or two sisters,' as the newspapers say—comfortable apartments, neat and tasty withal, and the civilest of all civil treatment from the host and hostess. But who would ever have dreamt of such a notice? Lodgings to let in our village!

CHAPTER XVII

THE COPSE

April 18th. Sad wintry weather; a north-east wind; a sun that puts out one's eyes, without affording the slightest warmth; dryness that chaps lips and hands like a frost in December; rain that comes chilling and arrowy like hail in January; nature at a dead pause; no seeds up in the garden; no leaves out in the hedgerows; no cowslips swinging their pretty bells in the fields; no nightingales in the dingles; no swallows skimming round the great pond; no cuckoos (that ever I should miss that rascally sonneteer!) in any part! Nevertheless there is something of a charm in this wintry spring, this putting back of the seasons. If the flower-clock must stand still for a month or two, could it choose a better time than that of the primroses and violets? I never remember (and for such gauds my memory, if not very good for aught of wise or useful, may be trusted) such an affluence of the one or such a duration of the other. Primrosy is the epithet which this year will retain in my recollection. Hedge, ditch, meadow, field, even the very paths and highways, are set with them; but their chief habitat is a certain copse, about a mile off, where they are spread like a carpet, and where I go to visit them rather oftener than quite comports with the dignity of a lady of mature age. I am going thither this very afternoon, and May and her company are going too.

This Mayflower of mine is a strange animal. Instinct and imitation make in her an approach to reason which is sometimes almost startling. She mimics all that she sees us do, with the dexterity of a monkey, and far more of gravity and apparent purpose; cracks nuts and eats them; gathers currants and severs them from the stalk with the most delicate nicety; filches and munches apples and pears; is as dangerous in an orchard as a schoolboy; smells to flowers; smiles at meeting; answers in a pretty lively voice when spoken to (sad pity that the language should be unknown), and has greatly the advantage of us in a conversation, inasmuch as our meaning is certainly clear to her—all this, and a thousand amusing prettinesses (to say nothing of her canine feat of bringing her game straight to her master's feet, and refusing to resign it to any hand but his), does my beautiful greyhound perform untaught, by the mere effect of imitation and sagacity. Well, May, at the end of the coursing season, having lost Brush, our old spaniel, her great friend, and the blue greyhound Mariette, her comrade and rival, both of which four-footed worthies were sent out to keep for the summer, began to find solitude a weary condition, and to look abroad for company. Now it so happened that the same suspension of sport which had reduced our little establishment from three dogs to one, had also dispersed the splendid kennel of a celebrated courser in our neighbourhood, three of whose finest young dogs came home to 'their walk' (as the sporting phrase goes) at the collar-maker's in our village. May, accordingly, on the first morning of her solitude (she had never taken the slightest notice of her neighbours before, although they had sojourned in our street upwards of a fortnight), bethought herself of the timely resource offered to her by the vicinity of these canine beaux, and went up boldly and knocked at their stable door, which was already very commodiously on the half-latch. The three dogs came out with much alertness and gallantry, and May, declining apparently to enter their territories, brought them off to her own. This manœuvre has been repeated every day, with one variation: of the three dogs, the first a brindle, the second a yellow, and the third a black, the two first only are now admitted to walk or consort with her, and the last, poor fellow! for no fault that I can discover except May's caprice, is driven away not only by the fair lady, but even by his old companions—is, so to say, sent to Coventry. Of her two permitted followers, the yellow gentleman, Saladin by name, is decidedly the favourite. He is indeed May's shadow, and will walk with me whether I choose or not. It is quite impossible to get rid of him unless by discarding Miss May also—and to accomplish a walk in the country without her would be like an adventure of Don Quixote without his faithful squire Sancho.

So forth we set, May and I, and Saladin and the brindle
May and myself walking with the sedateness and decorum
befitting our sex and age (she is five years old this grass
rising six), the young things, for the soldan and the brindle
are (not meaning any disrespect) little better than puppies
frisking and frolicking as best pleased them.

Our route lay for the first part along the sheltered quiet
lanes which lead to our old habitation; a way never trodden
by me without peculiar and home-like feelings, full of the
recollections, the pains and pleasures, of other days. But we
are not to talk sentiment now—even May would not understand that maudlin language. We must get on. What a
wintry hedgerow this is for the 18th April! Primrosy to
be sure, abundantly spangled with those stars of the earth—
but so bare, so leafless, so cold! The wind whistles through
the brown boughs as in winter. Even the early elder
shoots, which do make an approach to springiness, look
brown, and the small leaves of the woodbine, which have also
ventured to peep forth, are of a sad purple, frost-bitten, like
a dairy-maid's elbows on a snowy morning. The very birds,
in this season of pairing and building, look chilly and uncomfortable, and their nests!——'Oh, Saladin! come away
from the hedge! Don't you see that what puzzles you and
makes you leap up in the air is a redbreast's nest? Don't
you see the pretty speckled eggs? Don't you hear the poor
hen calling as it were for help? Come here this moment,
sir!' And by good luck Saladin (who for a paynim has
tolerable qualities) comes, before he has touched the nest,
or before his playmate the brindle, the less manageable of
the two, has espied it.

Now we go round the corner and cross the bridge, where
the common, with its clear stream winding between clumps
of elms, assumes so park-like an appearance. Who is this
approaching so slowly and majestically, this square bundle
of petticoat and cloak, this road-wagon of a woman! It is,
it must be Mrs. Sally Mearing, the completest specimen
within my knowledge of farmeresses (may I be allowed that
innovation in language?) as they were. It can be nobody
else.

Mrs. Sally Mearing, when I first became acquainted with
her, occupied, together with her father (a superannuated

man of ninety), a large farm very near our former habitation.
It had been anciently a great manor farm or court-house,
and was still a stately substantial building, whose lofty halls
and spacious chambers gave an air of grandeur to the common offices to which they were applied. Traces of gilding
might yet be seen on the panels which covered the walls,
and on the huge carved chimney-pieces which rose almost to
the ceilings; and the marble tables and the inlaid oak staircase still spoke of the former grandeur of the court. Mrs.
Sally corresponded well with the date of her mansion,
although she troubled herself little with its dignity. She
was thoroughly of the old school, and had a most comfortable contempt for the new: rose at four in winter and summer, breakfasted at six, dined at eleven in the forenoon,
supped at five, and was regularly in bed before eight,
except when the hay-time or the harvest imperiously
required her to sit up till sunset—a necessity to which she
submitted with no very good grace. To a deviation from
these hours, and to the modern iniquities of white aprons,
cotton stockings, and muslin handkerchiefs (Mrs. Sally herself
always wore check, black worsted, and a sort of yellow
compound which she was wont to call *susy*), together
with the invention of drill ploughs and thrashing machines,
and other agricultural novelties, she failed not to attribute
all the mishaps or misdoings of the whole parish. The
last-mentioned discovery especially aroused her indignation. Oh! to hear her descant on the merits of the flail,
wielded by a stout right arm, such as she had known in her
youth (for by her account there was as great a deterioration in
bones and sinews as in the other implements of husbandry),
was enough to make the very inventor break his machine.
She would even take up her favourite instrument, and
thrash the air herself, by way of illustrating her argument,
and to say truth, few men, in these degenerate days, could
have matched the stout, brawny, muscular limb which Mrs.
Sally displayed at sixty-five.

In spite of this contumacious rejection of agricultural
improvements, the world went well with her at Court Farm.
A good landlord, an easy rent, incessant labour, unremit-
ting frugality, and excellent times, ensured a regular though
moderate profit; and she lived on, grumbling and prospering,

flourishing and complaining, till two misfortunes befell her
at once—her father died, and her lease expired. The loss
of her father, although a bed-ridden man turned of ninety,
who could not in the course of nature have been expected to
live long, was a terrible shock to a daughter who was not so
much younger as to be without fears for her own life, and who
had besides been so used to nursing the good old man, and
looking to his little comforts, that she missed him as a mother
would miss an ailing child. The expiration of the lease was
a grievance and a puzzle of a different nature. Her landlord would have willingly retained his excellent tenant, but
not on the terms on which she then held the land, which had
not varied for fifty years: so that poor Mrs. Sally had the
misfortune to find rent rising and prices sinking both at the
same moment—a terrible solecism in political economy.
Even this, however, I believe she would have endured,
rather than have quitted the house where she was born, and
to which all her ways and notions were adapted, had not a
priggish steward, as much addicted to improvement and
reform as she was to precedent and established usages,
insisted on binding her by lease to spread a certain number
of loads of chalk on every field. This tremendous innovation, for never had that novelty in manure whitened the
crofts and pightles of Court Farm, decided her at once. She
threw the proposals into the fire, and left the place in a week.

Her choice of a habitation occasioned some wonder and
much amusement in our village world. To be sure, upon
the verge of seventy, an old maid may be permitted to dispense with the more rigid punctilio of her class; but Mrs.
Sally had always been so tenacious on the score of character,
so very a prude, so determined an avoider of the 'men-
folk' (as she was wont contemptuously to call them), that
we all were conscious of something like astonishment, on
finding that she and her little handmaid had taken up their
abode in one end of a spacious farm-house belonging to the
bluff old bachelor, George Robinson, of the Lea. Now
Farmer Robinson was quite as notorious for his aversion to
petticoated things as Mrs. Sally for her hatred to the unfeathered bipeds who wear doublet and hose, so that there
was a little astonishment in that quarter too, and plenty of
jests, which the honest farmer speedily silenced, by telling

all who joked on the subject that he had given his lodger fair
warning, that, let people say what they would, he was quite
determined not to marry her; so that if she had any views
that way, it would be better for her to go elsewhere. This
declaration, which must be admitted to have been more
remarkable for frankness than civility, made, however, no
ill impression on Mrs. Sally. To the farmer's she went,
and at his house she lives still, with her little maid, her
tabby cat, a decrepit sheep-dog, and much of the lumber of
Court Farm, which she could not find in her heart to part
from. There she follows her old ways and her old hours,
untempted by matrimony, and unassailed (as far as I hear) by
love or by scandal, with no other grievance than an occasional dearth of employment for herself and her young lass
(even pewter dishes do not always want scouring), and now
and then a twinge of the rheumatism.

Here she is, that good relic of the olden time—for, in spite
of her whims and prejudices, a better and a kinder woman
never lived—here she is, with the hood of her red cloak
pulled over her close black bonnet, of that silk which once
(it may be presumed) was fashionable, since it is still called
mode, and her whole stout figure huddled up in a miscellaneous and most substantial covering of thick petticoats, gowns, aprons, shawls, and cloaks—a weight which
it requires the strength of a thrasher to walk under; here
she is, with her square honest visage, and her loud frank
voice; and we hold a pleasant disjointed chat of rheuma-
tisms and early chickens, bad weather, and hats with feathers
in them—the last exceedingly sore subject being introduced
by poor Jane Davis (a cousin of Mrs. Sally), who, passing us
in a beaver bonnet, on her road from school, stopped to drop
her little curtsy, and was soundly scolded for her civility.
Jane, who is a gentle, humble, smiling lass about twelve
years old, receives so many rebukes from her worthy relative,
and bears them so meekly, that I should not wonder if they
were to be followed by a legacy: I sincerely wish they may.
Well, at last we said good-bye; when, on inquiring my
destination, and hearing that I was bent to the ten-acre
copse (part of the farm which she ruled so long), she stopped
me to tell a dismal story of the two sheep-stealers who
sixty years ago were found hidden in that copse, and only

taken after great difficulty and resistance, and the maim-
ing of a peace officer. 'Pray don't go there, miss! For
mercy's sake don't be so venturesome! Think if they should
kill you!' were the last words of Mrs. Sally.

Many thanks for her care and kindness! But, without
being at all foolhardy in general, I have no great fear of the
sheep-stealers of sixty years ago. Even if they escaped
hanging for that exploit, I should greatly doubt their
being in case to attempt another. So on we go: down the
short shady lane, and out on the pretty retired green, shut
in by fields and hedgerows, which we must cross to reach
the copse. How lively this green nook is to-day, half
covered with cows and horses and sheep! And how glad
these frolicsome greyhounds are to exchange the hard
gravel of the high road for this pleasant short turf, which
seems made for their gambols! How beautifully they are
at play, chasing each other round and round in lessening
circles, darting off at all kinds of angles, crossing and recrossing May, and trying to win her sedateness into a game
at romps, turning round on each other with gay defiance,
pursuing the cows and the colts, leaping up as if to catch
the crows in their flight—all in their harmless and innocent——'Ah, wretches! villains! rascals! four-footed mis-
chiefs! canine plagues! Saladin! Brindle!' They are
after the sheep—'Saladin, I say!' They have actually
singled out that pretty spotted lamb—'Brutes, if I catch
you! Saladin, Brindle!' We shall be taken up for sheep-
stealing presently ourselves. They have chased the poor
little lamb into a ditch, and are mounting guard over it,
standing at bay—'Ah, wretches, I have you now! For
shame, Saladin! Get away, Brindle! See how good May
is! Off with you, brutes! For shame! For shame!' and
brandishing a handkerchief, which could hardly be an
efficient instrument of correction, I succeeded in driving
away the two puppies, who after all meant nothing more
than play, although it was somewhat rough, and rather too
much in the style of the old fable of the boys and the frogs.
May is gone after them, perhaps to scold them: for she has
been as grave as a judge during the whole proceeding,
keeping ostentatiously close to me, and taking no part
whatever in the mischief.

CHAPTER XVIII

JACK HATCH

I PIQUE myself on knowing by sight, and by name, almost
every man and boy in our parish, from eight years old to
eighty—I cannot say quite so much for the women. They—
the elder of them at least—are more within doors, more
hidden. One does not meet them in the fields and highways; their duties are close housekeepers, and live under
cover. The girls, to be sure, are often enough in sight,
'true creatures of the element,' basking in the sun, racing
in the wind, rolling in the dust, dabbling in the water—
hardier, dirtier, noisier, more sturdy defiers of heat and
cold and wet than boys themselves. One sees them quite
often enough to know them; but then the little elves alter
so much at every step of their approach to womanhood that
recognition becomes difficult, if not impossible. It is not
merely growing—boys grow—it is positive, perplexing, and
perpetual change: a butterfly hath not undergone more
transmogrifications in its progress through this life, than a
village belle in her arrival at the age of seventeen.

The first appearance of the little lass is something after
the manner of a caterpillar, crawling and creeping upon the
grass, set down to roll by some tired little nurse of an elder
sister, or mother with her hands full. There it lies—a fat,
boneless, rosy piece of health, aspiring to the accomplishments of walking and talking; stretching its chubby limbs;
scrambling and sprawling; laughing and roaring. There it
sits, in all the dignity of the baby, adorned in a pink-
checked frock, a blue spotted pinafore, and a little white
cap, tolerably clean, and quite whole. One is forced to
ask if it be boy or girl, for these hardy country rogues
are all alike, open-eyed and weather-stained, and nothing
fearing. There is no more mark of sex in the countenance
than in the dress.

In the next stage, dirt-encrusted enough to pass for the

chrysalis, if it were not so very unquiet, the gender remains
equally uncertain. It is a fine, stout, curly-pated creature
of three or four, playing and rolling about amongst grass
or mud all day long; shouting, jumping, screeching—the
happiest compound of noise and idleness, rags and rebellion,
that ever trod the earth.

Then comes a sun-burnt gipsy of six, beginning to grow
tall and thin, and to find the cares of the world gathering
about her; with a pitcher in one hand, a mop in the other,
an old straw bonnet of ambiguous shape, half hiding her
tangled hair; a tattered stuff-petticoat, once green, hanging
below an equally tattered cotton frock, once purple; her
longing eyes fixed on a game of baseball at the corner of the
green, till she reaches the cottage door, flings down the
mop and pitcher, and darts off to her companions, quite
regardless of the storm of scolding with which the mother
follows her runaway steps.

So the world wags till ten; then the little damsel gets
admission to the charity school, and trips mincingly thither
every morning, dressed in the old-fashioned blue gown and
white cap and tippet and bib and apron of that primitive
institution, looking as demure as a nun, and as tidy; her
thoughts fixed on buttonholes and spelling-books—those
ensigns of promotion; despising dirt and baseball, and all
their joys.

Then at twelve the little lass comes home again, uncapped
untippeted, unschooled; brown as a berry, wild as a colt,
busy as a bee—working in the fields, digging in the garden,
frying rashers, boiling potatoes, shelling beans, darning
stockings, nursing children, feeding pigs—all these employments varied by occasional fits of romping and flirt-
ing and idle play, according as the nascent coquetry or the
lurking love of sport happens to preponderate; merry and
pretty and good with all her little faults. It would be
well if a country girl could stand at thirteen. Then she is
charming. But the clock will move forward, and at fourteen she gets a service in a neighbouring town; and her next
appearance is in the perfection of the butterfly state,
fluttering, glittering, inconstant, vain—the gayest and
gaudiest insect that ever skimmed over a village green. And
this is the true progress of a rustic beauty, the average lot of

our country girls—so they spring up, flourish, change, and
disappear. Some indeed marry and fix amongst us, and
then ensues another set of changes, rather more gradual
perhaps, but quite as sure, till grey hairs, wrinkles, and
linsey-woolsey wind up the picture.

All this is beside the purpose. If woman be a mutable
creature, man is not. The wearers of smock frocks, in spite
of the sameness of the uniform, are almost as easily distinguished by an interested eye, as a flock of sheep by the
shepherd, or a pack of hounds by the huntsman; or, to come
to less affronting similes, the members of the House of
Commons by the Speaker, or the gentlemen of the Bar by
the Lord Chief Justice. There is very little change in them
from early boyhood. 'The child is father to the man' in
more senses than one. There is a constancy about them;
they keep the same faces, however ugly; the same habits,
however strange; the same fashions, however unfashionable;
they are in nothing new-fangled. Tom Cooper, for instance,
man and boy, is and has been addicted to posies—from the
first polyanthus to the last China rose, he has always a
nosegay in his buttonhole; George Simmons may be known
a mile off by an eternal red waistcoat; Jem Tanner, summer
and winter, by the smartest of all smart straw hats; and Joel
Brent, from the day that he left off petticoats, has always,
in every dress and every situation, looked like a study for a
painter—no mistaking him. Yes! I know every man and
boy of note in the parish, with one exception—one most
signal exception, which 'haunts and startles and waylays'
me at every turn. I do not know, and I begin to fear that
I never shall know, Jack Hatch.

The first time I had occasion to hear of this worthy was on
a most melancholy occurrence. We have lost—I do not
like to talk about it, but I cannot tell my story without—
we have lost a cricket match, been beaten, and soundly too,
by the men of Beech Hill, a neighbouring parish. How this
accident happened I cannot very well tell; the melancholy
fact is sufficient. The men of Beech Hill, famous players,
in whose families cricket is an hereditary accomplishment,
challenged and beat us. After our defeat we began to
comfort ourselves by endeavouring to discover how this
misfortune could possibly have befallen. Every one that

has ever had a cold must have experienced the great consolation that is derived from puzzling out the particular act of imprudence from which it sprang, and we, on the same principle, found our affliction somewhat mitigated by the endeavour to trace it to its source. One laid the catastrophe to the wind—a very common scapegoat in the catarrhal calamity—which had, as it were, played us booty, carrying our adversaries' balls right and ours wrong; another laid it to a certain catch missed by Tom Willis, by which means Farmer Thackum, the pride and glory of the Beech Hillers, had two innings; a third to the aforesaid Thackum's remarkable manner of bowling, which is circular, so to say, that is, after taking aim he makes a sort of *chassé* on one side before he delivers his ball, which pantomimic motion had a great effect on the nerves of our eleven, unused to such quadrilling; a fourth imputed our defeat to the over-civility of our umpire, George Gosseltine, a sleek, smooth, silky, soft-spoken person, who stood with his little wand under his arm, smiling through all our disasters—the very image of peace and good humour; whilst their umpire, Bob Coxe, a roystering, roaring, bullying blade, bounced and hectored and blustered from his wicket, with the voice of a twelve-pounder; the fifth assented to this opinion, with some extension, asserting that the universal impudence of their side took advantage of the meekness and modesty of ours (N.B. it never occurred to our modesty that they might be the best players), which flattering persuasion appeared likely to prevail in fault of a better, when all on a sudden the true reason of our defeat seemed to burst at once from half a dozen voices, re-echoed like a chorus by all the others: 'It was entirely owing to the want of Jack Hatch! How could we think of playing without Jack Hatch!'

This was the first time I heard of him. My inquiries as to this great player were received with utter astonishment. 'Who is Jack Hatch?' 'Not know Jack Hatch!' There was no end to the wonder—'not to know him, argued myself unknown.' 'Jack Hatch—the best cricketer in the parish, in the county, in the country! Jack Hatch, who had got seven notches at one hit! Jack Hatch, who had trolled and caught out a whole eleven! Jack Hatch, who, besides these marvellous gifts in cricket, was the best bowler and the best musician in the hundred—could dance a hornpipe and a minuet, sing a whole song-book, bark like a dog, mew like a cat, crow like a cock, and go through Punch from beginning to end! Not know Jack Hatch!'

Half ashamed of my non-acquaintance with this Admirable Crichton of rural accomplishments, I determined to find him out as soon as possible, and I have been looking for him more or less ever since.

The cricket ground and the bowling green were of course the first places of search; but he was always just gone, or not come, or he was there yesterday, or he is expected to-morrow—a to-morrow, which as far as I am concerned never arrives; the stars were against me. Then I directed my attention to his other acquirements, and once followed a ballad-singer half a mile, who turned out to be a strapping woman in a man's greatcoat, and another time pierced a whole mob of urchins to get at a capital Punch—when behold it was the genuine man of puppets, the true squeakery, the 'real Simon Pure,' and Jack was as much to seek as ever.

At last I thought that I had actually caught him, and on his own peculiar field, the cricket ground. We abound in rustic fun and good humour, and of course in nicknames. A certain senior of fifty, or thereabout, for instance, of very juvenile habits and inclinations, who plays at ball and marbles and cricket with all the boys in the parish, and joins a kind merry buoyant heart to an aspect somewhat rough and care-worn, has no other appellation that ever I heard but 'Uncle'; I don't think, if by any strange chance he were called by it, that he would know his own name. On the other hand, a little stunted pragmatical urchin, son and heir of Dick Jones, an absolute old man cut shorter, so slow and stiff and sturdy and wordy, passes universally by the title of 'Grandfather'—I have not the least notion that he would answer to Dick. Also a slim, grim-looking, white-headed lad, whose hair is bleached, and his skin browned by the sun, till he is as hideous as an Indian idol, goes—good lack!—by the pastoral misnomer of the 'Gentle Shepherd.' Oh, manes of Allan Ramsay—the Gentle Shepherd!

Another youth, regular at cricket, but never seen except then, of unknown parish and parentage, and singular

uncouthness of person, dress, and demeanour, rough as a
badger, ragged as a colt, and sour as verjuice, was known
far more appropriately by the cognomen of 'Oddity.'
Him, in my secret soul, I pitched on for Jack Hatch. In
the first place, as I had in the one case a man without a
name, and in the other a name without a man, to have
found these component parts of individuality meet in the
same person, to have made the man to fit the name, and the
name fit the man, would have been as pretty a way of
solving two enigmas at once, as hath been heard of since
Œdipus his day. But besides the obvious convenience and
suitability of this belief, I had divers other corroborating
reasons. Oddity was young, so was Jack—Oddity came
up the hill from leaward, so must Jack—Oddity was a
capital cricketer, so was Jack—Oddity did not play in our
unlucky Beech Hill match, neither did Jack—and last of
all, Oddity's name was Jack, a fact I was fortunate enough
to ascertain from a pretty damsel who walked up with him
to the ground one evening, and who, on seeing him bowl out
Tom Cooper, could not help exclaiming in soliloquy, as
she stood a few yards behind us, looking on with all her
heart, 'Well done, Jack!' That moment built up all my
hopes; the next knocked them down. I thought I had
clutched him, but willing to make assurance doubly sure,
I turned to my pretty neighbour (Jack Hatch too had a
sweetheart) and said in a tone half affirmative, half inter-
rogatory: 'That young man who plays so well is Jack
Hatch?' 'No, ma'am, Jack Bolton!'—and Jack Hatch
remained still a sound, a name, a mockery.

Well, at last I ceased to look for him, and might possibly
have forgotten my curiosity had not every week produced
some circumstance to relumine that active female passion.

I seemed beset by his name, and his presence, invisibly as
it were. Will-o'-the-wisp is nothing to him; Puck, in that
famous *Midsummer Dream*, was a quiet goblin compared to
Jack Hatch. He haunts one in dark places. The fiddler,
whose merry tones come ringing across the orchard in a
winter's night from Farmer White's barn, setting the whole
village a-dancing, is Jack Hatch. The whistler, who trudges
homeward at dusk up Kibe's lanes, out-piping the nightingale in her own month of May, is Jack Hatch. And the

indefatigable learner of the bassoon, whose drone all last harvest might be heard in the twilight, issuing from the sexton's dwelling on the Little Lea, 'making night hideous,' that iniquitous practiser is Jack Hatch.

The name meets me all manner of ways. I have seen it in the newspaper for a prize of pinks, and on the back of warrant on the charge of poaching. (N.B. the constable had my luck, and could not find the culprit, otherwise I might have had some chance of seeing him on that occasion.) Things the most remote and discrepant issue in Jack Hatch. He caught Dame Wheeler's squirrel; the magpie at the 'Rose' owes to him the half-dozen phrases with which he astounds and delights the passers-by; the very dog Tero—an animal of singular habits, who sojourns occasionally at half the houses in the village, making each his home till he is affronted—Tero himself, best and ugliest of finders—a mongrel compounded of terrier, cur, and spaniel—Tero, most remarkable of ugly dogs, inasmuch as he constantly squints, and commonly goes on three legs, holding up first one and then the other, out of a sort of quadrupedal economy to ease those useful members—Tero himself is said to belong of right and origin to Jack Hatch.

Everywhere that name meets me. 'Twas but a few weeks ago that I heard him asked in church, and a day or two afterwards I saw the tail of the wedding procession, the little lame clerk handing the bridesmaid, and a girl from the 'Rose' running after them with pipes, passing by our house. Nay, this very morning, someone was speaking—Dead! what dead? Jack Hatch dead?—a name, a shadow, a jack-o'-lantern! Can Jack Hatch die? Hath he the property of mortality? Can the bell toll for him? Yes! there is the coffin and the pall—all that I shall ever see of him is there! There are his comrades following in decent sorrow—and the poor pretty bride, leaning on the little clerk. My search is over—Jack Hatch is dead!

CHAPTER XIX

THE WOOD

April 20th. Spring is actually come now, with the fullness and almost the suddenness of a northern summer. To-day is completely April—clouds and sunshine, wind and showers; blossoms on the trees, grass in the fields, swallows by the ponds, snakes in the hedgerows, nightingales in the thickets, and cuckoos everywhere. My young friend Ellen G——is going with me this evening to gather wood-sorrel. She never saw that most elegant plant, and is so delicate an artist that the introduction will be a mutual benefit; Ellen will gain a subject worthy of her pencil, and the pretty weed will live—no small favour to a flower almost as transitory as the gum cistus: duration is the only charm which it wants, and that Ellen will give it. The weather is, to be sure, a little threatening, but we are not people to mind the weather when we have an object in view; we shall certainly go in quest of the wood-sorrel, and will take May, provided we can escape May's followers; for since the adventure of the lamb, Saladin has had an affair with a gander, furious in defence of his goslings, in which rencontre the gander came off conqueror; and as geese abound in the wood to which we are going (called by the country people the Pinge), and the victory may not always incline to the right side, I should be very sorry to lead the Soldan to fight his battles over again. We will take nobody but May.

So saying, we proceeded on our way through winding lanes, between hedgerows tenderly green, till we reached the hatch-gate, with the white cottage beside it embosomed in fruit trees, which forms the entrance to the Pinge, and in a moment the whole scene was before our eyes.

'Is not this beautiful, Ellen?' The answer could hardly be other than a glowing rapid 'Yes!' A wood is generally a very pretty place; but this wood—— Imagine a smaller forest, full of glades and sheep-walks, surrounded by irregular cottages with their blooming orchards, a clear stream winding about the brakes, and a road intersecting it and giving life and light to the picture, and you will have a faint idea of the Pinge. Every step was opening a new point of view, a fresh combination of glade and path and thicket. The accessories too were changing every moment. Ducks, geese, pigs, and children, giving way, as we advanced into the wood, to sheep and forest ponies; and they again disappearing as we became more entangled in its mazes, till we heard nothing but the song of the nightingale, and saw only the silent flowers.

What a piece of fairyland! The tall elms overhead just bursting into tender vivid leaf, with here and there a hoary oak or a silver-barked beech; every twig swelling with the brown buds, and yet not quite stripped of the tawny foliage of autumn: tall hollies and hawthorn beneath, with their crisp brilliant leaves mixed with the white blossoms of the sloe, and woven together with garlands of woodbines and wild-briers—what a fairyland!

Primroses, cowslips, pansies, and the regular open-eyed white blossom of the wood anemone (or, to use the more elegant Hampshire name, the windflower) were set under our feet as thick as daisies in a meadow; but the pretty weed that we came to seek was coyer, and Ellen began to fear that we had mistaken the place or the season. At last she had herself the pleasure of finding it under a brake of holly: 'Oh, look! look! I am sure that this is the woodsorrel! Look at the pendent white flower, shaped like a snowdrop and veined with purple streaks, and the beautiful trefoil leaves folded like a heart—some, the young ones, so vividly yet tenderly green, that the foliage of the elm and the hawthorn would show dully at their side; others of a deeper tint, and lined, as it were, with a rich and changeful purple! Don't you see them?' pursued my dear young friend, who is a delightful piece of life and sunshine, and was half inclined to scold me for the calmness with which, amused by her enthusiasm, I stood listening to her ardent exclamations: 'Don't you see them? Oh, how beautiful, and in what quantity—what profusion! See how the dark shade of the holly sets off the light and delicate colouring of the flower!—and see that other bed of them springing from the rich moss in the roots of that old beech tree! Pray let us gather some. Here are baskets.' So quickly and carefully we began gathering leaves, blossoms, roots and all, for the plant is so fragile that it will not brook separation; quickly and carefully we gathered, encountering divers petty misfortunes in spite of all our care, now caught by the veil in a holly bush, now hitching our shawls in a bramble, still gathering on, in spite of scratched fingers, till we had nearly filled our baskets and began to talk of our departure.

'But where is May? May! May! No going home without her. May! Here she comes galloping, the beauty!' Ellen is almost as fond of May as I am. 'What has she got in her mouth?—that rough, round, brown substance which she touches so tenderly? What can it be? A bird's nest? Naughty May!'

'No! as I live, a hedgehog! Look, Ellen, how it has coiled itself into a thorny ball! Off with it, May! Don't bring it to me!' And May, somewhat reluctant to part with her prickly prize, however troublesome of carriage, whose change of shape seemed to me to have puzzled her sagacity more than any event I ever witnessed, for in general she has perfectly the air of understanding all that is going forward—May at last dropped the hedgehog, continuing, however, to pat it with her delicate catlike paw, cautiously and daintily applied, and caught back suddenly and rapidly after every touch, as if her poor captive had been a red-hot coal. Finding that these pats entirely failed in solving the riddle (for the hedgehog shammed dead, like the lamb the other day, and appeared entirely motionless), she gave him so spirited a nudge with her pretty black nose, that she not only turned him over, but sent him rolling some little way along the turfy path—an operation which that sagacious quadruped endured with the most perfect passiveness, the most admirable non-resistance. No wonder that May's discernment was at fault; I myself, if I had not been aware of the trick, should have said that the ugly rough thing which she was trundling along, like a bowl or a cricket ball, was an inanimate substance, something devoid of sensation and of will. At last my poor pet, thoroughly perplexed and tired out, fairly relinquished the contest, and came slowly away, turning back once or twice to look at the object of her curiosity, as if half inclined to return and try the event of another shove. The sudden flight of a wood-pigeon effectually diverted her attention, and Ellen amused herself by fancying how the hedgehog was scuttling away, till our notice was also attracted by a very different object.

We had nearly threaded the wood, and were approaching an open grove of magnificent oaks on the other side, when sounds other than of nightingales burst on our ear, the deep and frequent strokes of the woodman's axe; and emerging from the Pinge we discovered the havoc which that axe had committed. Above twenty of the finest trees lay stretched on the velvet turf. There they lay in every shape and form of devastation; some bare trunks stripped ready for the timber carriage, with the bark built up in long piles at the side; some with the spoilers busy about them, stripping, hacking, hewing; others with their noble branches, their brown and fragrant shoots all fresh as if they were alive—majestic corses, the slain of to-day! The grove was like a field of battle. The young lads who were stripping the bark, the very children who were picking up the chips, seemed awed and silent, as if conscious that death was around them. The nightingales sang faintly and interruptedly—a few low frightened notes like a requiem.

Ah! here we are at the very scene of the murder, the very tree that they are felling; they have just hewn round the trunk with those slaughtering axes, and are about to saw it asunder. After all it is a fine and thrilling operation, as the work of death usually is. Into how grand an attitude was that young man thrown as he gave the final strokes round the root; and how wonderful is the effect of that supple and apparently powerless saw, bending like a riband, and yet overmastering that giant of the woods, conquering and overthrowing that thing of life! Now it has passed half through the trunk, and the woodman has begun to calculate which way the tree will fall; he drives a wedge to direct its course—now a few more movements of the noiseless saw; and then a larger wedge. See how the branches tremble! Hark how the trunk begins to crack! Another stroke of the huge hammer on the wedge, and the tree quivers, as with a mortal agony, shakes, reels, and falls. How slow and solemn and awful it is! How like to death, to human death in its grandest form! Caesar in the Capitol, Seneca in the bath, could not fall more sublimely than that oak.

Even the heavens seem to sympathize with the devastation. The clouds have gathered into one thick low canopy, dark and vapoury as the smoke which overhangs London; the setting sun is just gleaming underneath with a dim and bloody glare, and the crimson rays spreading upward with a lurid and portentous grandeur, a subdued and dusky glow, like the light reflected on the sky from some vast conflagration. The deep flush fades away, and the rain begins to descend, and we hurry homeward rapidly, yet sadly, forgetful alike of the flowers, the hedgehog, and the wetting, thinking and talking only of the fallen tree.

CHAPTER XX

A VISIT TO LUCY

Lucy, who in her single state bore so striking a resemblance to Jenny Dennison, in the number and variety of her lovers, continues to imitate that illustrious original in her married life, by her dexterous and excellent management, of which I have been lately an amused and admiring witness. Not having seen her for a long time, tempted by the fineness of the day, the first day of summer, and by the pleasure of carrying to her a little housewifely present from her sometime mistress, we resolved to take a substantial luncheon at two o'clock, and drive over to drink tea with her at five, such being, as we well knew, the fashionable visiting hour at S——.

The day was one glow of sunshine, and the road wound through a beautiful mixture of hill and dale and rich woodland, clothed in the brightest foliage, and thickly studded with gentlemen's seats, and prettier cottages, their gardens gay with the blossoms of the plum and the cherry, tossing their snowy garlands across the deep blue sky. So we journeyed on through pleasant villages and shady lanes till we emerged into the opener and totally different scenery of M—— common—a wild district, always picturesque and romantic, but now peculiarly brilliant, and glowing with the luxuriant orange flowers of the furze in its height of bloom, stretching around us like a sea of gold, and loading the very air with its rich almond odour. Who could have believed that this brown, barren, shaggy heath could have assumed such splendour, such majesty? The farther we proceeded, the more beautiful it appeared, the more gorgeous, the more brilliant. Whether climbing up the steep bank, and mixing with the thick plantation of dark firs, or chequered with brown heath and green turf on the open plain, where the sheep and lambs were straying, or circling round the pool covered with its bright white flowers, or edging the dark morass inlaid with the silky tufts of the cotton grass, or creeping down the deep dell where the alders grow, or mixing by the roadside with the shining and varied bark, now white, now purplish, and the light tremulous leaves of the feathery birch-tree—in every form or variety this furze was beauty itself. We almost lamented to leave it as we wound down the steep hill of M—— West End, that most picturesque village, with its long open sheds for broom- and faggot-making; its little country inn, the 'Red Lion'; its pretty school just in the bottom, where the clear stream comes bubbling over the road, and the romantic foot-bridge is flung across; and with cottages straggling up the hill on the opposite ascent, orchards backed by meadows, and the light wreaths of smoke sailing along the green hill-side, the road winding amidst all, beside another streamlet, whose deep rust-coloured scum gives token of a chalybeate spring.

Even this sweet and favourite scene, which, when I would think of the perfection of village landscape, of a spot to live and die in, rises unbidden before my eyes—this dear and cherished picture, which I generally leave so reluctantly— was hurried over now, so glad were we to emerge once more from its colder colouring into the full glory of the waving furze on S—— common, brighter even than that of M—— which we left behind us. Even Lucy's house was unheeded till we drove up to the door, and found, to our great satisfaction, that she was at home.

The three years that have elapsed since her marriage have changed the style of her beauty. She is grown very fat, and rather coarse; and having moreover taken to loud speaking (as I apprehend a village schoolmistress must do in pure self-defence, that her voice may be heard in the mêlée), our airy sparkling soubrette, although still handsome, has been transmuted somewhat suddenly into a bustling merry country dame, looking her full age, if not a little older. It is such a transition as a rosebud experiences when turned into a rose, such as might befall the pretty coquette mistress Anne Page when she wedded Master Fenton, and became one of the merry wives of Windsor. Lucy, however, in her dark gown and plain cap (for her dress hath undergone as much alteration as her person), her smiles and her rosiness, is still as fair a specimen of country comeliness as heart can desire.

We found her very busy, superintending the operations of a certain she-tailor, a lame woman, famous for buttonholes, who travels from house to house in that primitive district, making and repairing men's gear, and who was at that moment endeavouring to extract a smart waistcoat for our friend the schoolmaster out of a remnant of calico and a blemished waistcoat-piece, which had been purchased at half-price for his behoof by his frugal helpmate. The more material parts of the cutting out had been effected before my arrival, considerably at the expense of the worthy pedagogue's comfort, although to the probable improvement of his shape, for certainly the new fabric promised to be at least an inch smaller than the pattern; that point, however, had been by dint of great ingenuity satisfactorily adjusted, and I found the lady of the shears and the lady of the rod in the midst of a dispute on the question of buttons, which the tailoress insisted must be composed of metal or mother-of-pearl, or anything but covered moulds, inasmuch as there would be no stuff left to cover them; whilst Lucy on her side insisted that there was plenty, that anything (as all the world knew) would suffice to cover buttons if people were clever and careful, and that certain most diminutive and irregular scraps, which she gathered from the table and under it, and displayed with great ostentation, were amply sufficient for the purpose. 'If the pieces are not big enough,' continued she, 'you have nothing to do but to join them.' And as Lucy had greatly the advantage both in loudness of voice and fluency of thought and word over the itinerant sempstress, who was a woman of slow quiet speech, she carried her point in the argument most triumphantly, although whether the unlucky waistcoat-maker will succeed in stretching her materials so as to do the impossible remains to be proved, the button question being still undecided when I left S——.

Her adversary being fairly silenced, Lucy laid aside her careful thoughts and busy looks; and leaving the poor woman to her sewing and stitching, and a little tidy lass (a sort of half-boarder, who acts half as servant, half as pupil) to get all things ready for tea, she prepared to accompany me to a pleasant coppice in the neighbourhood, famous for wild lilies of the valley, to the love of which delicate flower she, not perhaps quite unjustly, partly attributed my visit.

Nothing could be more beautiful than the wood where they are found, which we reached by crossing first the open common, with its golden waves of furze, and then a clover field intensely green, deliciously fresh and cool to the eye and the tread. The copse was just in its pleasantest state, having luckily been cut last year, and being too thinly clothed with timber to obstruct the view. It goes sloping down a hill, till it is lost in the green depths of P—— Forest, with an abruptness of descent which resembles a series of terraces or rather ledges, so narrow that it is sometimes difficult to find a space on which to walk. The footing is more precarious, as even the broader paths are intersected and broken by hollows and caves, where the ground has given way and been undermined by fox earths. On the steepest and highest of these banks, in a very dry unsheltered situation, the lily of the valley grows so profusely, that the plants almost cover the ground with their beautiful broad leaves and the snowy white bells, which envelop the most delicate of odours. All around grow the fragile wind-flowers, pink as well as white; the coral blossoms of the whortleberry; the graceful wood-sorrel; the pendent drops of the stately Solomon's seal, which hang like waxen tassels under the full and regular leaves; the bright wood-vetch; the unobtrusive woodroof, whose scent is like new hay, and which retains and communicates it when dried; and lastly, those strange freaks of nature the orchises, where the portrait of an insect is so quaintly depicted in a flower. The bee orchis abounds also in the Mapledurham woods— those woods where whilom flourished the two stately but unlovely flowers Martha and Teresa Blount of *Popish* fame, and which are still in the possession of their family. But, although it is found at Mapledurham as well as in these copses of North Hampshire, yet in the little slip of Berks which divides Hants from Oxfordshire, I have never been able to discover it. The locality of flowers is a curious puzzle. The field tulip, for instance, through whose superb pendent blossoms chequered with puce and lilac the sun shines as gloriously as through stained glass, and which, blended with a still more elegant white variety, covers whole acres of the Kennet meadows, can by no process be coaxed into another habitation, however apparently similar in situation and soil. Treat them as you may, they pine and die and disappear. The Duke of Marlborough only succeeded in naturalizing them at White-Knights by the magnificent operation of transplanting half an acre of meadow, grass, and earth and all, to the depth of two feet, and even there they seem dwindling. The wood-sorrel, which I was ambitious of fixing in the shrubberies of our old place, served me the provoking trick of living a year or two, and bearing leaves, but never flowers; and that far rarer but less beautiful plant the field-star of Bethlehem—a sort of large hyacinth of the hue of the mistletoe, which, in its pale and shadowy stalk and blossom, has something to me awful, unearthly, ghastly, mystical, druidical—used me still worse, not only refusing to grow in a corner of our orchard where I planted it, but vanishing from the spot where I procured the roots, although I left at least twenty times as many as I took.

Nothing is so difficult to tame as a wild flower; and wisely so, for they generally lose much of their characteristic beauty by any change of soil or situation. That very wood-sorrel now, which I coveted so much, I saw the other day in a greenhouse! By what chance my fellow-amateur persuaded that swamp-loving, cold-braving, shade-seeking plant to blossom in the very region of light and heat and dryness, I cannot imagine; but there it was in full bloom, as ugly a little abortion as ever showed its poor face, smaller far than in its native woods, the flowers unveined and colourless, and bolt upright, the leaves full spread and stiff— no umbrella fold, no pendent grace, no changing hue! None but a lover's eye would have recognized the poor beauty of the woods in the faded prisoner of the greenhouse. No caged bird ever underwent such a change. I will never try to domesticate that pretty blossom again—content to visit it in its own lovely haunts, the bed of moss or the beech-root sofa.

The lily of the valley we may perhaps try to transplant. The garden is its proper home; it seems thrown here by accident; we cannot help thinking it an abasement, a condescension. The lily must be transportable. For the present, however, we were content to carry away a basket of blossoms, reserving till the autumn our design of peopling a shady border in our own small territories, the identical border where in summer our geraniums flourish, with that simplest and sweetest of flowers.

We then trudged back to Lucy's to tea, talking by the way of old stories, old neighbours, and old friends—mixed on her part with a few notices of her new acquaintance, lively, shrewd, and good-humoured as usual. She is indeed a most agreeable and delightful person; I think the lately developed quality at which I hinted in my opening remarks, the slight tinge of Jenny-Dennisonism, only renders her conversation more piquant and individualized, and throws her merits into sharper relief. We talked of old stories and new, and soon found she had lost none of her good gifts in gossipry; of her thousand and one lovers, about whom, although she has quite left off coquetry, she inquired with a kindly interest; of our domestic affairs, and above all of her own. She has no children—a circumstance which I sometimes think she regrets; I do not know why, except that my dear mother having given her on her marriage, amongst a variety of parting gifts, a considerable quantity of baby things, she probably thinks it a pity that they should not be used. And yet the expensiveness of children might console her on the one hand, and the superabundance of them with which she is blest in school-time on the other. Indeed, she has now the care of a charity Sunday school, in addition to her work-day labours—a circumstance which has by no means altered her opinion of the inefficacy and inexpediency of general education.

I suspect that the irregularity of payment is one cause of her dislike to the business; and yet she is so ingenious a contriver in the matter of extracting money's worth from those who have no money, that we can hardly think her unreasonable in requiring the *hen-tailor* to cover buttons out of nothing. Where she can get no cash, she takes the debt in kind; and, as most of her employers are in that predicament, she lives in this respect like the Loochooans who never heard of a currency. She accommodates herself to this state of things with admirable facility. She has sold her cow, because she found she could be served with milk and butter by the wife of a small farmer who has four children at her school; and has parted with her poultry and pigs, and left off making bread, because the people of both shops are customers to her husband in his capacity of shoemaker, and she gets bread and eggs and bacon for nothing. On the same principle, she has commenced brewing, because the maltster's son and daughter attend her seminary, and she procured three new barrels, coolers, tubs, etc., from a cooper who was in debt to her husband for shoes. 'Shoes,' or 'children,' is indeed the constant answer to the civil notice which one is accustomed to take of any novelty in the house. 'Shoes' produced the commodious dressing-table and washing-stand, coloured like rose-wood, which adorn her bed-chamber; 'children' were the source of the good-as-new roller and wheelbarrow which stand in the court; and to 'shoes and children' united are they indebted for the excellent double hedgerow of grubbed wood which she took me to see in returning from the copse—'a brand (as she observed) snatched out of the fire; for the poor man who owed them the money must break, and had nothing useful to give them except this wood, which was useless to him, as he had not money to get it grubbed up. If he holds on till the autumn,' continued Lucy, 'we shall have a good crop of potatoes from the hedgerow. We have planted them on the chance.' The ornamental part of her territory comes from the same fertile source. Even the thrift which adorns the garden (fit emblem of its mistress!) was a present from the drunken gardener of a gentleman in the neighbour-hood. 'He does not pay his little girl's schooling very regularly,' quoth she, 'but then he is so civil, poor man! Anything in the garden is at our service.'

'Shoes and children' are the burden of the song. The united professions react on each other in a remarkable manner—shoes bring scholars and scholars consume shoes. The very charity school before mentioned, a profitable concern, of which the payment depends on rich people and not on poor, springs indirectly from a certain pair of purple kid boots, a capital fit (I must do our friend the pedagogue the justice to say that he understands the use of his awl, no man better!) which so pleased the vicar's lady, who is remarkable for a neat ankle, that she not only gave a magnificent order for herself, and caused him to measure her children, but actually prevailed on her husband to give the appointment of Sunday schoolmaster to this matchless cordwainer. I should not wonder if, through her powerful patronage, he should one day rise to be parish clerk.

Well, the tea and the bread and butter were discussed with the appetite produced by a two hours' ride and a three hours' walk—to say nothing of the relish communicated to our viands by the hearty hospitality of our hostess, who 'gaily pressed and smiled.' And then the present, our ostensible errand, a patch-work quilt, long the object of Lucy's admiration, was given with due courtesy, and received with abundance of pleased and blushing thanks.

At last the evening began to draw in; her husband, who had been absent, returned, and we were compelled to set out homewards, and rode back with our basket of lilies through a beautiful twilight world, inhaling the fragrance of the blossomed furze, listening to the nightingales, and talking of Lucy's good management.

CHAPTER XXI

THE BLACK VELVET BAG

HAVE any of my readers ever found great convenience in the loss, the real loss, of actual tangible property, and been exceedingly provoked and annoyed when such property was restored to them? If so, they can sympathize with a late unfortunate recovery, which has brought me to great shame and disgrace. There is no way of explaining my calamity but by telling the whole story.

Last Friday fortnight was one of those anomalies in weather with which we English people are visited for our sins; a day of intolerable wind, an insupportable dust; an equinoctial gale out of season; a piece of March unnaturally foisted into the very heart of May; just as, in the almost parallel misarrangement of the English counties, one sees (perhaps out of compliment to this peculiarity of climate, to keep the weather in countenance as it were) a bit of Wiltshire plumped down in the very middle of Berkshire, whilst a great island of the county palatine of Durham figures in the centre of canny Northumberland. Be this as it may, on that remarkably windy day did I set forth to the good town of B——, on the feminine errand called shopping. Every lady who lives far in the country, and seldom visits great towns, will understand the full force of that comprehensive word; and I had not been shopping for a long time. I had a dread of the operation, arising from a consciousness of weakness. I am a true daughter of Eve, a dear lover of bargains and bright colours; and knowing this have generally been wise enough to keep, as much as I can, out of the way of temptation. At last a sort of necessity arose for some slight purchases, in the shape of two new gowns from London, which cried aloud for making. Trimmings, ribands, sewing-silk, and lining—all were called for. The shopping was inevitable, and I undertook the whole concern at once, most heroically resolving to spend just so much and no more; and half comforting myself that I had a full morning's work of indispensable business, and should have no time for extraneous extravagance.

There was, to be sure, a prodigious accumulation of errands and wants. The evening before, they had been set down in great form, on a slip of paper, headed thus—'things wanted.' To how many and various catalogues that title would apply, from the red bench of the peer, to the oaken settle of the cottager—from him who wants a blue riband, to him who wants bread and cheese! My list was astounding. It was written in double columns, in an invisible hand; the long intractable words were brought into the ranks by the Procrustes mode—abbreviation; and as we approached the bottom, two or three were crammed into one lot, clumped as the bean-setters say, and designated by a sort of shorthand, a hieroglyphic of my own invention. In good open printing my list would have cut a respectable figure as a catalogue, and filled a decent number of pages—a priced catalogue too; for, as I had a given sum to carry to market, I amused myself with calculating the proper and probable cost of every article; in which process I most egregiously cheated the shopkeeper and myself, by copying, with the credulity of hope, from the puffs in newspapers, and expecting to buy fine solid wearable goods at advertising prices. In this way I stretched my money a great deal farther than it would go, and swelled my catalogue, so that at last, in spite of compression and shorthand, I had no room for another word, and was obliged to crowd several small, but important articles, such as cotton, laces, pins, needles, shoe-strings, etc., into that very irregular and disorderly storehouse—that place where most things deposited are lost — *my memory*, by courtesy so called.

The written list was safely consigned, with a well-filled purse, to my usual repository, a black velvet bag; and, the next morning, I and my bag, with its nicely balanced contents of wants and money, were safely conveyed in a little open carriage to the good town of B——. There I dismounted, and began to bargain most vigorously, visiting the cheapest shops, cheapening the cheapest articles, yet wisely buying the strongest and the best; a little astonished at first to find everything so much dearer than I had set it down, yet soon reconciled to this misfortune by the magical influence which shopping possesses over a woman's fancy—all the sooner reconciled, as the monitory list lay unlooked at, and unthought of, in its grave receptacle, the black velvet bag. On I went, with an air of cheerful business, of happy importance, till my money began to wax small. Certain small aberrations had occurred too in my economy. One article that had happened, by rare accident, to be below my calculation, and indeed, below any calculation, calico at ninepence, fine, thick, strong, wide calico, at ninepence (did ever man hear of anything so cheap?), absolutely enchanted me, and I took the whole piece; then after buying for M—— a gown, according to order, I saw one that I liked better, and bought that too. Then I fell in love, was actually captivated, with a sky-blue sash and handkerchief — not the poor, thin, greeny colour which usually passes under that dishonoured name, but the rich full tint of the noonday sky, and a cap-riband, really pink, that might have vied with the inside leaves of a moss-rose. Then, in hunting after cheapness, I got into obscure shops, where, not finding what I asked for, I was fain to take something that they had, purely to make a proper compensation for the trouble of lugging out drawers and answering questions. Lastly, I was fairly coaxed into some articles by the irresistibility of the sellers—by the demure and truth-telling look of a pretty quaker, who could almost have persuaded the head off one's shoulders, and who did persuade me that ell-wide muslin would go as far as yard and a half; and by the fluent impudence of a lying shopman, who under cover of a well-darkened window, affirmed, on his honour, that his brown satin was a perfect match to my green pattern, and forced the said satin down my throat accordingly. With these helps, my money melted all too fast; at half-past five my purse was entirely empty; and, as shopping with an empty purse has by no means the relish and savour of shopping with a full one, I was quite willing and ready to go home to dinner, pleased as a child with my purchases, and wholly unsuspecting the sins of omission, the errands unperformed, which were the natural result of my unconsulted memoranda and my treacherous memory.

Home I returned, a happy and proud woman, wise in my own conceit, a thrifty fashion-monger, laden like a pedlar, with huge packages in stout brown holland, tied up with whipcord, and genteel little parcels, papered and packthreaded in shopmanlike style. At last we were safely stowed in the pony-chaise, which had much ado to hold us, my little black bag lying, as usual, in my lap; when, as we ascended the steep hill out of B——, a sudden puff of wind took at once my cottage-bonnet and my large cloak, blew the bonnet off my head, so that it hung behind me, suspended by the riband, and fairly snapped the string of the cloak, which flew away, much in the style of John Gilpin's, renowned in story. My companion, pitying my plight, exerted himself manfully to regain the fly-away garments, shoved the head into the bonnet, or the bonnet over the head (I do not know which phrase best describes the manœuvre), with one hand, and recovered the refractory cloak with the other. This last exploit was certainly the most difficult. It is wonderful what a tug he was forced to give before that obstinate cloak could be brought round: it was swelled with the wind like a bladder, animated, so to say, like a living thing, and threatened to carry pony and chaise and riders and packages backward down the hill, as if it had been a sail and we a ship. At last the contumacious garment was mastered. We righted; and by dint of sitting sideways and turning my back on my kind comrade, I got home without any further damage than the loss of my bag, which, though not missed before the chaise had been unladen, had undoubtedly gone by the board in the gale; and I lamented my old and trusty companion, without in the least foreseeing the use it would probably be of to my reputation.

Immediately after dinner (for in all cases, even when one has bargains to show, dinner must be discussed) I produced my purchases. They very much admired; and the quantity, when spread out in our little room, being altogether dazzling and the quality satisfactory, the cheapness was never doubted. Everybody thought the bargains were exactly such as I meant to get—for nobody calculated; and the bills being really lost in the lost bag, and the particular prices just as much lost in my memory (the ninepence calico was the only article whose cost occurred to me), I passed, without telling anything like a fib, merely by a discreet silence, for the best and thriftiest bargainer that ever went shopping. After some time spent very pleasantly in admiration on one side and display on the other, we were interrupted by the demand for some of the little articles which I had forgotten. 'The sewing silk, please, ma'am, for my mistress's gown.' 'Sewing silk! I don't know—look about.' Ah, she might look long enough—no sewing-silk was there. 'Very strange!' Presently came other inquiries: 'Where's the tape, Mary?' 'The tape?' 'Yes, my dear; and the needles, pins, cotton, stay-laces, boot-laces!' 'The bobbin, the ferret, shirt-buttons, shoe-strings?' quoth she of the sewing-silk, taking up the cry, and forthwith began a search as bustling, as active, and as vain, as that of our old spaniel Brush after a hare that had stolen away from her form. At last she suddenly desisted from her rummage. 'Without doubt, ma'am, they are in the reticule, and all lost,' said she, in a very pathetic tone. 'Really,' cried I, a little conscience-stricken, 'I don't recollect; perhaps I might forget.' 'Depend on it, my love, that Harriet's right,' interrupted one, whose interruptions are always kind; 'those are just the little articles that people put in reticules, and you never could forget so many things; besides, you wrote them down.' 'I don't know—I am not sure.' But I was not listened to; Harriet's conjecture had been metamorphosed into a certainty; all my sins of omission were stowed in the reticule, and before bedtime the little black bag held forgotten things enough to fill a sack.

Never was reticule so lamented by all but its owner; a boy was immediately dispatched to look for it, and, on his returning empty-handed, there was even a talk of having it cried. My care, on the other hand, was all directed to prevent its being found. I had had the good luck to lose it in a suburb of B—— renowned for filching, and I remembered that the street was, at that moment, full of people; the bag did actually contain more than enough to tempt those who were naturally disposed to steal for stealing's sake, so I went to bed in the comfortable assurance that it was gone for ever. But there is nothing certain in this world—not even a thief's dishonesty. Two old women, who had

pounced at once on my valuable property, quarrelled about
the plunder, and one of them, in a fit of resentment at being
cheated in her share, went to the mayor of B—— and informed against her companion. The mayor, an intelligent
and active magistrate, immediately took the disputed bag
and all its contents into his own possession, and as he is also
a man of great politeness, he restored it as soon as possible
to the right owner. The very first thing that saluted my
eyes when I awoke in the morning, was a note from Mr.
Mayor, with a sealed packet. The fatal truth was visible;
I had recovered my reticule, and lost my reputation. There
it lay, that identical black bag, with its name-tickets, its
cambric handkerchief, its empty purse, its unconsulted
list, its thirteen bills, and its two letters; one from a good
sort of lady-farmer, inquiring the character of a cook, with
half a sonnet written on the blank pages; the other from a
literary friend, containing a critique on the plot of a play,
advising me not to kill the king too soon, with other good
counsel, such as might, if our mayor had not been a man of
sagacity, have sent a poor authoress, in a Mademoiselle-
Scuderi-mistake, to the Tower. That catastrophe would
hardly have been worse than the real one. All my omissions
have been found out. My price list has been compared with
the bills. I have forfeited my credit for bargaining. I am
become a byword for forgetting. Nobody trusts me to
purchase a paper of pins, or to remember the cost of a penny
riband. I am a lost woman. My bag is come back, but
my fame is gone.

CHAPTER XXII

THE DELL

May 2nd. A delicious evening—bright sunshine; light summer air; a sky almost cloudless; and a fresh yet delicate verdure on the hedges and in the fields—an evening that seems made for a visit to my newly discovered haunt, the mossy dell, one of the most beautiful spots in the neighbourhood, which after passing, times out of number, the field which it terminates, we found out about two months ago from the accident of May's killing a rabbit there. May has had a fancy for the place ever since, and so have I.

Thither accordingly we bend our way — through the village—up the hill—along the common—past the avenue—across the bridge—and by the mill. How deserted the road is to-night! We have not seen a single acquaintance, except poor blind Robert, laden with his sack of grass plucked from the hedges, and the little boy that leads him. A singular division of labour! Little Jem guides Robert to the spots where the long grass grows, and tells him where it s most plentiful; and then the old man cuts it close to the roots, and between them they fill the sack, and sell the contents in the village. Half the cows in the street—for our baker, our wheelwright, and our shoemaker, has each his Alderney—owe the best part of their maintenance to blind Robert's industry.

Here we are at the entrance of the corn-field which leads to the dell, and which commands so fine a view of the Loddon, the mill, the great farm, with its picturesque outbuildings, and the range of woody hills beyond. It is impossible not to pause a moment at that gate; the landscape, always beautiful, is so suited to the season and the hour—so bright and gay and spring-like. But May, who has the chance of another rabbit in her pretty head, has galloped forward to the dingle, and poor May, who follows me so faithfully in all my wanderings, has a right to a little indulgence in hers. So to the dingle we go.

At the end of the field, which when seen from the road seems terminated by a thick dark coppice, we come suddenly to the edge of a ravine, on one side fringed with a low growth of alder, birch, and willow, on the other mossy, turfy, and bare, or only broken by bright tufts of blossomed broom. One or two old pollards almost conceal the winding road that leads down the descent, by the side of which a spring as bright as crystal runs gurgling along. The dell itself is an irregular piece of broken ground, in some parts very deep, intersected by two or three high banks of equal irregularity, now abrupt and bare and rock-like, now crowned with tufts of the feathery willow or magnificent old thorns. Everywhere the earth is covered by short fine turf, mixed with mosses, soft, beautiful, and various, and embossed with the speckled leaves and lilac flowers of the arum, the paler blossoms of the common orchis, the enamelled blue of the wild hyacinth, so splendid in this evening light, and large tufts of oxlips and cowslips rising like nosegays from the short turf.

The ground on the other side of the dell is much lower than the field through which we came, so that it is mainly to the labyrinthine intricacy of these high banks that it owes its singular character of wildness and variety. Now we seem hemmed in by those green cliffs, shut out from all the world, with nothing visible but those verdant mounds and the deep blue sky; now by some sudden turn we get a peep at an adjoining meadow, where the sheep are lying, dappling its sloping surface like the small clouds on the summer heaven. Poor harmless quiet creatures, how still they are! Some socially lying side by side; some grouped in threes and fours; some quite apart. Ah! there are lambs amongst them—pretty, pretty lambs!—nestled in by their mothers. Soft, quiet, sleepy things! Not all so quiet, though! There is a party of these young lambs as wide awake as heart can desire; half a dozen of them playing together, frisking, dancing, leaping, butting, and crying in the young voice, which is so pretty a diminutive of the full-grown bleat. How beautiful they are with their innocent spotted faces, their mottled feet, their long curly tails, and their light flexible forms, frolicking like so many kittens, but with a gentleness, an assurance of sweetness and innocence, which no kitten, nothing that ever is to be a cat, can have. How complete and perfect is their enjoyment of existence! Ah, little rogues, your play has been too noisy; you have awakened your mammas, and two or three of the old ewes are getting up; and one of them marching gravely to the troop of lambs has selected her own, given her a gentle butt, and trotted off, the poor rebuked lamb following meekly, but every now and then stopping and casting a longing look at its playmates, who, after a moment's awed pause, had resumed their gambols, whilst the stately dam every now and then looked back in her turn, to see that her little one was following. At last she lay down, and the lamb by her side. I never saw so pretty a pastoral scene in my life. [1]

Another turning of the dell gives a glimpse of the dark coppice by which it is backed, and from which we are separated by some marshy, rushy ground, where the springs have formed into a pool, and where the moor-hen loves to build her nest. Aye, there is one scudding away now—I can hear her plash into the water, and the rustling of her wings amongst the rushes. This is the deepest part of the wild dingle. How uneven the ground is! Surely these excavations, now so thoroughly clothed with vegetation, must originally have been huge gravel pits; there is no other way of accounting for the labyrinth, for they do dig gravel

---

[1] I have seen one which affected me much more. Walking in the Church Lane with one of the young ladies of the vicarage, we met a large flock of sheep, with the usual retinue of shepherds and dogs. Lingering after them and almost out of sight, we encountered a straggling ewe, now trotting along, now walking, and every now and then stopping to look back, and bleating. A little behind her came a lame lamb, bleating occasionally, as if in answer to its dam, and doing its very best to keep up with her. It was a lameness of both the fore feet; the knees were bent, and it seemed to walk on the very edge of the hoof—on tiptoe, if I may venture such an expression. My young friend thought that the lameness proceeded from original malformation; I am rather of opinion that it was accidental, and that the poor creature was wretchedly foot-sore. However that might be, the pain and difficulty with which it took every step were not to be mistaken; and the distress and fondness of the mother, her perplexity as the flock passed gradually out of sight, the effort with which the poor lamb contrived to keep up a sort of trot, and their mutual calls and lamentations, were really so affecting, that Ellen and I, although not at all larmoyant sort of people, had much ado not to cry. We could not find a boy to carry the lamb, which was too big for us to manage; but I was quite sure that the ewe would not desert it, and as the dark was coming on, we both trusted that the shepherds on folding their flock would miss them and return for them; and so I am happy to say it proved.

in such capricious meanders; but the quantity seems incredible. Well, there is no end of guessing! We are getting amongst the springs, and must turn back. Round this corner, where on ledges like fairy terraces the orchises and arums grow, and we emerge suddenly on a new side of the dell, just fronting the small homestead of our good neighbour, Farmer Allen.

This rustic dwelling belongs to what used to be called in this part of the country 'a little bargain': thirty or forty acres, perhaps, of arable land, which the owner and his sons cultivated themselves, whilst the wife and daughters assisted in the husbandry, and eked out the slender earnings by the produce of the dairy, the poultry yard, and the orchard—an order of cultivators now passing rapidly away, but in which much of the best part of the English character, its industry, its frugality, its sound sense, and its kindness might be found. Farmer Allen himself is an excellent specimen, the cheerful venerable old man, with his long white hair, and his bright grey eye, and his wife still finer. They have had a hard struggle to win through the world and keep their little property undivided; but good management and good principles and the assistance afforded them by an admirable son, who left our village a poor 'prentice boy, and is now a partner in a great house in London, have enabled them to overcome all the difficulties of these trying times, and they are now enjoying the peaceful evening of a well-spent life as free from care and anxiety as their best friends could desire.

Ah! there is Mr. Allen in the orchard, the beautiful orchard, with its glorious garlands of pink and white, its pearly pear-blossoms and coral apple-buds. What a flush of bloom it is! How brightly delicate it appears, thrown into strong relief by the dark house and the weather-stained barn, in this soft evening light. The very grass is strewed with the snowy petals of the pear and the cherry. And there sits Mrs. Allen, feeding her poultry, with her three little granddaughters from London, pretty fairies from three years old to five (only two-and-twenty months elapsed between the birth of the eldest and the youngest), playing round her feet.

Mrs. Allen, my dear Mrs. Allen, has been that rare thing, a

beauty, and although she be now an old woman, I had almost said that she is so still. Why should I not say so? Nobleness of feature and sweetness of expression are surely as delightful in age as in youth. Her face and figure are much like those which are stamped indelibly on the memory of every one who ever saw that grand specimen of woman— Mrs. Siddons. The outline of Mrs. Allen's face is exactly the same; but there is more softness, more gentleness, a more feminine composure in the eye and in the smile. Mrs. Allen never played Lady Macbeth. Her hair, almost as black as at twenty, is parted on her large fair forehead, and combed under her exquisitely neat and snowy cap; a muslin neckerchief, a grey stuff gown, and a white apron complete the picture.

There she sits under an old elder-tree which flings its branches over her like a canopy, whilst the setting sun illumines her venerable figure and touches the leaves with an emerald light; there she sits, placid and smiling, with her spectacles in her hand and a measure of barley on her lap, into which the little girls are dipping their chubby hands and scattering the corn amongst the ducks and chickens with unspeakable glee. But those ingrates, the poultry, don't seem so pleased and thankful as they ought to be; they mistrust their young feeders. All domestic animals dislike children, partly from an instinctive fear of their tricks and their thoughtlessness, partly, I suspect, from jealousy. Jealousy seems a strange tragic passion to attribute to the inmates of the *basse-cour*—but only look at that strutting fellow of a bantam cock (evidently a favourite), who sidles up to his old mistress with an air half affronted and half tender, turning so scornfully from the barley-corns which Annie is flinging towards him, and say if he be not as jealous as Othello! Nothing can pacify him but Mrs. Allen's notice and a dole from her hand. See, she is calling to him and feeding him, and now how he swells out his feathers, and flutters his wings, and erects his glossy neck, and struts and crows and pecks, proudest and happiest of bantams, the pet and glory of the poultry yard!

In the meantime my own pet May, who has all this while been peeping into every hole, and penetrating every nook and winding of the dell, in hopes to find another rabbit, has returned to my side, and is sliding her snake-like head into my hand, at once to invite the caress which she likes so well, and to intimate, with all due respect, that it is time to go home. The setting sun gives the same warning; and in a moment we are through the dell, the field, and the gate, past the farm and the mill, and hanging over the bridge that crosses the Loddon river.

What a sunset! How golden! How beautiful! The sun just disappearing, and the narrow liny clouds, which a few minutes ago lay like soft vapoury streaks along the horizon, lighted up with a golden splendour that the eye can scarcely endure, and those still softer clouds which floated above them, wreathing and curling into a thousand fantastic forms, as thin and changeful as summer smoke, now defined and deepened into grandeur, and edged with ineffable, insufferable light! Another minute and the brilliant orb totally disappears, and the sky above grows every moment more varied and more beautiful as the dazzling golden lines are mixed with glowing red and gorgeous purple, dappled with small dark specks, and mingled with such a blue as the egg of the hedge-sparrow. To look up at that glorious sky, and then to see that magnificent picture reflected in the clear and lovely Loddon water, is a pleasure never to be described and never forgotten. My heart swells and my eyes fill as I write of it, and think of the immeasurable majesty of nature, and the unspeakable goodness of God, who has spread an enjoyment so pure, so peaceful, and so intense before the meanest and the lowliest of His creatures.

CHAPTER XXIII

THE OLD HOUSE AT ABERLEIGH

June 25th. What a glowing glorious day! Summer in its richest prime, noon in its most sparkling brightness, little white clouds dappling the deep blue sky, and the sun, now partially veiled, and now bursting through them with an intensity of light! It would not do to walk to-day, professedly to walk—we should be frightened at the very sound—and yet it is probable that we may be beguiled into a pretty long stroll before we return home. We are going to drive to the old house at Aberleigh, to spend the morning under the shade of those balmy firs, and amongst those luxuriant rose-trees, and by the side of that brimming Loddon river. 'Do not expect us before six o'clock,' said I, as I left the house. 'Six at soonest!' added my charming companion; and off we drove in our little pony-chaise, drawn by our old mare, and with the good-humoured urchin, Henry's successor, a sort of younger Scrub, who takes care of horse and chaise, and cow and garden, for our charioteer.

My comrade in this homely equipage was a young lady of high family and higher endowments, to whom the novelty of the thing, and her own naturalness of character and simplicity of taste, gave an unspeakable enjoyment. She danced the little chaise up and down as she got into it, and laughed for very glee like a child. Lizzy herself could not have been more delighted. She praised the horse and the driver, and the roads and the scenery, and gave herself fully up to the enchantment of a rural excursion in the sweetest weather of this sweet season. I enjoyed all this too; for the road was pleasant to every sense, winding through narrow lanes, under high elms, and between hedges garlanded with woodbine and rose-trees, whilst the air was scented with the delicious fragrance of blossomed beans. I enjoyed it all—but I believe my principal pleasure was derived from my companion herself.

Emily I—— is a person whom it is a privilege to know. She is quite like a creation of the older poets, and might pass for one of Shakespeare's or Fletcher's women stepped into life; just as tender, as playful, as gentle, and as kind. She is clever too, and has all the knowledge and accomplishments that a carefully conducted education, acting on a mind of singular clearness and ductility, matured and improved by the very best company, can bestow. But one never thinks of her acquirements. It is the charming artless character, the bewitching sweetness of manner, the real and universal sympathy, the quick taste and the ardent feeling, that one loves in Emily. She is Irish by birth, and has in perfection the melting voice and soft caressing accent by which her fair countrywomen are distinguished. Moreover she is pretty—I think her beautiful, and so do all who have heard as well as seen her—but pretty, very pretty, all the world must confess; and perhaps that is a distinction more enviable, because less envied, than the 'palmy state' of beauty. Her prettiness is of the prettiest kind—that of which the chief character is youthfulness. A short but pleasing figure, all grace and symmetry, a fair blooming face, beaming with intelligence and good humour; the prettiest little feet and the whitest hand in the world—such is Emily I——.

She resides with her maternal grandmother, a venerable old lady, slightly shaken with the palsy; and when together (and they are so fondly attached to each other that they are seldom parted) it is one of the loveliest combinations of youth and age ever witnessed. There is no seeing them without feeling an increase of respect and affection for both grandmother and granddaughter—always one of the tenderest and most beautiful of natural connections—as Richardson knew when he made such exquisite use of it in his matchless book. I fancy that Grandmamma Shirley must have been just another venerable lady as Mrs. S——, and our sweet Emily—— Oh, no—Harriet Byron is not half good enough for her! There is nothing like her in the whole seven volumes.

But here we are at the bridge! Here we must alight! 'This is the Loddon, Emily. Is it not a beautiful river?—rising level with its banks, so clear and smooth and peaceful, giving back the verdant landscape and the bright blue sky, and bearing on its pellucid stream the snowy water-lily, the purest of flowers, which sits enthroned on its own cool leaves, looking chastity itself, like the lady in Comus. That queenly flower becomes the water, and so do the stately swans who are sailing so majestically down the stream, like those who

> On St. Mary's lake
> Float double, swan and shadow.

We must dismount here, and leave Richard to take care of our equipage under the shade of these trees, whilst we walk up to the house. See, there it is! We must cross this stile; there is no other way now.'

And crossing the stile we were immediately in what had been a drive round a spacious park, and still retained something of the character, though the park itself had long been broken into arable fields—and in full view of the Great House, a beautiful structure of James the First's time, whose glassless windows and dilapidated doors form a melancholy contrast with the strength and entireness of the rich and massive front.

The story of that ruin—for such it is—is always to me singularly affecting; it is that of the decay of an ancient and distinguished family, gradually reduced from the highest wealth and station to actual poverty. The house and park, and a small estate around it, were entailed on a distant cousin, and could not be alienated; and the late owner, the last of his name and lineage, after long struggling with debt and difficulty, farming his own lands, and clinging to his magnificent home with a love of place almost as tenacious as that of the younger Foscari, was at last forced to abandon it, retired to a paltry lodging in a paltry town, and died there about twenty years ago, broken-hearted. His successor, bound by no ties of association to the spot, and rightly judging the residence to be much too large for the diminished estate, immediately sold the superb fixtures, and would have entirely taken down the house, if, on making the attempt, the masonry had not been found so solid that the materials were not worth the labour. A great part, however, of one side is laid open, and the splendid chambers, with their carving and gilding, are exposed to the wind and rain—sad memorials of past grandeur! The grounds have been left in a merciful neglect; the park, indeed, is broken up, the lawn mown twice a year like a common hay-field, the grotto mouldering into ruin, and the fish-ponds choked with rushes and aquatic plants; but the shrubs and flowering trees are undestroyed, and have grown into a magnificence of size and wildness of beauty, such as we may imagine them to attain in their native forests. Nothing can exceed their luxuriance, especially in the spring, when the lilac and laburnum and double-cherry put forth their gorgeous blossoms. There is a sweet sadness in the sight of such floweriness amidst such desolation; it seems the triumph of nature over the destructive power of man. The whole place, in that season more particularly, is full of a soft and soothing melancholy, reminding me, I scarcely know why, of some of the descriptions of natural scenery in the novels of Charlotte Smith, which I read when a girl, and which, perhaps for that reason, hang on my memory.

But here we are, in the smooth grassy ride, on the top of a steep turfy slope descending to the river, crowned with enormous firs and limes of equal growth, looking across the winding waters into a sweet peaceful landscape of quiet meadows, shut in by distant woods. What a fragrance is in the air from the balmy fir-trees and the blossomed limes! What an intensity of odour! And what a murmur of bees in the lime-trees! What a coil those little winged people make over our heads! And what a pleasant sound it is! —the pleasantest of busy sounds, that which comes associated with all that is good and beautiful—industry and forecast, and sunshine and flowers. Surely these lime-trees might store a hundred hives; the very odour is of a honeyed richness, cloying, satiating.

Emily exclaimed in admiration as we stood under the deep, strong, leafy shadow, and still more when honey-suckles trailed their untrimmed profusion in our path, and roses, really trees, almost intercepted our passage.

'On, Emily, farther yet! Force your way by that jasmine—it will yield; I will take care of this stubborn white rose bough.' 'Take care of yourself! Pray take care,' said my fairest friend; 'let me hold back the branches.' After we had won our way through the strait, at some expense of veils and flounces, she stopped to contemplate and admire the tall graceful shrub, whose long thorny stems, spreading in every direction, had opposed our progress, and now waved their delicate clusters over our heads. 'Did I ever think,' exclaimed she, 'of standing under the shadow of a white rose tree! What an exquisite fragrance! And what a beautiful flower—so pale and white and tender, and the petals thin and smooth as silk! What rose is it?' 'Don't you know? Did you never see it before? It is rare now, I believe, and seems rarer than it is, because it only blossoms in very hot summers; but this, Emily, is the musk-rose — that very musk-rose of which Titania talks, and which is worthy of Shakespeare and of her. Is it not? No, do not smell to it; it is less sweet so than other roses; but one cluster in a vase, or even that bunch in your bosom, will perfume a large room, as it does the summer air.' 'Oh! we will take twenty clusters,' said Emily. 'I wish grandmamma were here! She talks so often of a musk-rose tree that grew against one end of her father's house. I wish she were here to see this!'

Echoing her wish, and well laden with musk-roses, planted perhaps in the days of Shakespeare, we reached the steps that led to a square summer-house or banqueting-room, overhanging the river; the under part was a boat-house, whose projecting roof, as well as the walls and the very top of the little tower, was covered with ivy and woodbine, and surmounted by tufted barberries, bird-cherries, acacias, covered with their snowy chains, and other pendent and flowering trees. Beyond rose two poplars of unrivalled magnitude, towering like stately columns over the dark tall firs, and giving a sort of pillared and architectural grandeur to the scene.

We were now close to the mansion; but it looked sad and desolate, and the entrance, choked with brambles and nettles, seemed almost to repel our steps. The summer-house, the beautiful summer-house, was free and open and inviting, commanding from the unglazed windows, which hung high above the water, a reach of the river terminated by a rustic mill.

There we sat, emptying our little basket of fruit and country cakes, till Emily was seized with a desire of viewing from the other side of the Loddon the scenery which had so much enchanted her. 'I must,' said she, 'take a sketch of the ivied boat-house, and of this sweet room, and this pleasant window—grandmamma would never be able to walk from the road to see the place itself, but she must see its likeness.' So forth we sallied, not forgetting the dear musk-roses.

We had no way of reaching the desired spot but by retracing our steps a mile, during the heat of the hottest hour of the day, and then following the course of the river to an equal distance on the other side; nor had we any materials for sketching, except the rumpled paper which had contained our repast, and a pencil without a point, which I happened to have about me. But these small difficulties are pleasures to gay and happy youth. Regardless of such obstacles, the sweet Emily bounded on like a fawn, and I followed delighting in her delight. The sun went in, and the walk was delicious; a reviving coolness seemed to breathe over the water, wafting the balmy scent of the firs and limes; we found a point of view presenting the boat-house, the water, the poplars, and the mill, in a most felicitous combination; the little straw fruit-basket made a capital table; and refreshed and sharpened and pointed by our trusty lackey's excellent knife (your country boy is never without a good knife—it is his prime treasure) the pencil did double duty—first in the skilful hands of Emily, whose faithful and spirited sketch does equal honour to the scene and to the artist, and then in the humbler office of attempting a faint transcript of my own impressions in the following sonnet:

> It was an hour of calmest noon, a day
>   Of ripest summer: o'er the deep blue sky
>   White speckled clouds came sailing peacefully,
> Half shrouding in a chequer'd veil the ray
> Of the sun, too ardent else—what time we lay
>   By the smooth Loddon, opposite the high
>   Steep bank, which as a coronet gloriously
> Wore its rich crest of firs and lime-trees, gay
>   With their pale tassels; while from out a bower
> Of ivy (where those column'd poplars rear
>   Their heads) the ruin'd boat-house, like a tower,
> Flung its deep shadow on the waters clear.
>   My Emily! forgot not that calm hour,
> Nor that fair scene, by thee made doubly dear!

CHAPTER XXIV

THE OLD GIPSY

WE have few gipsies in our neighbourhood. In spite of our tempting green lanes, our woody dells and heathy commons, the rogues don't take to us. I am afraid that we are too civilized, too cautious; that our sheep-folds are too closely watched; our barn-yards too well guarded; our geese and ducks too fastly penned; our chickens too securely locked up; our little pigs too safe in their sty; our game too scarce; our laundresses too careful. In short, we are too little primitive: we have a snug brood of vagabonds and poachers of our own, to say nothing of their regular followers, constables and justices of the peace; we have stocks in the village, and a treadmill in the next town; and therefore we go gipsyless—a misfortune of which every landscape painter, and every lover of that living landscape, the country, can appreciate the extent. There is nothing under the sun that harmonizes so well with nature, especially in her woodland recesses, as that picturesque people, who are, so to say, the wild genus—the pheasants and roebucks of the human race.

Sometimes, indeed, we used to see a gipsy procession passing along the common, like an eastern caravan, men, women, and children, donkeys and dogs; and sometimes a patch of bare earth, strewed with ashes and surrounded by scathed turf, on the broad green margin of some cross-road, would give token of a gipsy halt; but a regular gipsy encampment has always been so rare an event that I was equally surprised and delighted to meet with one in the course of my walks last autumn, particularly as the party was of the most innocent description, quite free from those tall, dark, lean Spanish-looking men, who it must be confessed, with all my predilection for the caste, are rather startling to meet when alone in an unfrequented path; and a path more solitary than that into which the beauty of a bright October morning had tempted me could not well be imagined.

Branching off from the high road, a little below our village, runs a wide green lane, bordered on either side by a row of young oaks and beeches just within the hedge, forming an avenue, in which, on a summer afternoon, you may see the squirrels disporting from tree to tree, whilst the rooks, their fellow-denizens, are wheeling in noisy circles over their heads. The fields sink gently down on each side, so that, being the bottom of a natural winding valley, and crossed by many little rills and rivulets, the turf exhibits even in the dryest summers an emerald verdure. Scarcely any one passes the end of that lane without wishing to turn into it; but the way is in some sort dangerous and difficult for foot passengers, because the brooklets which intersect it are in many instances bridgeless, and in others bestridden by planks so decayed that it were rashness to pass them; and the nature of the ground, treacherous and boggy, and in many places as unstable as water, renders it for carriages wholly impracticable.

I, however, who do not dislike a little difficulty where there is no absolute danger, and who am moreover almost as familiar with the one only safe track as the heifers who graze there, sometimes venture along this seldom-trodden path, which terminates, at the end of a mile and a half, in a spot of singular beauty. The hills become abrupt and woody, the cultivated enclosures cease, and the long narrow valley ends in a little green, bordered on one side by a fine old park, whose mossy paling, overhung with thorns and hollies, comes sweeping round it, to meet the rich coppices which clothe the opposite acclivity. Just under the high and irregular paling, shaded by the birches and sycamores of the park, and by the venerable oaks which are scattered irregularly on the green, is a dark deep pool, whose broken banks, crowned with fern and wreathed with brier and bramble, have an air of wildness and grandeur that might have suited the pencil of Salvator Rosa.

In this lonely place (for the mansion to which the park belongs has long been uninhabited) I first saw our gipsies. They had pitched their tent under one of the oak-trees, perhaps from a certain dim sense of natural beauty, which those who live with nature in the fields are seldom totally without; perhaps because the neighbourhood of the coppices and of the deserted hall was favourable to the acquisition of game, and of the little fuel which their hardy habits required. The party consisted only of four—an old crone, in a tattered red cloak and black bonnet, who was stooping over a kettle, of which the contents were probably as savoury as that of Meg Merrilies, renowned in story; a pretty black-eyed girl, at work under the trees; a sun-burnt urchin of eight or nine, collecting sticks and dead leaves to feed their out-of-door fire, and a slender lad two or three years older, who lay basking in the sun, with a couple of shabby dogs, of the sort called mongrel, in all the joy of idleness, whilst a grave patient donkey stood grazing hard by. It was a pretty picture, with its soft autumnal sky, its rich woodiness, its sunshine, its verdure, the light smoke curling from the fire, and the group disposed around it so harmless, poor outcasts, and so happy—a beautiful picture! I stood gazing on it till I was half ashamed to look longer, and came away half afraid that they should depart before I could see them again.

This fear I soon found to be groundless. The old gipsy was a celebrated fortune-teller, and the post having been so long vacant, she could not have brought her talents to a better market. The whole village rang with the predictions of this modern Cassandra—unlike her Trojan predecessor, inasmuch as her prophecies were never of evil. I myself could not help admiring the real cleverness, the genuine gipsy tact with which she adapted her foretellings to the age, the habits, and the known desires and circumstances of her clients.

To our little pet, Lizzy, for instance, a damsel of seven, she predicted a fairing; to Ben Kirby, a youth of thirteen, head batter of the boys, a new cricket ball; to Ben's sister Lucy, a girl some three years his senior, and just promoted to that ensign of womanhood a cap, she promised a pink top-knot; whilst for Miss Sophia Matthews, our old-maidish schoolmistress, who would be heartily glad to be a girl again, she foresaw one handsome husband, and for the smart widow Simmons, two. These were the least of her triumphs. George Davis, the dashing young farmer of the hill-house, a gay sportsman who scoffed at fortune-tellers and matrimony, consulted her as to whose greyhound would win the courser's cup at the beacon meeting; to which she replied that she did not know to whom the dog would belong, but that the winner of the cup would be a white greyhound, with one blue ear, and a spot on its side, being an exact description of Mr. George Davis's favourite Helen, who followed her master's steps like his shadow, and was standing behind him at this very instant. This prediction gained our gipsy half a crown; and master Welles—the thriving thrifty yeoman of the Lea—she managed to win sixpence from his hard honest frugal hand, by a prophecy that his old brood mare, called Blackfoot, should bring forth twins; and Ned the blacksmith, who was known to court the tall nurse-maid at the mill—she got a shilling from Ned, simply by assuring him that his wife should have the longest coffin that ever was made in our wheelwright's shop. A most tempting prediction, ingeniously combining the prospect of winning and of surviving the lady of his heart— a promise equally adapted to the hot and cold fits of that ague, called love; lightening the fetters of wedlock; uniting in a breath the bridegroom and the widower. Ned was the best pleased of all her customers, and enforced his suit with such vigour that he and the fair giantess were asked in church the next Sunday, and married at the fortnight's end.

No wonder that all the world—that is to say, all our world—were crazy to have their fortunes told—to enjoy the pleasure of hearing from such undoubted authority that what they wished to be should be. Amongst the most eager to take a peep into futurity was our pretty maid Harriet, although her desire took the not unusual form of disclamation—'nothing should induce her to have her fortune told, nothing upon earth! She never thought of the gipsy, not she!'—and to prove the fact she said so at least twenty times a day. Now Harriet's fortune seemed told already; her destiny was fixed. She, the belle of the village, was engaged, as everybody knows, to our village beau, Joel Brent; they were only waiting for a little more money to marry; and as Joel was already head carter to our head farmer, and had some prospect of a bailiff's place, their union did not appear very distant. But Harriet, besides being a beauty, was a coquette, and her affection for her betrothed did not interfere with certain flirtations which came in like Isabella, 'by the by,' and occasionally cast a shadow of coolness between the lovers, which, however, Joel's cleverness and good humour generally contrived to chase away. There had probably been a little fracas in the present instance, for at the end of one of her daily professions of unfaith in gipsies and their predictions, she added 'that none but fools did believe them; that Joel had had his fortune told, and wanted to treat her to a prophecy —but she was not such a simpleton.'

About half an hour after the delivery of this speech, I happened in tying up a chrysanthemum to go to our wood-yard for a stick of proper dimensions, and there, enclosed between the faggot-pile and the coal-shed, stood the gipsy, in the very act of palmistry, conning the lines of fate in Harriet's hand. Never was a stronger contrast than that between the old withered sibyl, dark as an Egyptian, with bright laughing eyes and an expression of keen humour under all her affected solemnity, and our village beauty, tall and plump and fair, blooming as a rose and simple as a dove. She was listening too intently to see me, but the fortune-teller did, and stopped so suddenly that her attention was awakened, and the intruder discovered.

Harriet at first meditated a denial. She called up a pretty innocent unconcerned look; answered my silence (for I never spoke a word) by muttering something about 'coals for the parlour,' and catching up my new-painted green watering-pot instead of the coal-scuttle, began filling it with all her might, to the unspeakable discomfiture of that useful utensil—on which the dingy dust stuck like bird-lime—and of her own clean apron, which exhibited a curious interchange of black and green on a white ground. During the process of filling the watering-pot, Harriet made divers signs to the gipsy to decamp. The old sibyl, however, budged not a foot, influenced probably by two reasons, one, the hope of securing a customer in the new-comer, whose appearance is generally, I am afraid, the very reverse of dignified, rather merry than wise; the other, a genuine fear of passing through the yard gate, on the outside of which a much more imposing person, my greyhound May-flower, who has a sort of beadle instinct anent drunkards and pilferers and disorderly persons of all sorts, stood barking most furiously.

This instinct is one of May's remarkable qualities. Dogs are all, more or less, physiognomists and commonly pretty determined aristocrats, fond of the fine and averse to the shabby, distinguishing, with a nice accuracy, the master castes from the pariahs of the world. But May's power of perception is another matter, more, as it were, moral. She has no objection to honest rags; can away with dirt, or age, or ugliness, or any such accident, and, except just at home, makes no distinction between kitchen and parlour. Her intuition points entirely to the race of people commonly called suspicious, on whom she pounces at a glance. What a constable she would have made! What a jewel of a thief-taker! Pity that those four feet should stand in the way of her preferment—she might have risen to be a Bow Street officer. As it is we make the gift useful in a small way. In the matter of hiring and marketing the whole village likes to consult May. Many a chap has stared when she has been whistled up to give her opinion as to his honesty; and many a pig bargain has gone off on her veto. Our neighbour, mine host of the 'Rose,' used constantly to follow her judgment in the selection of his lodgers. His house was never so orderly as when under her government. At last he found out that she abhorred tipplers as well as thieves—indeed, she actually barked away three of his best customers; and he left off appealing to her sagacity, since which he has at different times lost three silver spoons and a leg of mutton. With every one else May is an oracle. Not only in the case of wayfarers and vagrants, but amongst our own people, her fancies are quite a touchstone. A certain hump-backed cobbler, for instance—May cannot abide him, and I don't think he has had so much as a job of heel-piecing to do since her dislike became public. She really took away his character.

Longer than I have taken to relate Mayflower's accomplishments stood we, like the folks in the *Critic*, at a dead-lock; May, who probably regarded the gipsy as a sort of

rival, an interloper on her oracular domain, barking with
the voice of a lioness—the gipsy trying to persuade me into
having my fortune told—and I endeavouring to prevail on
May to let the gipsy pass. Both attempts were unsuc-
cessful: and the fair consulter of destiny, who had by this
time recovered from the shame of her detection, extricated
us from our dilemma by smuggling the old woman away
through the house.

Of course Harriet was exposed to some raillery, and a
good deal of questioning about her future fate, as to which
she preserved an obstinate, but evidently satisfied, silence.
At the end of three days, however—my readers are, I hope,
learned enough in gipsy lore to know that unless kept
secret for three entire days, no prediction can come true—
at the end of three days, when all the family except herself
had forgotten the story, our pretty soubrette, half bursting
with the long retention, took the opportunity of lacing on
my new half-boots to reveal the prophecy. 'She was to see
within the week, and this was Saturday, the young man,
the real young man, whom she was to marry.' 'Why,
Harriet, you know poor Joel.' 'Joel, indeed! The gipsy
said that the young man, the real young man, was to ride
up to the house dressed in a dark greatcoat (and Joel never
wore a greatcoat in his life—all the world knew that he
wore smock-frocks and jackets) and mounted on a white
horse—and where should Joel get a white horse?' 'Had
this real young man made his appearance yet?' 'No; there
had not been a white horse past the place since Tuesday;
so it must certainly be to-day.'

A good look out did Harriet keep for white horses during
this fateful Saturday, and plenty did she see. It was the
market day at B——, and team after team came by with
one, two, and three white horses; cart after cart, and gig
after gig, each with a white steed; Colonel M——'s carriage,
with its prancing pair—but still no horseman. At length
one appeared; but he had a greatcoat whiter than the
animal he rode; another, but he was old farmer Lewington,
a married man; a third, but he was little Lord L——, a
schoolboy, on his Arabian pony. Besides, they all passed
the house; and as the day wore on, Harriet began, alternately, to profess her old infidelity on the score of fortune-

telling, and to let out certain apprehensions that, if the gipsy did really possess the power of foreseeing events, and no such horseman arrived, she might possibly be unlucky enough to die an old maid—a fate for which, although the proper destiny of a coquette, our village beauty seemed to entertain a very decided aversion.

At last, just at dusk, just as Harriet, making believe to close our casement shutters, was taking her last peep up the road, something white appeared in the distance coming leisurely down the hill. Was it really a horse? Was it not rather Titus Strong's cow driving home to milking? A minute or two dissipated that fear; it certainly was a horse and as certainly it had a dark rider. Very slowly he descended the hill, pausing most provokingly at the end of the village, as if about to turn up the Vicarage lane. He came on, however, and after another short stop at the 'Rose,' rode up full to our little gate, and catching Harriet's hand as she was opening the wicket, displayed to the half-pleased, half-angry damsel the smiling triumphant face of her own Joel Brent, equipped in a new greatcoat, and mounted on his master's newly purchased market nag. Oh, Joel! Joel! The gipsy! the gipsy!

CHAPTER XXV

THE YOUNG GIPSY

THE weather continuing fine and dry, I did not fail to revisit my gipsy encampment, which became more picturesque every day in the bright sun-gleams and lengthening shadows of a most brilliant autumn. A slight frost had strewed the green lane with the light yellow leaves of the elm—those leaves on whose yielding crispness it is so pleasant to tread, and which it is so much pleasanter to watch whirling along, 'thin dancers upon air,' in the fresh October breeze; whilst the reddened beech and spotted sycamore, and the rich oaks dropping with acorns, their foliage just edging into its deep orange-brown, added all the magic of colour to the original beauty of the scenery. It was undoubtedly the prettiest walk in the neighbourhood, and the one which I frequented the most.

Ever since the adventure of May, the old fortune-teller and I understood each other perfectly. She knew that I was no client, no patient, no customer (which is the fittest name for a goosecap who goes to a gipsy to ask what is to befall her?), but she also knew that I was no enemy to either her or her profession; for after all, if people choose to amuse themselves by being simpletons, it is no part of their neighbours' business to hinder them. I, on my side, liked the old gipsy exceedingly; I liked both her humour and her good humour, and had a real respect for her cleverness. We always interchanged a smile and a nod, meet where we might. May, too, had become accustomed to the whole party. The gift of a bone from the cauldron—a bare bone—your well-fed dog likes nothing so well as such a windfall, and if stolen the relish is higher—a bare bone brought about that reconciliation. I am sorry to accuse May of accepting a bribe, but such was the fact. She now looked at the fortune-teller with great complacency, would let the boys stroke her long neck, and in her turn would condescend to frolic with their shabby curs, who, trained to a cat-like caution and mistrust of their superiors, were as much alarmed at her advances as if a lioness had offered herself as their playfellow. There was no escaping her civility, however, so they submitted to their fate, and really seemed astonished to find themselves alive when the gambol was over. One of them, who from a tail turned over his back like a squirrel, and an amazingly snub nose, had certainly some mixture of the pug in his composition, took a great fancy to her when his fright was past, which she repaid by the sort of scornful kindness, the despotic protection, proper to her as a beauty and a favourite and a high-blooded greyhound—always a most proud and stately creature. The poor little mongrel used regularly to come jumping to meet her, and she as regularly turned him over and over and over, and round and round and round, like a teetotum. He liked it apparently, for he never failed to come and court the tossing whenever she went near him.

The person most interesting to me of the whole party was the young girl. She was remarkably pretty, and of the peculiar prettiness which is so frequently found amongst that singular people. Her face resembled those which Sir Joshua has often painted—rosy, round, and bright, set in such a profusion of dark curls, lighted by such eyes, and such a smile, and she smiled whenever you looked at her—she could not help it. Her figure was light and small, of low stature, and with an air of great youthfulness. In her dress she was, for a gipsy, surprisingly tidy. For the most part, that ambulatory race have a preference for rags, as forming their most appropriate wardrobe, being a part of their tools of trade, their insignia of office. I do not imagine that Harriet's friend, the fortune-teller, would have exchanged her stained tattered cloak for the thickest and brightest red cardinal that ever came out of a woollen-draper's shop. And she would have been a loser if she had. Take away that mysterious mantle, and a great part of her reputation would go too. There is much virtue in an old cloak. I question if the simplest of her clients, even Harriet herself, would have consulted her in a new one. But the young girl was tidy; not only accurately clean, and with clothes neatly and nicely adjusted to her trim little form, but with the rents darned and the holes patched in a way that I should be glad to see equalled by our own villagers.

Her manners were quite as ungipsy-like as her apparel, and so was her conversation; for I could not help talking to her, and was much pleased with her frankness and innocence, and the directness and simplicity of her answers. She was not the least shy; on the contrary, there was a straightforward look, a fixing of her sweet eyes full of pleasure and reliance right upon you, which in the description might seem almost too assured, but which in reality no more resembled vulgar assurance than did the kindred artlessness of Shakespeare's Miranda. It seems strange to liken a gipsy girl to that loveliest creation of genius; but I never saw that innocent gaze without being sure that just with such a look of pleased attention, of affectionate curiosity, did the island princess listen to Ferdinand.

All that she knew of her little story she told without scruple, in a young liquid voice, and with a little curtsy between every answer, that became her extremely. 'Her name,' she said, 'was Fanny. She had no father or mother; they were dead; and she and her brothers lived with her grandmother. They lived always out of doors, sometimes in one place—sometimes in another; but she should like always to live under that oak-tree, it was so pleasant. Her grandmother was very good to them all, only rather particular. She loved her very much; and she loved Dick (her eldest brother), though he was a sad unlucky boy, to be sure. She was afraid he would come to some bad end.'

And indeed, Dick at that moment seemed in imminent danger of verifying his sister's prediction. He had been trying for a gleaning of nuts amongst the tall hazels on the top of a bank, which, flanked by a deep ditch, separated the coppice from the green. We had heard him for the last five minutes smashing and crashing away at a prodigious rate, swinging himself from stalk to stalk, and tugging and climbing like a sailor or a monkey; and now at the very instant of Fanny's uttering this prophecy, having missed a particularly venturesome grasp, he was impelled forward by the rebound of the branches, and fell into the ditch with a tremendous report, bringing half the nuttery after him, and giving us all a notion that he had broken his neck.

His time, however, was not yet come: he was on his feet
again in half a minute, and in another half-minute we again
heard him rustling among the hazel boughs; and Fanny and
I went on with our talk, which the fright and scolding,
consequent on this accident, had interrupted. My readers
are of course aware that when any one meets with a fall
the approved medicament of the most affectionate relatives
is a good dose of scolding.

'She liked Dick,' she continued, 'in spite of his unlucki-
ness—he was so quick and good-humoured; but the person
she loved most was her younger brother, Willy. Willy
was the best boy in the world; he would do anything she
told him' (indeed the poor child was in the very act of
picking up acorns under her inspection, to sell, as I afterwards found, in the village), 'and never got into mischief,
or told a lie in his life; she had had the care of him ever since
he was born, and she wished she could get him a place.'
By this time the little boy had crept towards us, and still
collecting the acorns in his small brown hands, had turned
up his keen intelligent face, and was listening with great
interest to our conversation. 'A place!' said I, much
surprised. 'Yes,' replied she firmly, 'a place. 'Twould
be a fine thing for my poor Willy to have a house over him
in the cold winter nights.' And with a grave tenderness
that might have beseemed a young mother, she stooped her
head over the boy and kissed him. 'But *you* sleep out
of doors in the cold winter nights, Fanny?' 'Me! Oh, I
don't mind it, and sometimes we creep into a barn. But
poor Willy! If I could but get Willy a place, my lady!'

This 'my lady,' the first gipsy words that Fanny had
uttered, lost all that it would have had of unpleasing in
the generosity and affectionateness of the motive. I could
not help promising to recommend her Willy, although I
could not hold out any very strong hopes of success, and
we parted, Fanny following me, with thanks upon thanks,
almost to the end of the lane.

Two days after I again saw my pretty gipsy; she was
standing by the side of our gate, too modest even to enter
the court, waiting for my coming out to speak to me. I
brought her into the hall, and was almost equally delighted
to see her and to hear her news; for although I had most

faithfully performed my promise, by mentioning master Willy to everybody likely to want a servant of his qualifications, I had seen enough in the course of my canvass to convince me that a gipsy boy of eight years old would be a difficult protégé to provide for.

Fanny's errand relieved my perplexity. She came to tell me that Willy had got a place: 'That Thomas Lamb, my lord's head gamekeeper, had hired him to tend his horse and his cow, and serve the pigs, and feed the dogs, and dig the garden, and clean the shoes and knives, and run on errands—in short, to be a man of all work. Willy was gone that very morning. He had cried to part with her, and she had almost cried herself, she should miss him so—he was like her own child. But then it was such a great place; and Thomas Lamb seemed such a kind master—talked of new clothing him, and meant him to wear shoes and stockings, and was very kind indeed. But poor Willy had cried sadly at leaving her'—and the sweet matronly elder sister fairly cried too.

I comforted her all I could, first by praises of Thomas Lamb, who happened to be of my acquaintance, and was indeed the very master whom, had I had the choice, I would have selected for Willy; and secondly, by the gift of some unconsidered trifles, which one should have been ashamed to offer to any one who had ever had a house over her head, but which the pretty gipsy girl received with transport, especially some working materials of the commonest sort. Poor Fanny had never known the luxury of a thimble before; it was as new to her finger as shoes and stockings were likely to be to Willy's feet. She forgot her sorrows, and tripped home to her oak-tree, the happiest of the happy.

Thomas Lamb, Willy's new master, was, as I have said, of my acquantance. He was a remarkably fine young man, and as well mannered as those of his calling usually are. Generally speaking, there are no persons, excepting real gentlemen, so gentlemanly as gamekeepers. They keep good company. The beautiful and graceful creatures whom they at once preserve and pursue, and the equally noble and generous animals whom they train, are their principal associates; and even by their masters they are regarded rather as companions than as servants. They attend them in their sports more as guides and leaders than as followers, pursuing a common recreation with equal enjoyment, and often with superior skill. Gamekeepers are almost always well behaved, and Thomas Lamb was eminently so. He had quite the look of a man of fashion: the person, the carriage, the air. His figure was tall and striking; his features delicately carved, with a paleness of complexion and a slight appearance of ill-health that added to their elegance. In short, he was exactly what the ladies would have called interesting in a gentleman; and the gentleness of his voice and manner, and the constant propriety of his deportment, tended to confirm the impression.

Luckily for him, however, this delicacy and refinement lay chiefly on the surface. His constitution, habits, and temper were much better fitted to his situation, much hardier and heartier than they appeared to be. He was still a bachelor, and lived by himself in a cottage, almost as lonely as if it had been placed in a desert island. It stood in the centre of his preserves, in the midst of a wilderness of coppice and woodland, accessible only by a narrow winding path, and at least a mile from the nearest habitation. When you had threaded the labyrinth, and were fairly arrived in Thomas's dominion, it was a pretty territory. A low thatched cottage, very irregularly built, with a porch before the door, and a vine half covering the casements; a garden a good deal neglected (Thomas Lamb's four-footed subjects, the hares, took care to eat up all his flowers: hares are animals of taste, and are particularly fond of pinks and carnations, the rogues!), an orchard and a meadow completed the demesne. There was also a commodious dog-kennel, and a stable, of which the outside was completely covered with the trophies of Thomas's industry—kites, jackdaws, magpies, hawks, crows, and owls, nailed by the wings, *displayed*, as they say in heraldry, against the wall, with polecats, weasels, stoats, and hedgehogs figuring at their side, a perfect menagerie of dead game-killers. [1]

[1] Foxes, the destruction of which is so great an object in a pheasant preserve, never are displayed, especially if there be a pack of hounds in the neighbourhood. That odious part of a gamekeeper's occupation is as quietly and unostentatiously performed as any operation of gunnery can be. Lords of manors will even affect to preserve foxes—Heaven forgive them!—just as an unpopular ministry is sure to talk of protecting the liberty of the subject.

But the prettiest part of this woodland cottage was the real living game that flitted about it, as tame as barn-door fowls, partridges flocking to be fed, as if there were not a dog or a gun or a man in the world; pheasants—glorious creatures!—coming at a call; hares almost as fearless as Cowper's, that would stand and let you look at them: would let you approach quite near, before they raised one quivering ear and darted off; and that even then, when the instinct of timidity was aroused, would turn at a safe distance to look again. Poor, pretty things! What a pity it seemed to kill them!

Such was to be Willy's future habitation. The day after he entered upon his place, I had an opportunity of offering my double congratulations, to the master on his new servant, to the servant on his new master. Whilst taking my usual walk, I found Thomas Lamb, Dick, Willy, and Fanny, about half-way up the lane, engaged in the animating sport of unearthing a weasel, which one of the gipsy dogs followed into a hole by the ditch-side. The boys showed great sportsmanship on this occasion: and so did their poor curs, who with their whole bodies inserted into the different branches of the burrow, and nothing visible but their tails (the one, the long puggish brush, of which I have already made mention, the other a terrier-like stump, that maintained an incessant wag), continued to dig and scratch, throwing out showers of earth, and whining with impatience and eagerness. Every now and then, when quite gasping and exhausted, they came out for a moment's air, whilst the boys took their turn, poking with a long stick, or loosening the ground with their hands, and Thomas stood by, superintending and encouraging both dog and boy, and occasionally cutting a root or a bramble that impeded their progress. Fanny also entered into the pursuit with great interest, dropping here and there a word of advice, as nobody can help doing when they see others in perplexity. In spite of all these aids, the mining operation proceeded so slowly that the experienced keeper sent off his new attendant for a spade to dig out the vermin, and I pursued my walk.

After this encounter it so happened that I never went near the gipsy tent without meeting Thomas Lamb—sometimes on foot, sometimes on his pony; now with a gun, and now without; but always loitering near the oak-tree, and always, as it seemed, reluctant to be seen. It was very unlike Thomas's usual manner to seem ashamed of being caught in any place, or in any company; but so it was. Did he go to the ancient sibyl to get his fortune told, or was Fanny the attraction? A very short time solved the query.

One night, towards the end of the month, the keeper presented himself at our house on justice business. He wanted a summons for some poachers who had been committing depredations in the preserve. Thomas was a great favourite, and was, of course, immediately admitted, his examination taken, and his request complied with. 'But how,' said the magistrate, looking up from the summons which he was signing, 'how can you expect, Thomas, to keep your pheasants, when that gipsy boy with his finders has pitched his tent just in the midst of your best coppices, killing more game than half the poachers in the country?' 'Why, as to the gipsy, sir,' replied Thomas, 'Fanny is as good a girl——' 'I was not talking of Fanny,' interrupted the man of warrants, smiling. '—as good a girl——' pursued Thomas. 'A very pretty girl,' ejaculated his worship. '—as good a girl,' resumed Thomas, 'as ever trod the earth!' 'A sweet pretty creature, certainly,' was again the provoking reply. 'Ah, sir, if you could but hear how her little brother talks of her!' 'Why, Thomas, this gipsy has made an impression.' 'Ah, sir, she is such a good girl!' And the next day they were married.

It was a measure to set every tongue in the village wagging; for Thomas, besides his personal good gifts, was well to do in the world—my lord's head keeper, and prime favourite. He might have pretended to any farmer's daughter in the parish: everybody cried out against the match. It was rather a bold measure, certainly; but I think it will end well. They are, beyond a doubt, the handsomest couple in these parts; and as the fortune-teller and her eldest grandson have had the good sense to decamp, and Fanny, besides being the most grateful and affectionate creature on earth, turns out clever and docile, and comports herself just as if she had lived in a house all her days, there are some hopes that in process of time her sin of gipsyism may be forgiven, and Mrs. Lamb be considered as visitable, at least by her next neighbours, the wives of the shoemaker and the parish clerk. At present, I am sorry to say that those worthy persons have sent both Thomas and her to Coventry—a misfortune which they endure with singular resignation.

CHAPTER XXVI

A CHRISTMAS PARTY

THE wedding of Jacob Frost and Hester Hewit took place on a Monday morning; and, on the next day (Tuesday), as I was walking along the common—blown along would be the properer phrase, for it was a wind that impelled one onward like a steam-engine—what should I see but the well-known fish-cart sailing in the teeth of that raging gale, and Jacob and his old companions, the grey mare and the black sheep-dog, breasting, as well as they might, the fury of the tempest. As we neared, I caught occasional sounds of 'Herrings—oysters! Oysters—herrings!' although the words, being as it were blown away, came scatteringly and feebly on the ear; and when we at last met, and he began in his old way to recommend, as was his wont, these oysters of a week old (note that the rogue was journeying coastwise, outward bound), with a profusion of praises and asseverations which he never vented on them when fresh—and when I also perceived that Jacob had donned his old garments, and that his company had doffed their bridal favours—it became clear that our man of oysters did not intend to retire yet awhile to the landlordship of the 'Bell'; and it was soon equally certain that the fair bride, thus deserted in the very outset of the honeymoon, intended to maintain a full and undisputed dominion over her own territories, she herself, and her whole establishment — the lame ostler, who still called her Mistress Hester, the red-haired charity girl, and the tabby cat—still remaining in full activity; whilst the very inscription of her maiden days, 'Hester Hewit's home-brewed,' still continued to figure above the door of that respectable hostelry. Two days after the wedding, that happy event seemed to be most comfortably forgotten by all the parties concerned—the only persons who took any note of the affair being precisely those who had nothing to do with the matter; that is to say, all the gossips of the neighbourhood, male and female—who did, it must be confessed, lift up their hands, and shake their heads, and bless themselves, and wonder what this world would come to.

On the succeeding Saturday, however, his regular day, Jacob reappeared on the road, and, after a pretty long traffic in the village, took his way to the 'Bell'; and, the next morning, the whole *cortège*, bride and bridegroom, lame ostler, red-haired lass, grey mare, and black sheep-dog, adorned exactly as on the preceding Monday, made their appearance at church; Jacob looking, as aforetime, very knowing—Hester, as usual, very demure. After the service there was a grand assemblage of Master Frost's acquaintances; for, between his customers and his playmates, Jacob was on intimate terms with half the parish, and many jokes were prepared on his smuggled marriage and subsequent desertion; but he of the brown jerkin evaded them all, by handing his fair lady into the cart, lifting the poor parish girl beside her, and even lending a friendly hoist to the lame ostler; after which he drove off, with a knowing nod, in total silence; being thereunto prompted partly by his wife's entreaties, partly by a sound more powerful over his associations—an impatient neigh from the old grey mare, who, never having attended church before, had begun to weary of the length of the service, and to wonder on what new course of duty she and her master were entering.

By this dispatch, our new-married couple certainly contrived to evade the main broadside of jokes prepared for their reception; but a few random jests, flung after them at a venture, hit notwithstanding; and one amongst them, containing an insinuation that Jacob had stolen a match to avoid keeping the wedding, touched our bridegroom, a man of mettle in his way, on the very point of honour—the more especially as it proceeded from a bluff old bachelor of his own standing—honest George Bridgwater, of the Lea—at whose hospitable gate he had discussed many a jug of ale and knoll of bacon, whilst hearing and telling the news of the country-side. George Bridgwater to suspect him of stinginess!—the thought was insupportable. Before he reached the 'Bell' he had formed, and communicated to Hester, the spirited resolution of giving a splendid party in the Christmas week—a sort of wedding feast or house-warming; consisting of smoking and cards for the old, dancing and singing for the young, and eating and drinking for all ages; and, in spite of Hester's decided disapprobation, invitations were given and preparations entered on forthwith.

Sooth to say, such are the sad contradictions of poor human nature, that Mrs. Frost's displeasure, albeit a bride in the honeymoon, not only entirely failed in persuading Master Frost to change his plan, but even seemed to render him more confirmed and resolute in his purpose. Hester was a thrifty housewife; and although Jacob was apparently, after his fashion, a very gallant and affectionate husband, and although her interest had now become his—and of his own interest none had ever suspected him to be careless—yet he did certainly take a certain sly pleasure in making an attack at once on her hoards and her habits, and forcing her into a gaiety and an outlay which made the poor bride start back aghast.

The full extent of Hester's misfortune in this ball did not, however, come upon her at once. She had been accustomed to the speculating hospitality of the Christmas parties at the 'Rose,' whose host was wont at tide times to give a supper to his customers, that is to say, to furnish the eatables thereof—the leg of mutton and turnips, the fat goose and apple sauce, and the huge plum-puddings, of which light viands that meal usually consisted—on an understanding that the aforesaid customers were to pay for the drinkables therewith consumed; and, from the length of the sittings, as well as the reports current on such occasions, Hester was pretty well assured that the expenditure had been most judicious, and that the leg of mutton and trimmings had been paid for over and over. She herself being, as she expressed it, 'a lone woman, and apt to be put upon,' had never gone farther in these matters than a cup of hyson and muffins, and a glass of hot elder-wine, to some of her cronies in the neighbourhood; but, having considerable confidence both in the extent of Jacob's connections and their tippling propensities, as well as in that faculty of getting tipsy and making tipsy in Jacob himself, which she regarded 'with one auspicious and one dropping eye,' as good and bad for her trade, she had at first no very great objection to try for once the experiment of a Christmas party; nor was she so much startled at the idea of a dance— dancing, as she observed, being a mighty provoker of thirst; neither did she very greatly object to her husband's engaging old Timothy, the fiddler, to officiate for the evening, on condition of giving him as much ale as he chose to drink, although she perfectly well knew what that promise implied; Timothy's example being valuable on such an occasion. But when the dreadful truth stared her in the face, that this entertainment was to be a bona fide treat—that not only the leg of mutton, the fat goose, and the plum-puddings, but the ale, wine, spirits, and tobacco were to come out of her coffers, then party, dancing, and fiddler became nuisances past endurance, the latter above all.

Old Timothy was a person of some note in our parish, known to every man, woman, and child in the place, of which, indeed, he was a native. He had been a soldier in his youth, and having had the good luck to receive a sabre wound on his skull, had been discharged from the service as infirm of mind, and passed to his parish accordingly; where he led a wandering, pleasant sort of life, sometimes in one public-house, sometimes in another—tolerated, as Hester said, for his bad example, until he had run up a score that became intolerable, at which times he was turned out, with the workhouse to go to, for a *pis aller*, and a comfortable prospect that his good humour, his good-fellowship, and his fiddle would in process of time be missed and wanted, and that he might return to his old haunts and run up a fresh score. When half-tipsy, which happened nearly every day in the week, and at all hours, he would ramble up and down the village, playing snatches of tunes at every corner, and collecting about him a never-failing audience of eight- and ten-year-old urchins of either sex, amongst which small mob old Timothy, with his jokes, his songs, and his antics, was incredibly popular. Against justice and constable, treadmill and stocks, the sabre-cut was a protection, although I must candidly confess that I do not think the crack in the crown ever made itself visible in his demeanour until a sufficient quantity of ale had gone down his throat to account for any aberration of conduct, supposing the broadsword in question never to have approached his skull. That weapon served, however, as a most useful shield to our modern Timotheus, who, when detected in any outrageous fit of drunkenness, would immediately summon sufficient recollection to sigh and look pitiful, and put his poor, shaking, withered hand to the seam which the wound had left, with an air of appeal, which even I, with all my scepticism, felt to be irresistible.

In short, old Timothy was a privileged person; and terrible sot though he were, he almost deserved to be so, for his good humour, his contentedness, his constant festivity of temper, and his good will towards every living thing—a good will which met with its usual reward in being heartily and universally returned. Everybody liked old Timothy, with the solitary exception of the hostess of the 'Bell,' who, having once had him as an inmate during three weeks, had been so scandalized by his disorderly habits, that, after having with some difficulty turned him out of her house, she had never admitted him into it again, having actually resorted to the expedient of buying off her intended customer, even when he presented himself pence in hand, by the gift of a pint of home-brewed at the door, rather than suffer him to effect a lodgment in her tap-room—a mode of dismissal so much to Timothy's taste that his incursions had become more and more frequent, insomuch that 'to get rid of the fiddler and other scapegraces, who were apt to put upon a lone woman,' formed a main article in the catalogue of reasons assigned by Hester to herself and the world for her marriage with Jacob Frost. Accordingly, the moment she heard that Timothy's irregularities and ill example were likely to prove altogether unprofitable, she revived her old objection to the poor fiddler's morals, rescinded her consent to his admission, and insisted so vehemently on his being unordered, that her astonished husband, fairly out-talked and out-scolded, was fain to purchase a quiet evening by a promise of obedience. Having carried this point, she forthwith, according to the example of all prudent wives, began an attack on another, and, having compassed the unordering of Timothy, began to bargain for uninviting her next neighbour, the widow Glen.

Mrs. Martha Glen kept a baker's and chandler's shop in

a wide lane, known by the name of the Broadway, and
adorned with a noble avenue of oaks, terminating in the
green whereon stood the 'Bell,' a lane which, by dint of
two or three cottages peeping out from amongst the trees,
and two or three farm-houses, the smoke from whose chimneys sailed curlingly amongst them, might, in comparison
with that lonely nook, pass for inhabited. Martha was a
buxom widow, of about the same standing with Mistress
Frost. She had had her share of this world's changes,
being the happy relict of three several spouses; and was now
a comely, rosy dame, with a laughing eye and a merry
tongue. Why Hester should hate Martha Glen was one
of the puzzles of the parish. Hate her she did, with that
venomous and deadly hatred that never comes to words;
and Martha repaid the obligation in kind, as much as a
naturally genial and relenting temper would allow, although
certainly the balance of aversion was much in favour
of Mrs. Frost. An exceedingly smooth, genteel, and civil
hatred it was on both sides; such a one as would have done
honour to a more polished society. They dealt with each
other, curtsied to each other, sat in the same pew at church,
and employed the same charwoman—which last accordance,
by the way, may partly account for the long duration of
discord between the parties; Betty Clarke, the help in
question, being a sharp, shrewish, vixenish woman, with a
positive taste for quarrels, who regularly reported every
cool innuendo uttered by the slow and soft-spoken Mrs.
Frost, and every hot retort elicited from the rash and hasty
Martha, and contrived to infuse her own spirit into each.
With such an auxiliary on either side, there could be no
great wonder at the continuance of this animosity; how it
began was still undecided. There were, indeed, rumours of
an early rivalry between the fair dames for the heart of a
certain gay shepherd, the first husband of Martha; other
reports assigned as a reason the unlucky tricks of Tom Higgs,
the only son of Mrs. Glen by her penultimate spouse, and
the greatest pickle within twenty miles; a third party had,
since the marriage, discovered the jealousy of Jacob to be
the proximate cause, Martha Glen having been long his
constant customer, dealing with him in all sorts of fishery
and fruitery for herself and her shop, from red herrings to

golden pippins; whilst a fourth party, still more scandalous, placed the jealousy, to which they also attributed the aversion, to the score of a young and strapping Scotch pedlar, Sandy Frazer by name, who travelled the country with muslins and cottons, and for whom certain malicious gossips asserted both ladies to entertain a lurking penchant, and whose insensibility towards the maiden was said to have been the real origin of her match with Jacob Frost, whose proffer she had accepted out of spite. For my own part, I disbelieve all and each of these stories, and hold it very hard that an innocent woman cannot entertain a little harmless aversion towards her next neighbour without being called to account for so natural a feeling. It seems that Jacob thought so too—for on Hester's conditioning that Mrs. Glen should be excluded from the party, he just gave himself a wink and a nod, twisted his mouth a little more on one side than usual, and assented without a word; and with the same facility did he relinquish the bough of mistletoe, which he had purposed to suspend from the bacon rack— the ancient mistletoe bough, on passing under which our village lads are apt to snatch a kiss from the village maidens: a ceremony which offended Hester's nicety, and which Jacob promised to abrogate; and, pacified by these concessions, the bride promised to make due preparation for the ball, whilst the bridegroom departed on his usual expedition to the coast.

Of the unrest of that week of bustling preparation, words can give but a faint image. Oh, the scourings, the cleanings, the sandings, the dustings, the scoldings of that disastrous week! The lame ostler and the red - haired parish girl were worked off their feet—'even Sunday shone no Sabbath day to them,' for then did the lame ostler trudge eight miles to the church of a neighbouring parish, to procure the attendance of a celebrated bassoon player to officiate in lieu of Timothy; whilst the poor little maid was sent nearly as far to the next town, in quest of an itinerant show-woman, of whom report had spoken at the 'Bell,' to beat the tambourine. The show-woman proved undiscoverable; but the bassoon player having promised to come, and to bring with him a clarinet, Mrs. Frost was at ease as to her music; and having provided more victuals than the whole

village could have discussed at a sitting, and having moreover adorned her house with berried holly, china-roses, and
chrysanthemums after the most tasteful manner, began to
enter into the spirit of the thing, and to wish for the return
of her husband, to admire and to praise.

Late on the great day Jacob arrived, his cart laden with
marine stores, for his share of the festival. Never had our
goodly village witnessed such a display of oysters, mussels,
periwinkles, and cockles, to say nothing of apples and
nuts, and two little kegs, snugly covered up, which looked
exceedingly as if they had cheated the revenue, a packet of
green tea, which had something of the same air, and a new
silk gown, of a flaming salmon colour, straight from Paris,
which he insisted on Hester's retiring to assume, whilst
he remained to arrange the table and receive the company,
who, it being now about four o'clock p.m.—our good rustics
can never have enough of a good thing—were beginning
to assemble for the ball.

The afternoon was fair and cold, and dry and frosty, and
Matthewses, Bridgwaters, Whites, and Joneses, in short
the whole farmerage and shopkeepery of the place, with a
goodly proportion of wives and daughters, came pouring
in apace. Jacob received them with much gallantry, un-
cloaking and unbonneting the ladies, assisted by his two
staring and awkward auxiliaries, welcoming their husbands
and fathers, and apologizing, as best he might, for the
absence of his helpmate; who, 'perplexed in the extreme' by
her new finery which, happening to button down the back,
she was fain to put on hind side before, did not make her
appearance till the greater part of the company had arrived,
and the music had struck up a country dance. An evil
moment, alas! did poor Hester choose for her entry: for the
first sound that met her ear was Timothy's fiddle, forming
a strange trio with the bassoon and the clarinet; and the
first persons whom she saw were Tom Higgs cracking
walnuts at the chimney-side, and Sandy Frazer saluting
the widow Glen under the mistletoe. How she survived
such sights and sounds does appear wonderful—but survive
them she did, for at three o'clock a.m., when our reporter
left the party, she was engaged in a sociable game at cards,
which, by the description, seems to have been long whist,

with the identical widow Glen, Sandy Frazer, and William Ford, and had actually won fivepence halfpenny of Martha's money; the young folks were still dancing gaily, to the sound of Timothy's fiddle, which fiddle had the good quality of going on almost as well drunk as sober, and it was now playing solo, the clarinet being *hors de combat* and the bassoon under the table. Tom Higgs, after showing off more tricks than a monkey, amongst the rest sewing the whole card party together by the skirts, to the probable damage of Mrs. Frost's gay gown, had returned to his old post by the fire, and his old amusement of cracking walnuts, with the shells of which he was pelting the little parish girl, who sat fast asleep on the other side; and Jacob Frost, in all his glory, sat in a cloud of tobacco smoke, roaring out catches with his old friend George Bridgwater, and half a dozen other 'drouthy cronies,' whilst 'aye the ale was growing better,' and the Christmas party went merrily on.

CHAPTER XXVII

THE TWO VALENTINES

VALENTINE'S DAY is one of great stir and emotion in our little village. In large towns—especially in London—the wicked habit of quizzing has entirely destroyed the romance and illusion of that tender anniversary. But we in the country are, for the most part, uninfected by 'over-wiseness' or 'over-niceness' (to borrow two of Sir Walter Raleigh's quaint but expressive phrases), and are content to keep the gracious festival of love-making and *billets-doux* as simply and confidingly as our ancestors of old. I do not mean to say that every one of our youths and maidens pair on that day, like the 'goldfinch, bullfinch, greenfinch, and all the finches of the grove.' Heaven forbid! Nor that the spirit of fun hath so utterly evaporated from us, that we have no display of innocent trick or harmless raillery on that licensed morn; all that I contend for is that, in our parts, some truth may be found lurking amidst the fictions of those annual rhymes, that many a village beau hath so broken the ice of courtship, and that many a village belle hath felt her heart throb, as she glanced at the emblematic scroll, and tried to guess the sender, in spite of the assumed careless-ness, the saucy head-tossings, and the pretty poutings with which she attempted to veil her real interest. In short, there is something like sincerity amongst us, even in a valentine—as witness the number of wooings begun on the 14th February, and finished in that usual end of courtships and comedies—a wedding—before Whitsuntide. Our little lame clerk, who keeps a sort of *catalogue raisonné* of marriages, as a companion to the parish register, computes those that issue from the bursting valentine-bag of our postman at not less than three and a half per annum—that is to say, seven between two years.

But, besides the matches which spring, directly or in-directly, from the *billets* commonly called valentines,

there is another superstition connected with the day,
which has no small influence on the destinies of our country
maidens. They hold that the first man whom they espy
in the morning—provided that such man be neither of kin
to them, nor married, nor an inmate of the same house—
is to pass for their valentine during the day; and, perhaps
(for this is the secret clause which makes the observation
important), to prove their husband for life. It is strange
how much faith they put in this kind of *sortes Virgilianae*—
this turning over the living leaf of destiny; and how much
pains they will take to cheat the fates, and see the man they
like best first in spite of the stars! One damsel, for instance,
will go a quarter of a mile about, in the course of her ordinary avocations, in order to avoid a youth whom she does
not fancy; another shall sit within doors, with her eyes
shut, half the morning, until she hears the expected voice
of the favourite swain; whilst, on their part, our country lads
take care to place themselves each in the way of his chosen
she; and a pretty lass would think herself overlooked, if
she had not three or four standing round her door, or saunter-
ing beneath her window, before sunrise.

Now, one of the prettiest girls in our parish is, undoubtedly, Sally North. Pretty is hardly the proper
phrase—Sally is a magnificent girl—tall, far above the
common height of woman, and large in proportion—but
formed with the exactest symmetry, and distinguished
by the firm, erect, and vigorous carriage, and the light,
elastic step, peculiar to those who are early accustomed to
walk under burthens. Sally's father is an eminent baker
—the most celebrated personage in our village; besides
supplying half the next town with genuine country bread,
which he carries thither himself in his huge tilted cart, he
hath struck into other arts of the oven, and furnishes all
the breakfast-tables within five miles with genuine London
rolls. No family of gentility can possibly get through the
first meal without them. The rolls, to be sure, are—just
like other rolls—very good, and nothing more; but some
whim of a great man, or caprice of a fine lady, has put them
in fashion; and so Sally walks round the parish every
morning, with her great basket, piled to the very brim,
poised on her pretty head—now lending it the light support

of one slender hand, and now of another; the dancing black eyes, and the bright blushing smile, that flash from under her burthen, as well as the perfect ease and grace with which she trips along, entirely taking away all painful impression of drudgery or toil. She is quite a figure for a painter, is Sally North—and the gipsy knows it. There is a gay, good-humoured consciousness of her power and her beauty, as she passes on her morning round, carolling as merrily as the lark over her head, that makes no small part of her charm. The lass is clever, too—sharp and shrewd in her dealings—and, although sufficiently civil and respectful to her superiors, and never actually wanting in decorum, is said to dismiss the compliments of some of her beaux with a repartee generally brusque, and frequently poignant.

Of beaux—between the lackeys of the houses that she takes in her circuit, and the wayfarers whom she picks up on the road—Sally hath more than a court beauty; and two of them—Mr. Thompson, my lord's gentleman, a man of substance and gravity, not much turned of fifty; and Daniel Tubb, one of Sir John's gardeners, a strapping, red-haired youth, as comely and merry as herself—were severally recommended, by the old and the young, as fitting matches for the pretty mistress of the rolls. But Sally silenced Mr. Thompson's fine speeches by a very stout, sturdy, steady 'No'; and even inflicted a similar sentence (although so mildly that Daniel did not quite despair) on his young rival; for Sally, who was seventeen last Candlemas Day, had been engaged these three years!

The love affair had begun at the Free School at Aberleigh; and the object of it, by name Stephen Long, was the son of a little farmer in the neighbourhood, and about the same age with his fair mistress. There the resemblance ceased; for Stephen had been as incomparably the shortest and ugliest boy in the school, as Sally was the tallest and prettiest girl—being, indeed, of that stunted and large-headed appearance which betokens a dwarf, and is usually accompanied by features as unpleasant in their expression as they are grotesque in their form. But then he was the head boy; and being held up by the master as a miracle of reading, writing, and ciphering, was a personage of no small im-

portance at Aberleigh; and Sally being, with all her cleverness, something of a dunce, owed to Stephen much obligation for assistance in the school business. He arranged,
cast up, and set in order on the slate, the few straggling
figures which poor Sally called her sum—painted over, and
reduced to something like form, the misshapen and disjointed letters in her copy-book—learnt all her lessons
himself, and tried most ineffectually to teach them to her—
and, finally, covered her unconquerable want of memory by
the loudest and boldest prompting ever heard out of a
theatre. Many a rap of the knuckles have Sally North's
blunders cost Stephen Long, and vainly did the master
admonish him to hold his tongue. Prompt he would—
although so incorrigibly stupid was his fair mistress, that
even when the words were put into her mouth she stumbled
at repeating them; and Stephen's officious kindness commonly ended in their being punished in company—a con-
summation for his share of which the boy was gallant
enough to rejoice. She was fully sensible of this flattering
devotion, and repaid it, as far as lay in her power, by taking
him under her protection at playtimes, in return for the
services which he rendered her in school; and becoming
more and more bound to him by a series of mutual good
offices, finished by vindicating his ugliness, denying his
pedantry, and when twitted with his dwarfishness, boldly
predicting that he would grow. They walked together,
talked together, laughed, romped, and quarrelled—in short,
it was a decided attachment; and when our village Romeo
was taken as an apprentice by a cousin of his mother's—a
respectable hosier in Cheapside—it is on record that his
Juliet—the lightest-hearted personage in the neighbourhood—cried for an hour, and moped for a day. All the
school stood amazed at her constancy!

Stephen, on his side, bore the test of absence like a
knight of Amadis his day. Never was *preux chevalier* so
devoted to the lady of his love. Every letter home contained some tender message or fond inquiry; and although
the messages became gradually less and less intelligible, as
the small pedantry of the country schoolboy ripened into
the full-blown affectation of the London apprentice, still
Sally was far from quarrelling with a love message on so

small a ground as not understanding it; whilst, however mysterious his words might seem, his presents spoke his affection in a more homely and convincing language. Of such tokens there was no lack. The very first packet that he sent home, consisting of worsted mittens for his old grandmother, a pair of cotton hose for his sister, and a nightcap for his father, contained also a pair of scarlet garters for Sally; which attention was followed up at every opportunity by pincushions, ribbons, thimbles, needle-cases, and as great a variety of female ware as that with which Autolycus's basket was furnished. No wonder that Sally, in spite of occasional flirtations with Daniel Tubb, continued tolerably constant; especially as one of Stephen's sisters, who had been at service in London, affirmed that he was so much improved as to be one of the smartest beaux in all Cheapside.

So affairs continued until this identical Valentine's Day. Last spring, a written valentine, exceedingly choice in its decorations, had made its appearance at Master North's; rather out of date, it must be owned, since being enclosed in a packet, to save postage, and sent by an opportunity, as the country phrase goes, it had been detained, either by accident or waggery, till the 1st April; but this was none of Stephen's fault; there was the valentine in the newest London taste, consisting of a raised group of roses and heartsease, executed on a kind of paper cut-work, which, on being lifted up, turned into a cage enclosing a dove—tender emblem!—with all the rapidity of a change in a pantomime. There the valentine was—equally known for Stephen's by the savour of the verses and the flourish of the signature; the finest specimen of poetry and penmanship, as my friend the schoolmaster triumphantly asserted, that had ever been seen in Aberleigh. 'The force of *writing* could no farther go'; so, this year, our 'good apprentice' determined to come himself to be her personal valentine, and to renew, if not complete, their early engagement.

On this determination being announced to Sally, it occasioned no small perturbation in that fair damsel, equally alarmed at the mental accomplishments and the personal defects of her constant swain. In fact, her feeling towards Stephen had been almost as ideal and unsubstantial as the shadow of a rainbow. She liked to think of him when she had nothing better to do; or to talk of him when she had nothing better to say; or to be puzzled by his verses, or laughed at for his homage; but as a real substantial valentine, a present wooer, a future husband, and he so ugly, and a poet, too—oh dear! she was frightened to think of it! This impression first broke forth to his sister— who communicated the news of his intended arrival—in a variety of questions, as to Stephen's height, and size, and shape, and complexion; especially as compared with Daniel Tubb's! and was afterwards displayed to that rustic adorer himself; not by words, indeed, but by the encouraging silence and saucy smile with which she listened to his account of the debarkation of his cockney rival from the top of the B—— stage. 'He's tinier than ever,' quoth Daniel, 'and the smartest dandy that ever was seen. I shall be your valentine after all, Sally,' pursued her swain; 'for I could hide him with the shadow of my fist.'

This was Valentine's eve. Valentine's morn saw Sally eyeing the two rivals, through a peep-hole in her little check curtain, as they stood side by side on the green, watching for the first glimpse of their divinity. Never was seen such a contrast. Stephen, whose original square dwarfishness had fined down into a miniature dandy, sallow, strutting, and all over small—the very Tom Thumb of apprentices!—Daniel, taller, bigger, ruddier, and heartier than ever—the actual Goliath of country lads! Never was such a contrast seen. At length, Sally, laughing, blushing, and bridling, sallied forth from the cottage—her huge roll basket, but not as usual filled with rolls, carried, not on her head, but in her hands. 'I'm your valentine, Sally, am I not?' exclaimed Daniel Tubb, darting towards her. 'You saw me first; I know you saw me first,' continued the ardent lover, proceeding to claim the salute usual on such occasions. 'Pshaw! nonsense! let me alone then, Daniel, can't you?' was the reply of his mistress, advancing to Stephen, who, perhaps dazzled by the beauty, perhaps astounded by the height of the fair giantess, remained motionless and speechless on the other side of the road. 'Would you like a ride in my basket this fine morning, Mr. Stephen?' said the saucy lass, emptying all his gifts, garters, pincushions, ribbons, and valentines, from their huge reservoir, and depositing it on the ground at his feet. 'Don't be afraid; I 'll be bound to carry you as easily as the little Italian boy carries *his* tray of images. He 's not half the weight of the rolls—is he, Daniel?' pursued the unmerciful beauty. 'For my part, I think he has grown shorter. Come, do step in!' And, with the word, the triumphant Daniel lifted up the discomfited beau, placed him safely in the basket, and hoisted the burthen on Sally's head—to the unspeakable diversion of that saucy maiden, and the complete cure of Master Stephen's love. No need, after this, to declare which of the two rivals is Sally North's valentine. I think, with the little clerk, that they will be married at Whitsuntide, if not before.

CHAPTER XXVIII

A COUNTRY APOTHECARY

ONE of the important personages in a small country town is the apothecary. He takes rank next after the rector and the attorney, and before the curate; and could be much less easily dispensed with than either of those worthies, not merely as holding 'fate and physic' in his hand, but as the general, and as it were official, associate, adviser, comforter, and friend of all ranks and all ages, of high and low, rich and poor, sick and well. I am no despiser of dignities; but twenty emperors shall be less intensely missed in their wide dominions than such a man as my friend John Hallett in his own small sphere.

The spot which was favoured with the residence of this excellent person was the small town of Hazelby, in Dorsetshire; a pretty little place, where everything seems at a standstill. It was originally built in the shape of the letter T; a long, broad market-place (still so called, although the market be gone) serving for the perpendicular stem, traversed by a straight, narrow, horizontal street, to answer for the top line. Not one addition has occurred to interrupt this architectural regularity since; fifty years ago, a rich London tradesman built, at the west end of the horizontal street, a wide-fronted single house, with two low wings, iron palisades before, and a fish - pond opposite, which still goes by the name of New Place, and is balanced, at the east end of the street, by an erection of nearly the same date, a large, square, dingy mansion enclosed within high walls, inhabited by three maiden sisters, and called, probably by way of nickname, the Nunnery. New Place being on the left of the road, and the Nunnery on the right, the T has now something the air of the italic capital *T*, turned up at one end and down on the other. The latest improvements are the bow-window in the market-place, commanding the pavement both ways, which the late brewer, Andrews, threw out in his snug parlour some twenty years back, and where he used to sit smoking, with the sash up, in summer afternoons, enjoying himself, good man; and the great room at the 'Swan,' originally built by the speculative publican, Joseph Allwright, for an assembly-room. That speculation did not answer. The assembly, in spite of canvassing and patronage, and the active exertions of all the young ladies in the neighbourhood, dwindled away and died at the end of two winters; then it became a club-room for the hunt, but the hunt quarrelled with Joseph's cookery; then a market-room for the farmers; but the farmers (it was in the high-price time) quarrelled with Joseph's wine; then it was converted into the magistrates' room—the bench, but the bench and the market went away together, and there was an end of justicing; then Joseph tried the novel attraction (to borrow a theatrical phrase) of a billiard-table, but, alas! that novelty succeeded as ill as if it had been theatrical: there were not customers enough to pay the marker: at last, it has merged finally in that unconscious receptacle of pleasure and pain, a post office, although Hazelby has so little to do with traffic of any sort—even the traffic of correspondence—that a saucy mail-coach will often carry on its small bag, and as often forget to call for the London bag in return.

In short, Hazelby is an insignificant place—my readers will look for it in vain in the map of Dorsetshire; it is omitted, poor dear town! left out by the map-maker with as little remorse as a dropped letter—and it is also an old-fashioned place. It has not even a cheap shop for female gear. Everything in the one store which it boasts, kept by Martha Deane, linen-draper and haberdasher, is dear and good, as things were wont to be. You may actually get there thread made of flax, from the gouty, uneven, clumsy, shiny fabric, ycleped whited-brown, to the delicate commodity of Lisle, used for darning muslin. I think I was never more astonished than when, on asking, from the mere force of habit, for thread, I was presented, instead of the pretty lattice-wound balls or snowy reels of cotton with which that demand is usually answered, with a whole drawerful of skeins, peeping from their blue papers —such skeins as in my youth a thrifty maiden would

draw into the nicely-stitched compartments of that silken
repository, a housewife, or fold into a congeries of graduated
thread-papers, 'fine by degrees, and beautifully less.' The
very literature of Hazelby is doled out at the pastrycook's,
in a little one-windowed shop, kept by Matthew Wise.
Tarts occupy one end of the counter, and reviews the other;
whilst the shelves are parcelled out between books, and
dolls, and gingerbread. It is a question, by which of his
trades poor Matthew gains least; he is so shabby, so thread-
bare, and so starved.

Such a town would hardly have known what to do with a
highly informed and educated surgeon, such as one now
generally sees in that most liberal profession. My friend
John Hallett suited it exactly. His predecessor, Mr.
Simon Shuter, had been a small, wrinkled, spare old gentleman, with a short cough and thin voice, who always seemed
as if he needed an apothecary himself. He wore generally
a full suit of drab, a flaxen wig of the sort called a Bob
Jerom, and a very tight muslin stock: a costume which he
had adopted in his younger days in imitation of the most
eminent physician of the next city, and continued to the
time of his death. Perhaps the cough might have been
originally an imitation also, engrafted on the system by
habit. It had a most unsatisfactory sound, and seemed
more like a trick than a real effort of nature. His talk was
civil, prosy, and fidgety, much addicted to small scandal
and that kind of news which passes under the denomination
of tittle-tattle. He was sure to tell one half of the town
where the other drank tea, and recollected the blancmanges
and jellies on a supper-table, or described a new gown, with
as much science and unction as if he had been used to make
jellies and wear gowns in his own person. Certain professional peculiarities might have favoured the supposition.
His mode of practice was exactly that popularly attributed
to old women. He delighted in innocent remedies—manna,
magnesia, and camphor julep; never put on a blister in his
life; and would sooner, from pure complaisance, let a patient
die, than administer an unpalatable prescription.

So qualified, to say nothing of his gifts in tea-drinking,
casino, and quadrille (whist was too many for him), his
popularity could not be questioned. When he expired all

Hazelby mourned. The lamentation was general. The women of every degree (to borrow a phrase from that great phrasemonger, Horace Walpole) 'cried quarts'; and the procession to the churchyard—that very churchyard to which he had himself followed so many of his patients—was now attended by all of them that remained alive.

It was felt that the successor of Mr. Simon Shuter would have many difficulties to encounter. My friend, John Hallett, 'came, and saw, and overcame.' John was what is usually called a rough diamond. Imagine a short, clumsy, stout-built figure, almost as broad as it is long, crowned by a bullet head, covered with shaggy brown hair, sticking out in every direction; the face round and solid, with a complexion originally fair, but dyed one red by exposure to all sorts of weather; open, good-humoured eyes of a greenish cast, his admirers called them hazel; a wide mouth, full of large white teeth; a cocked-up nose, and a double chin; bearing altogether a strong resemblance to a print, which I once saw hanging up in an ale-house parlour, of 'the celebrated divine' (to use the identical words of the legend) 'Doctor Martin Luther.'

The condition of a country apothecary being peculiarly liable to the inclemency of the season, John's dress was generally such as might bid defiance to wind and rain or snow or hail. If anything, he wrapped up most in the summer, having a theory that people were never so apt to take cold as in hot weather. He usually wore a bearskin greatcoat, a silk handkerchief over his cravat, top-boots on those sturdy pillars, his legs, a huge pair of overalls, and a hat which, from the day in which it first came into his possession to that in which it was thrown aside, never knew the comfort of being freed from its oilskin—never was allowed to display the glossy freshness of its sable youth. Poor dear hat! how its vanity (if hats have vanity) must have suffered! For certain its owner had none, unless a lurking pride in his own bluffness and bluntness may be termed such. He piqued himself on being a plain down-right Englishman, and on a voice and address pretty much like his apparel, rough, strong, and warm, and fit for all weathers. A heartier person never lived.

In his profession he was eminently skilful, bold, confident, and successful. The neighbouring physicians liked to come after Mr. Hallett; they were sure to find nothing to undo. And blunt and abrupt as was his general manner, he was kind and gentle in a sick-room; only nervous disorders, the pet diseases of Mr. Simon Shuter, he could not abide. He made short work with them; frightened them away, as one does by children when they have the hiccup; or if the malady were pertinacious and would not go, he fairly turned off the patient. Once or twice, indeed, on such occasions, the patient got the start, and turned him off: Mrs. Emery, for instance, the lady's maid at New Place, most delicate and mincing of waiting-gentlewomen, motioned him from her presence; and Miss Deane, daughter of Martha Deane, haberdasher, who, after completing her education at a boarding-school, kept a closet full of millinery in a little den behind her mamma's shop, and was by many degrees the finest lady in Hazelby, was so provoked at being told by him that nothing ailed her, that, to prove her weakly condition, she pushed him by main force out of doors.

With these exceptions Mr. Hallett was the delight of the whole town, as well as of all the farm-houses within six miles round. He just suited the rich yeomanry, cured their diseases, and partook of their feasts; was constant at christenings, and a man of prime importance at weddings. A country merry-making was nothing without 'the doctor.' He was 'the very prince of good fellows'; had a touch of epicurism, which without causing any distaste of his own homely fare, made dainties acceptable when they fell in his way; was a most absolute carver; prided himself upon a sauce of his own invention, for fish and game—'Hazelby sauce' he called it; and was universally admitted to be the best compounder of a bowl of punch in the country.

Besides these rare convivial accomplishments, his gay and jovial temper rendered him the life of the table. There was no resisting his droll faces, his droll stories, his jokes, his tricks, or his laugh—the most contagious cachinnation that ever was heard. Nothing in the shape of fun came amiss to him. He would join in a catch or roar out a solo, which might be heard a mile off; would play at hunt the slipper or blind-man's-buff; was a great man in a country dance, and upon very extraordinary occasions would treat the company to a certain remarkable hornpipe, which put the walls in danger of tumbling about their ears, and belonged to him as exclusively as the Hazelby sauce. It was a sort of parody on a *pas seul* which he had once seen at the opera house, in which his face, his figure, his costume, his rich humour, and his strange, awkward, unexpected activity told amazingly. 'The force of frolic could no farther go' than 'the doctor's hornpipe.' It was the climax of jollity.

But the chief scene of Mr. Hallett's gaiety lay out of doors, in a very beautiful spot called the Down, a sloping upland about a mile from Hazelby; a side view of which, with its gardens and orchards, its pretty church peeping from amongst lime- and yew-trees, and the fine piece of water called Hazelby Pond, it commanded. The Down itself was an extensive tract of land covered with the finest verdure, backed by a range of hills, and surrounded by coppice-woods, large patches of which were scattered over the turf, like so many islands on an emerald sea. Nothing could be more beautiful or more impenetrable than these thickets; they were principally composed of birch, holly, hawthorn, and maple, woven together by garlands of woodbine, interwreathed and intertwisted by bramble and brier, till even the sheep, although the bits of their snowy fleece left on the bushes bore witness to the attempt, could make no way in the leafy mass. Here and there a huge oak or beech rose towering above the rich underwood; and all around, as far as the eye could pierce, the borders of this natural shrubbery were studded with a countless variety of woodland flowers. When the old thorns were in blossom, or when they were succeeded by the fragrant woodbine and the delicate brier-rose, it was like a garden, if it were possible to fancy any garden so peopled with birds.[1]

[1] A circumstance of some curiosity in natural history occurred for several successive years on this Down. There was constantly in one of the thickets a blackbird's nest, of which the young were distinguished by a striking peculiarity. The old birds (probably the same pair) were of the usual sable colour, but the plumage of their progeny was milk-white, as white as a swan, without a single discoloured feather. They were always taken, and sold at high prices to the curious in such freaks of nature. The late Bishop of Winchester had a pair of them for a long time in the aviary at Farnham Castle; they were hardy, and the male was a fine song-bird; but all attempts to breed from them failed. They died, 'and left the world no copy.'

The only human habitation on this charming spot was the cottage of the shepherd, old Thomas Tolfrey, who, with his granddaughter, Jemima, a light, pretty maiden of fourteen, tended the flocks on the Down; and the rustic carols of this little lass and the tinkling of the sheep-bells were usually the only sounds that mingled with the sweet songs of the feathered tribes. On May Days and holidays, however, the thickets resounded with other notes of glee than those of the linnet and the wood-lark. Fairs, revels, May games, and cricket matches—all were holden on the Down; and there would John Hallett sit, in his glory, universal umpire and referee of cricketer, wrestler, or backsword player, the happiest and greatest man in the field. Little Jemima never failed to bring her grandfather's armchair, and place it under the old oak for the good doctor; I question whether John would have exchanged his throne for that of the King of England.

On these occasions he certainly would have been the better for that convenience, which he piqued himself on not needing—a partner. Generally speaking, he really, as he used to boast, did the business of three men; but when a sickly season and a Maying happened to come together, I cannot help suspecting that the patients had the worst of it. Perhaps, however, a partner might not have suited him. He was sturdy and independent to the verge of a fault, and would not have brooked being called to account or brought to a reckoning by any man under the sun; still less would he endure the thought of that more important and durable co-partnery—marriage. He was a most determined bachelor; and so afraid of being mistaken for a wooer, or incurring the reputation of a gay deceiver, that he was as uncivil as his good nature would permit to every unwedded female from sixteen to sixty, and had nearly fallen into some scrapes on that account with the spinsters of the town, accustomed to the soft silkiness of Mr. Simon Shuter; but they got used to it—it was the man's way; and there was an indirect flattery in his fear of their charms which the maiden ladies, especially the elder ones, found very mollifying; so he was forgiven.

In his shop and his household he had no need either of partner or of wife: the one was excellently managed by an old rheumatic journeyman, slow in speech and of vinegar aspect, who had been a pedagogue in his youth, and now used to limp about with his Livy in his pocket, and growl, as he compounded the medicines, over the bad latinity of the prescriptions; the other was equally well conducted by an equally ancient housekeeper and a cherry-cheeked niece, the orphan daughter of his only sister, who kept everything within doors in the bright and shining order in which he delighted. John Hallett, notwithstanding the roughness of his aspect, was rather knick-knacky in his tastes; a great patron of small inventions, such as the improved *ne plus ultra* corkscrew and the latest patent snuffers. He also trifled with horticulture, dabbled in tulips, was a connoisseur in pinks, and had gained a prize for polyanthuses. The garden was under the especial care of his pretty niece, Miss Margaret, a grateful, warm-hearted girl, who thought she never could do enough to please her good uncle, and prove her sense of his kindness. He was indeed as fond of her as if he had been her father, and as kind.

Perhaps there was nothing very extraordinary in his goodness to the gentle and cheerful little girl, who kept his walks so trim and his parlour so neat, who always met him with a smile, and who (last and strongest tie to a generous mind) was wholly dependent on him—had no friend on earth but himself. There was nothing very uncommon in that. But John Hallett was kind to every one, even where the sturdy old English prejudices, which he cherished as virtues, might seem most likely to counteract his gentler feelings. One instance of his benevolence and of his delicacy shall conclude this sketch.

Several years ago an old French *émigré* came to reside at Hazelby. He lodged at Matthew Wise's, of whose two-fold shop for cakes and novels I have before made honourable mention, in the low three-cornered room, with a closet behind it, which Matthew had the impudence to call his first floor. Little was known of him but that he was a thin, pale, foreign-looking gentleman, who shrugged his shoulders in speaking, took a great deal of snuff, and made a remarkably low bow. The few persons with whom he had any communication spoke with amusement of his bad English, and with admiration of his good-humour, and it soon appeared, from a written paper placed in a conspicuous part of Matthew's shop, that he was an abbé, and that he would do himself the honour of teaching French to any of the nobility or gentry of Hazelby who might think fit to employ him. Pupils dropped in rather slowly. The curate's daughters, and the attorney's son, and Miss Deane the milliner—but she found the language difficult, and left off, asserting that M. l'Abbé's snuff made her nervous. At last poor M. l'Abbé fell ill himself, really ill, dangerously ill, and Matthew Wise went in all haste to summon Mr. Hallett. Now Mr. Hallett had such an aversion to a Frenchman, in general, as a cat has to a dog; and was wont to erect himself into an attitude of defiance and wrath at the mere sight of the object of his antipathy. He hated and despised the whole nation, abhorred the language, and 'would as lief,' he assured Matthew, 'have been called in to a toad.' He went, however, grew interested in the case, which was difficult and complicated, exerted all his skill, and in about a month accomplished a cure.

By this time he had also become interested in his patient, whose piety, meekness, and resignation had won upon him in an extraordinary degree. The disease was gone, but a languor and lowness remained, which Mr. Hallett soon traced to a less curable disorder—poverty; the thought of the debt to himself evidently weighed on the poor abbé's spirits, and our good apothecary at last determined to learn French purely to liquidate his own long bill. It was the drollest thing in the world to see this pupil of fifty, whose habits were so entirely unfitted for a learner, conning his task; or to hear him conjugating the verb *avoir*, or blundering through the first phrases of the easy dialogues. He was a most unpromising scholar, shuffled the syllables together in a manner that would seem incredible, and stumbled at every step of the pronunciation, against which his English tongue rebelled amain. Every now and then he solaced himself with a fluent volley of execrations in his own language, which the abbé understood well enough to return, after rather a politer fashion, in French. It was a most amusing scene. But the motive! the generous, noble motive! M. l'Abbé, after a few lessons, detected this delicate artifice, and, touched almost to tears, insisted on dismissing his pupil, who, on his side, declared that nothing should induce him to abandon his studies. At last they came to a compromise. The cherry-cheeked Margaret took her uncle's post as a learner, which she filled in a manner much more satisfactory; and the good old Frenchman not only allowed Mr. Hallett to administer gratis to his ailments, but partook of his Sunday dinner as long as he lived.

CHAPTER XXIX

WHEAT-HOEING

May 3rd. Cold bright weather. All within doors, sunny and chilly; all without, windy and dusty. It is quite tantalizing to see that brilliant sun careering through so beautiful a sky, and to feel little more warmth from his presence than one does from that of his fair but cold sister, the moon. Even the sky, beautiful as it is, has the look of that one sometimes sees in a very bright moonlight night —deeply, intensely blue, with white, fleecy clouds driven vigorously along by a strong breeze, now veiling and now exposing the dazzling luminary around whom they sail. A beautiful sky! and, in spite of its coldness, a beautiful world! The effect of this backward spring has been to arrest the early flowers, to which heat is the great enemy; whilst the leaves and the later flowers have, nevertheless, ventured to peep out slowly and cautiously in sunny places —exhibiting, in the copses and hedgerows, a pleasant mixture of March and May. And we, poor chilly mortals, must follow, as nearly as we can, the wise example of the may-blossoms, by avoiding bleak paths and open commons, and creeping up the sheltered road to the vicarage—the pleasant, sheltered road, where the western sun steals in between two rows of bright green elms, and the east wind is fenced off by the range of woody hills which rise abruptly before us, forming so striking a boundary to the picture.

How pretty this lane is, with its tall elms, just dressed in their young leaves, bordering the sunny path, or sweeping in a semicircle behind the clear pools and the white cottages that are scattered along the way. You shall seldom see a cottage hereabout without an accompanying pond, all alive with geese and ducks, at the end of the little garden. Ah! here is Dame Simmons making a most original use of her piece of water, standing on the bank that divides it from her garden, and most ingeniously watering her onion-bed with a new mop—now a dip, and now a twirl! Really, I give her credit for the invention. It is as good an imitation of a shower as one should wish to see on a summer day. A squirt is nothing to it!

And here is another break to the tall line of elms—the gate that leads into Farmer Thorpe's great enclosures. Eight, ten, fourteen people in this large field, wheat-hoeing. The couple nearest the gate, who keep aloof from all the rest, and are hoeing this furrow so completely in concert, step by step and stroke for stroke, are Jem Tanner and Mabel Green. There is not a handsomer pair in the field or in the village. Jem, with his bright complexion, his curling hair, his clear blue eye, and his trim figure—set off to great advantage by his short jacket and trousers and new straw hat; Mabel, with her little stuff gown, and her white handkerchief and apron — defining so exactly her light and flexible shape—and her black eyes flashing from under a deep bonnet lined with pink, whose reflection gives to her bright, dark countenance and dimpled cheeks a glow innocently artificial, which was the only charm that they wanted.

Jem and Mabel are, beyond all doubt, the handsomest couple in the field, and I am much mistaken if each have not a vivid sense of the charms of the other. Their mutual admiration was clear enough in their work; but it speaks still more plainly in their idleness. Not a stroke have they done for these five minutes; Jem, propped on his hoe, and leaning across the furrow, whispering soft nonsense; Mabel, blushing and smiling, now making believe to turn away, now listening, and looking up with a sweeter smile than ever, and a blush that makes her bonnet-lining pale. Ah, Mabel! Mabel! Now they are going to work again— no! after three or four strokes, the hoes have somehow become entangled, and, without either advancing a step nearer the other, they are playing with these rustic implements as pretty a game at romps—showing off as nice a piece of rural flirtation—as ever was exhibited since wheat was hoed.

Ah, Mabel! Mabel! beware of Farmer Thorpe! He 'll see, at a glance, that little will his corn profit by such labours. Beware, too, Jem Tanner!—for Mabel is, in some sort, an heiress: being the real niece and adopted daughter of our little lame clerk, who, although he looks such a tattered ragamuffin that the very grave-diggers are ashamed of him, is well to pass in the world—keeps a scrub pony —indeed he can hardly walk up the aisle—hath a share in the county fire office, and money in the funds. Mabel will be an heiress, despite the tatterdemalion costume of her honoured uncle, which I think he wears out of coquetry, that the remarks which might otherwise fall on his miserable person—full as misshapen as that of any hunchback recorded in the Arabian Tales—may find a less offensive vent on his raiment. Certain such a figure hath seldom been beheld out of church or in. Yet will Mabel, nevertheless, be a fortune; and therefore she must inter-marry with another fortune, according to the rule made and provided in such cases; and the little clerk hath already looked her out a spouse, about his own standing—a widower in the next parish, with four children and a squint. Poor Jem Tanner! Nothing will that smart person or that pleasant speech avail with the little clerk; never will he officiate at your marriage to his niece — 'amen' would 'stick in his throat.' Poor things! in what a happy oblivion of the world and its cares, Farmer Thorpe and the wheat-hoeing, the squinting shopkeeper and the little clerk, are they laughing and talking at this moment! Poor things! poor things!

Well, I must pursue my walk. How beautiful a mixture of flowers and leaves is in the high bank under this north hedge—quite an illustration of the blended seasons of which I spoke. An old irregular hedgerow is always beautiful, especially in the springtime, when the grass, and mosses, and flowering weeds mingle best with the bushes and creeping plants that overhang them. But this bank is, most especially, various and lovely. Shall we try to analyse it? First, the clinging white-veined ivy, which crawls up the slope in every direction, the master-piece of that rich mosaic; then the brown leaves and the lilac blossoms of its fragrant namesake, the ground-ivy, which grows here so profusely; then the late-lingering primrose; then the delicate wood-sorrel; then the regular pink stars of the cranesbill, with its beautiful leaves; then

the golden oxlip and the cowslip, 'cinque-spotted'; then the
blue pansy, and the enamelled wild hyacinth; then the bright
foliage of the brier-rose, which comes trailing its green
wreaths amongst the flowers; then the bramble and the
woodbine, creeping round the foot of a pollard oak, with its
brown folded leaves; then a verdant mass—the blackthorn,
with its lingering blossoms—the hawthorn, with its swelling
buds—the bushy maple—the long stems of the hazel—and
between them, hanging like a golden plume over the bank,
a splendid tuft of the blossomed broom; then, towering
high above all, the tall and leafy elms. And this is but a
faint picture of this hedge, on the meadowy side of which
sheep are bleating, and where, every here and there, a
young lamb is thrusting its pretty head between the trees.

Who is this approaching? Farmer Thorpe? Yes, of a
certainty it is that substantial yeoman, sallying forth from
his substantial farm-house, which peeps out from between
two huge walnut-trees on the other side of the road, with
intent to survey his labourers in the wheat-field. Farmer
Thorpe is a stout, square, sturdy personage of fifty, or
thereabout, with a hard, weather-beaten countenance, of
that peculiar vermilion, all over alike, into which the action
of the sun and wind sometimes tans a fair complexion;
sharp, shrewd features, and a keen grey eye. He looks
completely like a man who will neither cheat nor be cheated:
and such is his character—an upright, downright English
yeoman; just always, and kind in a rough way, but given
to fits of anger, and filled with an abhorrence of pilfering,
and idleness, and trickery of all sorts, that makes him
strict as a master, and somewhat stern at workhouse and
vestry. I doubt if he will greatly relish the mode in which
Jem and Mabel are administering the hoe in his wheat-drills.
He will not reach the gate yet, for his usual steady, active
pace is turned, by a recent accident, into an unequal,
impatient halt—as if he were alike angry with his lameness
and the cause. I must speak to him as he passes—not
merely as a due courtesy to a good neighbour, but to give
the delinquents in the field notice to resume their hoeing;
but not a word of the limp—that is a sore subject.

'A fine day, Mr. Thorpe?'

'We want rain, ma'am!'

And on, with great civility, but without pausing a moment, he is gone. He 'll certainly catch Mabel and her love philandering over his wheat-furrows. Well, that may take its chance!—they have his lameness in their favour, only that the cause of that lameness has made the worthy farmer unusually cross. I think I must confide the story to my readers.

Gipsies and beggars do not in general much inhabit our neighbourhood; but, about half a mile off, there is a den so convenient for strollers and vagabonds that it sometimes tempts the rogues to a few days' sojourn. It is, in truth, nothing more than a deserted brick-kiln, by the side of a lonely lane. But there is something so snug and comfortable in the old building (always keeping in view gipsy notions of comfort); the blackened walls are so backed by the steep hill on whose side they are built—so fenced from the bleak north-east, and letting in so gaily the pleasant western sun; and the wide, rugged, impassable lane (used only as a road to the kiln, and with that abandoned) is at once so solitary and deserted, and so close to the inhabited and populous world, that it seems made for a tribe whose prime requisites in a habitation are shelter, privacy, and a vicinity to farmyards.

Accordingly, about a month ago, a pretty strong encampment, evidently gipsies, took up their abode in the kiln. The party consisted of two or three tall, lean, sinister-looking men, who went about the country mending pots and kettles, and driving a small trade in old iron; one or two children, unnaturally quiet, the spies of the crew; an old woman, who sold matches and told fortunes; a young woman, with an infant strapped to her back, who begged; several hungry-looking dogs, and three ragged donkeys. The arrival of these vagabonds spread a general consternation through the village. Gamekeepers and housewives were in equal dismay. Snares were found in the preserves —poultry vanished from the farmyards—a lamb was lost from the lea—and a damask tablecloth, belonging to the worshipful the Mayor of W——, was abstracted from the drying-ground of Rachel Strong, the most celebrated laundress in these parts, to whom it had been sent for the benefit of country washing. No end to the pilfering, and the stories of pilfering! The inhabitants of the kiln were not only thieves in themselves, but the cause of thievery in others. 'The gipsies!' was the answer general to every inquiry for things missing.

Farmer Thorpe, whose dwelling, with its variety of outbuildings—barns, ricks, and stables—is only separated by a meadow and a small coppice from the lane that leads to the gipsy retreat, was particularly annoyed by this visitation. Two couple of full-grown ducks, and a whole brood of early chickens, disappeared in one night; and Mrs. Thorpe fretted over the loss, and the farmer was indignant at the roguery. He set traps, let loose mastiffs, and put in action all the resources of village police—but in vain. Every night property went; and the culprits, however strongly suspected, still continued unamenable to the law.

At last, one morning, the great chanticleer of the farm-yard—a cock of a million, with an unrivalled crow, a matchless strut, and plumage all gold and green, and orange and purple—gorgeous as a peacock, and fierce as a he-turkey—chanticleer, the pride and glory of the yard, was missing! And Mrs. Thorpe's lamentations and her husband's anger redoubled. Vowing vengeance against the gipsies, he went to the door to survey a young blood-mare of his own breeding; and as he stood at the gate—now bemoaning chanticleer, now cursing the gipsies, now admiring the bay filly—his neighbour, Dame Simmons—the identical lady of the mop, who occasionally charred at the house—came to give him the comfortable information that she had certainly heard chanticleer—she was quite ready to swear to chanticleer's voice — crowing in the brick-kiln. No time, she added, should be lost, if Farmer Thorpe wished to rescue that illustrious cock, and to punish the culprits—since the gipsies, when she passed the place, were preparing to decamp.

No time *was* lost. In one moment Farmer Thorpe was on the bay filly's unsaddled back, with the halter for a bridle; and, in the next, they were on full gallop towards the kiln. But, alas! alas! 'the more haste the worse speed,' says the wisdom of nations. Just as they arrived at the spot from which the procession—gipsies, dogs, and donkeys,

and chanticleer in a sack, shrieking most vigorously—
were proceeding on their travels, the young blood-mare—
whether startled at the unusual *cortège*, or the rough ways,
or the hideous noise of her old friend, the cock—suddenly
reared and threw her master, who lay in all the agony of a
sprained ankle, unable to rise from the ground; whilst the
whole tribe, with poor chanticleer their prisoner, marched
triumphantly past him, utterly regardless of his threats
and imprecations. In this plight was the unlucky farmer
discovered, about half an hour afterwards, by his wife, the
constable, and a party of his own labourers, who came to
give him assistance in securing the culprits; of whom, notwithstanding an instant and active search through the
neighbourhood, nothing has yet transpired. We shall
hardly see them again in these parts, and have almost done
talking of them. The village is returned to its old state
of order and honesty; the Mayor of W—— has replaced his
tablecloth, and Mrs. Thorpe her cock; and the poor farmer's
lame ankle is all that remains to give token of the gipsies.

Here we are at the turning, which, edging round by the
coppice, branches off to their sometime den; the other
bend to the right leads up a gentle ascent to the vicarage,
and that is our way. How fine a view of the little parsonage
we have from hence, between those arching elms, which
enclose it like a picture in a frame! and how pretty a picture
it forms, with its three pointed roofs, its snug porch, and
its casement window glittering from amid the China roses!
What a nest of peace and comfort! Farther on, almost at
the summit of the hill, stands the old church with its massy
tower—a row of superb lime-trees running along one side
of the churchyard, and a cluster of dark yews shading
the other. Few country churches have so much to boast
in architectural beauty, or in grandeur of situation.

We lose sight of it as we mount the hill, the lane narrowing
and winding between deep banks, surmounted by high hedges,
excluding all prospects till we reach the front of the vicarage,
and catch across the gate of the opposite field a burst of
country the most extensive and the most beautiful—field
and village, mansion and cot, town and river, all smiling
under the sparkling sun of May, and united and harmonized
by the profusion of hedgerow timber in its freshest verdure,

giving a rich woodland character to the scene, till it is terminated in the distance by the blue line of the Hampshire hills almost melting into the horizon. Such is the view from the vicarage. But it is too sunny and too windy to stand about out of doors, and time to finish our ramble. Down the hill, and round the corner, and past Farmer Thorpe's house, and one glance at the wheat-hoers, and then we will go home.

Ah! it is just as I feared. Jem and Mabel have been parted: they are now at opposite sides of the field—he looking very angry, working rapidly and violently, and doing more harm than good; she looking tolerably sulky, and just moving her hoe, but evidently doing nothing at all. Farmer Thorpe, on his part, is standing in the middle of the field, observing, but pretending not to observe, the little humours of the separated lovers. There is a lurking smile about the corners of his mouth that bespeaks him more amused than angry. He is a kind person after all, and will certainly make no mischief. I should not even wonder if he espoused Jem Tanner's cause; and, for certain, if anyone can prevail on the little clerk to give up his squinting favourite in favour of true love, Farmer Thorpe is the man.

CHAPTER XXX

THE CHALK-PIT

ONE of the most admirable persons whom I have ever known is my friend Mrs. Mansfield, the wife of the good vicar of Aberleigh. Her daughters are just what might be expected from girls trained under such a mother. Of Clara, the youngest, I have spoken elsewhere. Ellen, the elder sister, is as delightful a piece of sunshine and gaiety as ever gladdened a country home. One never thinks whether she is pretty, there is such a play of feature, such a light in her dark eye, such an alternation of blush and smile on her animated countenance; for Ellen has her mother's trick of blushing, although her 'eloquent blood' speaks through the medium of a richer and browner skin. One forgets to make up one's mind as to her prettiness; but it is quite certain that she is charming.

She has, in the very highest degree, those invaluable everyday spirits which require no artificial stimuli, no public amusements, no company, no flattery, no praise. Her sprightliness is altogether domestic. Her own dear family, and a few dear friends, are all the listeners she ever thinks of. No one doubts but Ellen might be a wit, if she would: she is saved from that dangerous distinction as much by natural modesty as by a kind and constant consideration for the feelings of others. I have often seen a repartee flashing and laughing in her bright eyes, but seldom, very seldom, heard it escape her lips; never unless quite equally matched and challenged to such a bout of 'bated foils' by some admirer of her playful conversation. They who have themselves that splendid but delusive talent can best estimate the merit of such forbearance. Governed as it is in her, it makes the delight of the house, and supplies perpetual amusement to herself and to all about her.

Another of her delightful and delighting amusements is her remarkable skill in drawing flowers. I have never seen any portraits so exactly resembling the originals, as her carnations and geraniums. If they could see themselves in her paintings, they might think that it was their own pretty selves in their looking-glass, the water. One reason for this wonderful verisimilitude is that our fair artist never flatters the flowers that sit to her; never puts leaves that ought to be there but are not there; never makes them hold up their heads unreasonably, or places them in an attitude, or forces them into a group. Just as they are, she sets them down; and if she does make any slight deviation from her models, she is so well acquainted with their persons and habits that all is in keeping; you feel that so the plant might have looked. By the way, I do not know any accomplishment that I would more earnestly recommend to my young friends than this of flower-painting. It is a most quiet, unpretending, womanly employment; a great amusement within doors, and a constant pleasure without. The enjoyment of a country walk is much enhanced when the chequered fritillary or the tinted wood-anemone are to be sought, and found, and gathered, and made our own; and the dear domestic spots, haunted by

Retired leisure,
Who in trim gardens takes his pleasure,

are doubly gardens when the dahlias and China asters, after flourishing there for their little day, are to reblossom on paper. Then it supplies such pretty keepsakes, the uncostly remembrances which are so pleasant to give and to take; and, above all, it fosters and sharpens the habit of observation and the love of truth. How much of what is excellent in art, in literature, in conversation, and in conduct is comprised in that little word!

Ellen had great delight in comparing our sylvan flora with the minute and fairy blossoms of the South Downs, where she had passed the greater part of her life. She could not but admit the superior luxuriance and variety of our woodland plants, and yet she had a good deal to say in favour of the delicate, flowery carpet which clothes the green hills of Sussex; and in fact was, on that point of honour, a little jealous—a little, a very little, the least in the world, touchy. She loved her former abode, the abode of her childhood, with enthusiasm: the downs; the sea, whose sound, as she said, seemed to follow her to her inland home, to dwell within her as it does in the folds of the sea-shell; and, above all, she loved her old neighbours, high and low. I do not know whether Mrs. Mansfield or her daughters returned oftenest to the 'simple annals of the *Sussex* poor.' It was a subject of which they never wearied; and we to whom they came, liked them the more for their clinging and lingering affection for those whom they had left. We received it as a pledge of what they would feel for us when we became better acquainted—a pledge which has been amply redeemed. I flatter myself that Aberleigh now almost rivals their dear old parish; only that Clara, who has been here three years, and is now eighteen, says, very gravely, that 'people as they grow old cannot be expected to form the very strong local attachments which they did when they were young.' I wonder how old Clara will think herself when she comes to be eight-and-twenty?

Between Ellen's stories and her mother's there is usually a characteristic difference; those of the one being merry, those of the other grave. One occurrence, however, was equally impressed on the mind of either. I shall try to tell it as shortly and simply as it was told to me; but it will want the charm of Mrs. Mansfield's touching voice, and of Ellen's glistening eyes.

Toward the bottom of one of the green hills of the parish of Lanton was a large, deserted chalk-pit; a solemn and ghastly-looking place, blackened in one part by an old lime-kiln, whose ruinous fragments still remained, and in others mossy and weather-stained, and tinted with every variety of colour—green, yellow, and brown. The excavation extended far within the sides of the hill, and the hedges were fringed by brier and bramble and ivy, contrasting strongly with the smooth, level verdure of the turf above, whilst plants of a ranker growth, nettles, docks, and fumitory, sprang up beneath, adding to the wildness and desolation of the scene. The road that led by the pit was little frequented. The place had an evil name; none cared to pass it even in the glare of the noonday sun; and the villagers would rather go a mile about than catch a glimpse of it when the pale moonlight brought into full relief those cavernous white walls, and the dark briers and ivy waved fitfully in the night wind. It was a vague and shuddering feeling. None knew why he feared, or what; but the awe and the avoidance were general, and the owls and the bats remained in undisturbed possession of Lanton chalk-pit.

One October day, the lively work of ploughing, and wheat-sowing, and harrowing was going on all at once in a great field just beyond the dreaded spot: a pretty and an interesting scene, especially on sloping ground, and under a gleaming sun throwing an ever-shifting play of light and shadow over the landscape. Towards noon, however, the clouds began to gather, and one of the tremendous pelting showers, peculiar to the coast, came suddenly on. Seedsmen, ploughmen, and carters hastened home with their teams, leaving the boys to follow; and they, five in number, set out at their fullest speed. The storm increased apace; and it was evident that their thin jackets and old smock-frocks would be drenched through and through long before they could reach Lanton Great Farm. In this dilemma, James Goddard, a stout lad of fifteen, the biggest and boldest of the party, proposed to take shelter in the chalk-pit. Boys are naturally thoughtless and fearless; the real inconvenience was more than enough to counterbalance the imaginary danger, and they all willingly adopted the plan, except one timid child, eight years old, who shrank and hung back.

Harry Lee was a widow's son. His father, a fisherman, had perished at sea a few months after the birth of this only child; and his mother, a fond and delicate woman, had reared him delicately and fondly, beyond her apparent means. Night and day had she laboured for her poor Harry; and nothing but a long illness and the known kindness of the farmer in whose service he was placed had induced her to part with him at so early an age.

Harry was, indeed, a sweet and gracious boy, noticed by every stranger for his gentleness and beauty. He had a fair, blooming, open countenance; large, mild blue eyes, which seemed to ask kindness in every glance; and a quantity of shining, light hair, curling in ringlets round his neck. He was the best reader in Mrs. Mansfield's Sunday-school; and only the day before, Miss Clara had given him a dinner to carry home to his mother, in reward of his proficiency: indeed, although they tried to conceal it, Harry was the decided favourite of both the young ladies. James Goddard, under whom he worked, and to whose care he had been tearfully committed by the widow Lee, was equally fond of him, in a rougher way; and in the present instance, seeing the delicate boy shivering between cold and fear at the outside of the pit (for the same constitutional timidity which prevented his entering, hindered him from going home by himself), he caught him up in his arms, brought him in, and deposited him in the snuggest recess, on a heap of dry chalk. 'Well, Harry, is not this better than standing in the wet?' said he kindly, sitting down by his protégé, and sharing with him a huge luncheon of bread and cheese; and the poor child smiled in his face, thanked him, and kissed him, as he had been used to kiss his mother.

Half an hour had passed away in boyish talk, and still the storm continued. At last James Goddard thought that he heard a strange and unaccustomed sound, as of bursting or cracking—an awful and indescribable sound—low, and yet distinctly audible, although the wind and rain were raging, and the boys loud in mirth and laughter. He seemed to feel the sound, as he said afterwards; and was just about to question his companions if they too heard that unearthly noise, when a horseman passed along the road, making signs to them and shouting. His words were drowned in the tempest; James rushed out to inquire his meaning, and in that moment the side of the chalk-pit fell in! He heard a crash and a scream—the death scream!— felt his back grazed by the descending mass, and turning round saw the hill rent, as by an earthquake, and the excavation which had sheltered them filled, piled, heaped up by the still quivering and gigantic fragments—no vestige left to tell where it was, or where his wretched companions lay buried!

'Harry! Harry! the child! the child!' was his first thought and his first exclamation. 'Help! instant help!' was the next, and, assisted by the stranger horseman, whose speed had been stayed by the awful catastrophe, the village of Lanton was quickly alarmed, and its inhabitants assembled on the spot. Who may describe that scene? Fathers, brothers, kinsmen, friends digging literally for life, every nerve quivering with exertion, and yet all exertion felt to be unavailing! Mothers and sisters looking on in agony; and the poor widow Lee, and poor, poor James Goddard, the self-accuser! A thousand and a thousand times did he crave pardon of that distracted mother, for the peril—the death of her son; for James felt that there could be no hope for the helpless child, and tears, such as no personal calamity could have drawn from the strong-hearted lad, fell fast for his fate. Hour after hour the men of Lanton laboured, and all was in vain. The mass seemed impenetrable, inexhaustible. Toward sunset one boy appeared, crushed and dead; another, who showed some slight signs of life, and who still lives, a cripple; a third dead; and then, last of all, Harry Lee. Alas! only by his raiment could that fond mother know her child. His death must have been instantaneous. She did not linger long. The three boys were interred together in Lanton churchyard on the succeeding Sabbath; and before the end of the year the widow Lee was laid by her son.

CHAPTER XXXI

OUR MAYING

As party produces party and festival brings forth festival in higher life, so one scene of rural festivity is pretty sure to be followed by another. The boys' cricket match at Whitsuntide, which was won most triumphantly by our parish, and luckily passed off without giving cause for a coroner's inquest, or indeed without injury of any sort, except the demolition of Amos Stone's new straw hat, the crown of which (Amos's head being fortunately at a distance) was fairly struck out by the cricket ball—this match produced one between our eleven and the players of the neighbouring hamlet of Whitley; and being patronized by the young lord of the manor and several of the gentry round, and followed by jumping in sacks, riding donkey-races, grinning through horse-collars, and other diversions more renowned for their antiquity than their elegance, gave such general satisfaction, that it was resolved to hold a Maying in full form in Whitley Wood.

Now this wood of ours happens to be a common of twenty acres, with three trees on it, and the Maying was fixed to be held between hay-time and harvest; but 'what 's in a name?' Whitley Wood is a beautiful piece of greensward, surrounded on three sides by fields, and farm-houses, and cottages, and woody uplands, and on the other by a fine park; and the May-house was erected, and the May-games held in the beginning of July; the very season of leaves and roses, when the days are at the longest, and the weather at the finest, and the whole world is longing to get out of doors. Moreover, the whole festival was aided, not impeded, by the gentlemen amateurs, headed by that very genial person, our young lord of the manor; whilst the business part of the affair was confided to the well-known diligence, zeal, activity, and intelligence of that most popular of village landlords, mine host of the 'Rose.' How

230

could a Maying fail under such auspices? Everybody
expected more sunshine and more fun, more flowers and
more laughing, than ever was known at a rustic merry-
making—and really, considering the manner in which expectation had been raised, the quantity of disappointment
has been astonishingly small.

Landlord Sims, the master of the revels, and our very
good neighbour, is a portly, bustling man of five-and-forty,
or thereabout, with a hale, jovial visage, a merry eye, a
pleasant smile, and a general air of good fellowship. This
last qualification, whilst it serves greatly to recommend
his ale, is apt to mislead superficial observers, who generally
account him a sort of slenderer Boniface, and imagine that,
like that renowned hero of the spigot, Master Sims eats,
drinks, and sleeps on his own *anno Domini*. They were never
more mistaken in their lives; no soberer man than Master
Sims within twenty miles! Except for the good of the
house, he no more thinks of drinking beer than a grocer
of eating figs. To be sure when the jug lags he will take a
hearty pull, just by way of example, and to set the good
ale a-going. But, in general, he trusts to subtler and more
delicate modes of quickening its circulation. A good song,
a good story, a merry jest, a hearty laugh, and a most
winning habit of assentation; these are his implements.
There is not a better companion or a more judicious
listener in the county. His pliability is astonishing. He
shall say yes to twenty different opinions on the same
subject within the hour; and so honest and cordial does
his agreement seem, that no one of his customers, whether
drunk or sober, ever dreams of doubting his sincerity.
The hottest conflict of politics never puzzles him: Whig
or Tory, he is both, or either—'the happy Mercutio, that
curses both houses.' Add to this gift of conformity a
cheerful, easy temper, an alacrity of attention, a zealous
desire to please, which gives to his duties, as a landlord,
all the grace of hospitality and a perpetual civility and
kindness, even when he has nothing to gain by them, and
no one can wonder at Master Sims's popularity.

After his good wife's death, this popularity began to
extend itself in a remarkable manner amongst the females
of the neighbourhood; smitten with his portly person, his

smooth, oily manner, and a certain soft, earnest, whispering voice, which he generally assumes when addressing one of the fairer sex, and which seems to make his very 'How d' ye do' confidential and complimentary. Moreover, it was thought that the good landlord was well to do in the world; and though Betsy and Letty were good little girls, quick, civil, and active, yet, poor things, what could such young girls know of a house like the 'Rose'? All would go to rack and ruin without the eye of a mistress! Master Sims must look out for a wife. So thought the whole female world, and, apparently, Master Sims began to think so himself.

The first fair one to whom his attention was directed was a rosy, pretty widow, a pastrycook of the next town, who arrived in our village on a visit to her cousin, the baker, for the purpose of giving confectionery lessons to his wife. Nothing was ever so hot as that courtship. During the week that the lady of pie-crust stayed, her lover almost lived in the oven. One would have thought that he was learning to make the cream tarts without pepper by which Bedreddin Hassan regained his state and his princess. It would be a most suitable match, as all the parish agreed; the widow, for as pretty as she was (and one shan't often see a pleasanter open countenance, or a sweeter smile), being within ten years as old as her suitor, and having had two husbands already. A most proper and suitable match, said everybody; and when our landlord carried her back to B—— in his new-painted green cart, all the village agreed that they were gone to be married, and the ringers were just setting up a peal, when Master Sims returned alone, single, crestfallen, dejected; the bells stopped of themselves, and we heard no more of the pretty pastrycook. For three months after that rebuff, mine host, albeit not addicted to aversions, testified an equal dislike to women and tartlets, widows and plum-cake. Even poor Alice Taylor, whose travelling basket of lollipops and gingerbread he had whilom patronized, was forbidden the house: and not a bun or a biscuit could be had at the 'Rose,' for love or money.

The fit, however, wore off in time; and he began again to follow the advice of his neighbours, and to look out for a wife, up street and down; whilst at each extremity a fair object presented herself, from neither of whom had he the slightest reason to dread a repetition of the repulse which he had experienced from the blooming widow. The down-street lady was a widow also; the portly, comely relict of our drunken village blacksmith, who, in spite of her joy at her first husband's death, and an old spite at mine host of the 'Rose,' to whose good ale and good company she was wont to ascribe most of the aberrations of the deceased, began to find her shop, her journeymen, and her eight children (six unruly, obstreperous pickles of boys, and two tomboys of girls), rather more than a lone woman could manage, and to sigh for a helpmate to ease her of her cares, collect the boys at night, see the girls to school of a morning, break the larger imps of running away to revels and fairs, and the smaller fry of bird's-nesting and orchard-robbing, and bear a part in the lectures and chastisements which she deemed necessary to preserve the young rebels from the bad end which she predicted to them twenty times a day. Master Sims was the coadjutor on whom she had inwardly pitched; and, accordingly, she threw out broad hints to that effect every time she encountered him, which, in the course of her search for boys and girls, who were sure to be missing at school-time and bed-time, happened pretty often; and Master Sims was far too gallant and too much in the habit of assenting to listen unmoved; for really the widow was a fine, tall, comely woman; and the whispers, and smiles, and hand-pressings, when they happened to meet, were becoming very tender; and his admonitions and head-shakings, addressed to the young crew (who, nevertheless, all liked him), quite fatherly. This was his down-street flame.

The rival lady was Miss Lydia Day, the carpenter's sister; a slim, upright maiden, not remarkable for beauty, and not quite so young as she had been, who, on inheriting a small annuity from the mistress with whom she had spent the best of her days, retired to her native village to live on her means. A genteel, demure, quiet personage was Miss Lydia Day; much addicted to snuff and green tea, and not averse from a little gentle scandal—for the rest, a good sort of woman, and *un très bon parti* for Master Sims, who seemed to consider it a profitable speculation, and made love to her whenever she happened to come into his head, which, it must be confessed, was hardly so often as her merits and her annuity deserved. Remiss as he was, he had no lack of encouragement to complain of—for she 'to hear would seriously incline,' and put on her best silk, and her best simper, and lighted up her faded complexion into something approaching to a blush, whenever he came to visit her. And this was Master Sims's up-street love.

So stood affairs at the 'Rose' when the day of the Maying arrived; and the double flirtation, which, however dexterously managed, must have been sometimes, one would think, rather inconvenient to the inamorato, proved on this occasion extremely useful. Each of the fair ladies contributed her aid to the festival; Miss Lydia by tying up sentimental garlands for the May-house, and scolding the carpenters into diligence in the erection of the booths; the widow by giving her whole bevy of boys and girls a holiday and turning them loose on the neighbourhood to collect flowers as they could. Very useful auxiliaries were these light foragers; they scoured the country far and near— irresistible mendicants! pardonable thieves! coming to no harm, poor children, except that little George got a black eye in tumbling from the top of an acacia-tree at the Park, and that Sam (he's a sad pickle, is Sam!) narrowly escaped a horse-whipping from the head gardener at the Hall, who detected a bunch of his new rhododendron, the only plant in the county, forming the very crown and centre of the may-pole. Little harm did they do, poor children, with all their pilfery; and when they returned, covered with their flowery loads, like the May-day figure called 'Jack-of-the-Green,' they worked at the garlands and the May-houses, as none but children ever do work, putting all their young life and their untiring spirit of noise and motion into their pleasant labour. Oh, the din of that building! Talk of the Tower of Babel! that was a quiet piece of masonry compared to the May-house of Whitley Wood, with its walls of leaves and flowers, and its canvas booths at either end for refreshments and musicians. Never was known more joyous note of preparation.

The morning rose more quietly—I had almost said more dully—and promised ill for the fête. The sky was gloomy, the wind cold, and the green filled as slowly as a balloon seems to do when one is watching it. The entertainments of the day were to begin with a cricket match (two elevens to be chosen on the ground), and the wickets pitched at twelve o'clock precisely. Twelve o'clock came, but no cricketers—except, indeed, some two or three punctual and impatient gentlemen; one o'clock came, and brought no other reinforcement than two or three more of our young Etonians and Wykehamites—less punctual than their precursors, but not a whit less impatient. Very provoking, certainly, but not very uncommon. Your country cricketer, the peasant, the mere rustic, does love, on these occasions, to keep his betters waiting, if only to display his power; and when we consider that it is the one solitary opportunity in which importance can be felt and vanity gratified, we must acknowledge it to be perfectly in human nature that a few airs should be shown. Accordingly, our best players held aloof. Tom Coper would not come to the ground; Joel Brent came, indeed, but would not play; Samuel Long coquetted—he would and he would not. Very provoking, certainly! Then two young farmers, a tall brother and a short, Hampshire men, cricketers born, whose good humour and love of the game rendered them sure cards, had been compelled to go on business—the one, ten miles south; the other, fifteen north—that very morning. No playing without the Goddards! No sign of either of them on the B—— road or the F——. Most intolerably provoking, beyond a doubt! Master Sims tried his best coaxing and his best double X on the recusant players, but all in vain. In short, there was great danger of the match going off altogether, when, about two o'clock, Amos Stone, who was there with the crown of his straw hat sewed in wrong side outward—new thatched, as it were—and who had been set to watch the B—— highway, gave notice that something was coming as tall as the may-pole—which something turning out to be the long Goddard, and his brother approaching at the same moment in the opposite direction, hope, gaiety, and good humour revived again; and two elevens, including Amos and another urchin of his calibre, were formed on the spot.

I never saw a prettier match. The gentlemen, the

Goddards, and the boys being equally divided, the strength and luck of the parties were so well balanced that it produced quite a neck-and-neck race, won only by two notches. Amos was completely the hero on the day, standing out half of his side, and getting five notches at one hit. His side lost—but so many of his opponents gave him their ribbons (have not I said that Master Sims bestowed a set of ribbons?) that the straw hat was quite covered with purple trophies; and Amos, stalking about the ground, with a shy and awkward vanity, looked with his decorations like the sole conqueror—the Alexander or Napoleon of the day. The boy did not speak a word; but every now and then he displayed a set of huge white teeth in a grin of inexpressible delight. By far the happiest and proudest personage of that Maying was Amos Stone.

By the time the cricket match was over the world began to be gay at Whitley Wood. Carts and gigs, and horses and carriages, and people of all sorts arrived from all quarters; and, lastly, 'the blessed sun himself' made his appearance, adding a triple lustre to the scene. Fiddlers, ballad-singers, cake-baskets—Punch—Master Frost, crying cherries—a Frenchman with dancing dogs—a Bavarian woman selling brooms—half a dozen stalls with fruit and frippery—and twenty noisy games of quoits, and bowls, and ninepins—boys throwing at boxes—girls playing at ball—gave to the assemblage the bustle, clatter, and gaiety of a Dutch fair, as one sees it in Teniers's pictures. Plenty of drinking and smoking on the green—plenty of eating in the booths: the gentlemen cricketers, at one end, dining off a round of beef, which made the table totter; the players, at the other, supping off a gammon of bacon—Amos Stone crammed at both — and Landlord Sims bustling everywhere with an activity that seemed to confer upon him the gift of ubiquity, assisted by the little light-footed maidens, his daughters, all smiles and curtsies, and by a pretty black-eyed young woman—name unknown—with whom, even in the midst of his hurry, he found time, as it seemed to me, for a little philandering. What would the widow and Miss Lydia have said? But they remained in happy ignorance—the one drinking tea in most decorous primness in a distant marquee, disliking to mingle with so mixed an assembly; the other in full chase after the most unlucky of all her urchins, the boy called Sam, who had gotten into a *démêlé* with a showman, in consequence of mimicking the wooden gentleman Punch and his wife Judy—thus, as the showman observed, bringing his exhibition into disrepute.

Meanwhile, the band struck up in the May-house, and the dance, after a little demur, was fairly set afloat—an honest English country dance (there had been some danger of waltzing and quadrilling), with ladies and gentlemen at the top, and country lads and lasses at the bottom; a happy mixture of cordial kindness on the one hand, and pleased respect on the other. It was droll, though, to see the beplumed and beflowered French hats, the silks and the furbelows sailing and rustling amidst the straw bonnets and cotton gowns of the humbler dancers; and not less so to catch a glimpse of the little lame clerk, shabbier than ever, peeping through the canvas opening of the booth, with a grin of ineffable delight, over the shoulder of our vicar's pretty wife. Really, considering that Mabel Green and Jem Tanner were standing together at that moment at the top of the set, so deeply engaged in making love that they forgot when they ought to begin, and that the little clerk must have seen them, I cannot help taking his grin for a favourable omen to those faithful lovers.

Well, the dance finished, the sun went down, and we departed. The Maying is over, the booths carried away, and the May-house demolished. Everything has fallen into its old position, except the love affairs of Landlord Sims. The pretty lass with the black eyes, who first made her appearance at Whitley Wood, is actually staying at the Rose Inn, on a visit to his daughters; and the village talk goes that she is to be the mistress of the thriving hostelry, and the wife of its master; and both her rivals are jealous, after their several fashions—the widow in the tantrums, the maiden in the dumps. Nobody knows exactly who the black-eyed damsel may be—but she's young, and pretty, and civil, and modest; and, without intending to depreciate the merits of either of her competitors, I cannot help thinking that our good neighbour has shown his taste.

CHAPTER XXXII

THE BIRD-CATCHER

A LONDON fog is a sad thing, as every inhabitant of London knows full well: dingy, dusky, dirty, damp; an atmosphere black as smoke and wet as steam, that wraps round you like a blanket; a cloud reaching from earth to heaven; a 'palpable obscure,' which not only turns day into night, but threatens to extinguish the lamps and lanthorns with which the poor street-wanderers strive to illumine their darkness, dimming and paling the 'ineffectual fires,' until the volume of gas at a shop door cuts no better figure than a hedge glow-worm, and a duchess's flambeau would veil its glories to a will-o'-the-wisp. A London fog is, not to speak profanely, a sort of renewal and reversal of Joshua's miracle: the sun seems to stand still as on that occasion, only that now it stands in the wrong place, and gives light to the Antipodes. The very noises of the street come stifled and smothered through that suffocating medium; din is at a pause; the town is silenced; and the whole population, biped and quadruped, sympathize with the dead and chilling weight of the out-of-door world. Dogs and cats just look up from their slumbers, turn round, and go to sleep again; the little birds open their pretty eyes, stare about them, wonder that the night is so long, and settle themselves afresh on their perches. Silks lose their gloss, cravats their stiffness, hackney-coachmen their way; young ladies fall out of curl, and mammas out of temper; masters scold; servants grumble; and the whole city, from Hyde Park Corner to Wapping, looks sleepy and cross, like a fine gentleman roused before his time and forced to get up by candlelight. Of all detestable things, a London fog is the most detestable.

Now a country fog is quite another matter. To say nothing of its rarity, and in this dry and healthy midland country few of the many variations of our variable English climate are rarer; to say nothing of its unfrequent recurrence, there is about it much of the peculiar and characteristic beauty which almost all natural phenomena exhibit to those who have themselves that faculty, oftener perhaps claimed than possessed, a genuine feeling of nature. This last lovely autumn, when the flowers of all seasons seemed mingling as one sometimes sees them in a painter's garland —the violets and primroses reblossoming, and new crops of sweet-peas and mignonette blending with the chrysanthemum, the Michaelmas daisy, and the dahlia, the latest blossoms of the year—when the very leaves clung to the trees with a freshness so vigorous and so youthful that they seemed to have determined, in spite of their old bad habit, that for once they would not fall—this last lovely autumn has given us more foggy mornings, or rather more foggy days, than I ever remember to have seen in Berkshire: days beginning in a soft and vapoury mistiness, enveloping the whole country in a veil, snowy, fleecy, and light as the smoke which one often sees circling in the distance from some cottage chimney, or as the still whiter clouds which float around the moon; and finishing in sunsets of a surprising richness and beauty, when the mist is lifted up from the earth, and turned into a canopy of unrivalled gorgeousness, purple, rosy, and golden, disclosing the splendid autumn landscape, with its shining rivulets, its varied and mellow woodland tints, and its deep emerald pasture lands, every blade and leaf covered with a thousand little drops, as pure as crystal, glittering and sparkling in the sunbeams like the dew on a summer morning, or the still more brilliant scintillations of frost.

It was in one of these days, early in November, that we set out about noon to pay a visit to a friend at some distance. The fog was yet on the earth, only some brightening in the south-west gave token that it was likely to clear away. As yet, however, the mist held complete possession—a much prettier, lighter, and cleaner vapour than that which is defiled with London smoke, but every whit as powerful and as delusive. We could not see the shoemaker's shop across the road—no! nor our chaise when it drew up before our door; were fain to guess at our own laburnum-tree; and found the sign of the 'Rose' invisible even when we ran against the signpost. Our little maid, a kind and careful lass, who, perceiving the dreariness of the weather, followed us across the court with extra wraps, had wellnigh tied my veil round her master's hat, and enveloped me in his bearskin; and my dog Mayflower, a white greyhound of the largest size, who had a mind to give us the undesired honour of her company, carried her point, in spite of the united efforts of half a dozen active pursuers, simply because the fog was so thick that nobody could see her. It was a complete game at bo-peep. Even mine host of the 'Rose,' one of the most alert of her followers, remained invisible, although we heard his voice close beside us.

A misty world it was, and a watery; and I, that had been praising the beauty of the fleecy white fog every day for a week before, began to sigh, and shiver, and quake, as much from dread of an overturn as from damp and chilliness; whilst my careful driver and his sagacious steed went on groping their way through the woody lanes that lead to the Loddon. Nothing but the fear of confessing my fear, that feeling which makes so many cowards brave, prevented me from begging to turn back again. On, however, we went, the fog becoming every moment heavier as we approached that beautiful and brimming river, which always, even in the midst of summer, brings with it such images of coolness and freshness as haunt the fancy after reading *Undine*; and where on the present occasion we seemed literally to breathe the water—as Dr. Clarke said in passing the Danube. My companion, nevertheless, continued to assure me that the day would clear—nay, that it was already clearing; and I soon found that he was right. As we left the river we seemed to leave the fog; and before we had reached the pretty village of Barkham the mist had almost disappeared; and I began to lose at once my silent fears and my shivering chilliness, and to resume my cheerfulness and my admiration.

It was curious to observe how object after object glanced out of the vapour. First of all, the huge oak, at the corner of Farmer Locke's field, which juts out into the lane like a crag into the sea, forcing the road to wind around it, stood forth like a hoary giant, with its head lost in the clouds; then Farmer Hewitt's great barn—the house, ricks, and

stables still invisible; then a gate, and half a cow, her head
being projected over it in strong relief, whilst the hinder
part of her body remained in the haze; then, more and more
distinctly, hedgerows, cottages, trees, and fields, until, as
we reached the top of Barkham Hill, the glorious sun broke
forth, and the lovely picture lay before our eyes in its soft
and calm beauty, emerging gradually from the vapour that
overhung it, in such manner as the image of his sleeping
Geraldine is said to have been revealed to Surrey in the
magic glass.   A beautiful picture it forms at all times, that
valley of Barkham.   Fancy a road winding down a hill
between high banks, richly studded with huge forest trees,
oak and beech, to a sparkling stream, with a footbridge
thrown across, which runs gurgling along the bottom; then
turning abruptly, and ascending the opposite hill, whilst
the rich plantations and old paling of a great park 'come
cranking in' on one side, and two or three irregular cottages
go straggling up on the other; the whole bathed in the
dewy sunshine, and glowing with the vivid colouring of
autumn.   The picture had, at the moment of which I
speak, an additional interest, by presenting to our eyes the
first human being whom we had seen during our drive
(we had heard several); one, too, who, although he bore
little resemblance to the fair mistress of Lord Surrey, was
yet sufficiently picturesque, and in excellent keeping with
the surrounding scene.

It was a robust, sturdy old man, his long grey hair appear-
ing between his well-worn hat and his warm but weather-
beaten coat, with a large package at his back, covered with
oilskin, a bundle of short, regular poles in one hand, and a
large bunch of thistles in the other; and even before Mayflower, who now made her appearance, and was endeavouring to satisfy her curiosity by pawing and poking the
knapsack, thereby awakening the noisy fears of two call-
birds, who together with a large bird-net formed its contents
—before this audible testimony of his vocation, or the still
stronger assurance of his hearty, good-humoured visage,
my companion, himself somewhat of an amateur in the art,
had recognized his friend and acquaintance Old Robin, the
bird-catcher of B——.

We soon overtook the old man, and after apologizing

for Mayflower's misdemeanour, who, by the way, seemed
sufficiently disposed to renew the assault, we proceeded at
the same slow pace up the hill, holding disjointed chat on
the badness of the weather, these foggy mornings, and the
little chance there was of doing much good with the nets
so late in the afternoon. To which Robin gave a doleful
assent. He was, however, going, he said, to try for a few
linnets on the common beyond the Great House, and was in
hopes to get a couple of wood-larks from the plantations.
He wanted the wood-larks above all things, for Mrs. Bennet,
the alderman's lady of B——, whose husband had left the
old shop in the market-place, and built a fine white cottage
just beyond the turnpike gate—so madam had set her
heart on a couple of wood-larks, to hang up in her new
shrubbery, and make the place look rural.

'Hang up, Robin! Why, there is not a tree a foot high
in the whole plantation! Wood-larks! Why, they'll be
dead before Christmas!'

'That's sure enough, your honour,' rejoined Robin.

'A soft-billed bird that requires as much care as a nightingale!' continued my companion. 'By the way, Robin,
have you any nightingales now?'

'Two, sir; a hen——'

'A hen! That's something remarkable!'

'A great curiosity, sir; for your honour knows that we
always set the trap for nightingales by ear, like; the creature
is so shy that one can seldom see it, so one is forced to put
the mealworm near where one hears the song; and it's
the most uncommon thing that can be to catch a hen; but
I have one, and a fine cock too, that I caught last spring
just before building-time. Two as healthy birds as ever
were seen.'

'Is the cock in song still?'

'Aye, sir, in full song; piping away, jug, jug, jug, all the
day, and half the night. I wish your honour would come
and hear it.' And, with a promise to that effect, we parted,
each our several ways; we to visit our friend, he to catch, if
catch he could, a couple of wood-larks to make Mrs. Bennet's
villa look rural.

Old Robin had not always been a bird-catcher. He had,
what is called, fallen in the world. His father had been the

best accustomed and most fashionable shoemaker in the
town of B——, and Robin succeeded, in right of eldership,
to his house, his business, his customers, and his debts.
No one was ever less fitted for the craft. Birds had been
his passion from the time that he could find a nest or string
an egg; and the amusement of the boy became the pursuit
of the man. No sooner was he his own master than his
whole house became an aviary, and his whole time was
devoted to breeding, taming, and teaching the feathered
race; an employment that did not greatly serve to promote
his success as a cordwainer. He married; and an extravagant wife, and a neglected and, therefore, unprosperous
business, drove him more and more into the society of
the pretty creatures whose company he had always so
greatly preferred to that of the two-legged, unfeathered
animal called man. Things grew worse and worse; and
at length poor Robin appeared in the Gazette—ruined,
as his wife and his customers said, by birds; or, as he himself
said, by his customers and his wife. Perhaps there was
some truth on either side; at least, a thousand pounds of
bad debts on his books, and a whole pile of milliners' and
mantuamakers' bills, went nigh to prove the correctness of
his assertion. Ruined, however, he was; and a happy day
it was for him, since, his stock being sold, his customers gone,
and his prospects in trade fairly at an end, his wife (they
had no family) deserted him also, and Robin, thus left a
free man, determined to follow the bent of his genius, and
devote the remainder of his life to the breeding, catching,
and selling of birds.

For this purpose he hired an apartment in the ruinous
quarter of B—— called the Soak, a high, spacious attic,
not unlike a barn, which came recommended to him by
its cheapness, its airiness, and its extensive cage-room;
and his creditors having liberally presented him with all
the inhabitants of his aviary, some of which were very rare
and curious, as well as a large assortment of cages, nets,
traps, and seeds, he began his new business with great
spirit, and has continued it ever since with various success,
but with unabating perseverance, zeal, and good-humour—
a very poor and a very happy man. His garret in the
Soak is one of the boasts of B——; all strangers go to see

the birds and the bird-catcher, and most of his visitors are induced to become purchasers, for there is no talking with Robin on his favourite subject without catching a little of his contagious enthusiasm. His room is quite a menagerie, something like what the feathered department of the ark must have been—as crowded, as numerous, and as noisy.

The din is really astounding. To say nothing of the twitter of whole legions of linnets, goldfinches, and canaries, the latter of all ages; the chattering and piping of magpies, parrots, jackdaws, and bullfinches, in every stage of their education; the deeper tones of blackbirds, thrushes, larks, and nightingales never fail to swell the chorus, aided by the cooing of doves, the screechings of owls, the squeakings of guinea-pigs, and the eternal grinding of a barrel-organ, which a little damsel of eight years old, who officiates under Robin as feeder and cleaner, turns round, with melancholy monotony, to the loyal and patriotic tunes of *Rule, Britannia!* and *God save the King*, the only airs, as her master observes, which are sure not to go out of fashion.

Except this young damsel and her music, the apartment exhibits but few signs of human habitation. A macaw is perched on the little table, and a cockatoo chained to the only chair; the roof is tenanted by a choice breed of tumbler pigeons, and the floor cumbered by a brood of curious bantams, unrivalled for ugliness.

Here Robin dwells, in the midst of the feathered population, except when he sallies forth at morning or evening to spread his nets for goldfinches or bullfinches on the neighbouring commons, or to place his trap-cages for the larger birds. Once or twice a year, indeed, he wanders into Oxfordshire, to meet the great flocks of linnets, six or seven hundred together, which congregate on those hills, and may be taken by dozens; and he has had ambitious thoughts of trying the great market of Covent Garden for the sale of his live stock. But in general he remains quietly at home. That nest in the Soak is too precious a deposit to leave long; and he is seldom without some especial favourite to tend and fondle. At present, the hen nightingale seems his pet; the last was a white blackbird; and once he had a whole brood of gorgeous kingfishers, seven glorious creatures, for whose behoof he took up a new trade and turned fisherman, dabbling all day with a hand-net in the waters of the Soak. It was the prettiest sight in the world to see them snatch the minnows from his hand, with a shy, mistrustful tameness, glancing their bright heads from side to side, and then darting off like bits of the rainbow. I had an entire sympathy with Robin's delight in his kingfishers. He sold them to his chief patron, Mr. Jay, a little fidgety old bachelor, with a sharp face, a hooked nose, a brown complexion, and a full suit of snuff-colour, not much un-like a bird himself; and that worthy gentleman's mis-management and a frosty winter killed the kingfishers every one. It was quite affecting to hear poor Robin talk of their death. But Robin has store of tender anecdotes; and any one who has a mind to cry over the sorrows of a widowed turtle-dove, and to hear described to the life her vermilion eye, black gorget, soft plumage, and plain-tive note, cannot do better than pay a visit to the garret in the Soak, and listen for half an hour to my friend the bird-catcher.

CHAPTER XXXIII

THE MOLE-CATCHER

THERE are no more delightful or unfailing associations than those afforded by the various operations of the husbandman, and the changes on the fair face of nature. We all know that busy troops of reapers come with the yellow corn; whilst the yellow leaf brings a no less busy train of ploughmen and seedsmen preparing the ground for fresh harvests; that woodbines and wild roses, flaunting in the blossomy hedgerows, give token of the gay bands of haymakers which enliven the meadows; and that the primroses, which begin to unfold their pale stars by the side of the green lanes, bear marks of the slow and weary female processions, the gangs of tired yet talkative bean-setters, who defile twice a day through the intricate mazes of our cross-country roads. These are general associations, as well known and as universally recognized as the union of mince-pies and Christmas. I have one, more private and peculiar, one, perhaps, the more strongly impressed on my mind because the impression may be almost confined to myself. The full flush of violets which, about the middle of March, seldom fails to perfume the whole earth, always brings to my recollection one solitary and silent coadjutor of the husbandman's labours, as unlike a violet as possible— Isaac Bint, the mole-catcher.

I used to meet him every spring, when we lived at our old house, whose park-like paddock, with its finely-clumped oaks and elms, and its richly-timbered hedgerows, edging into wild, rude, and solemn fir-plantations, dark, and rough, and hoary, formed for so many years my constant and favourite walk. Here, especially under the great horse-chestnut, and where the bank rose high and naked above the lane, crowned only with a tuft of golden broom; here the sweetest and prettiest of wild flowers, whose very name hath a charm, grew like a carpet under one's feet, enamelling the young green grass with their white and purple blossoms, and loading the air with their delicious fragrance; here I used to come almost every morning during the violet-tide; and here almost every morning I was sure to meet Isaac Bint.

I think that he fixed himself the more firmly in my memory by his singular discrepancy with the beauty and cheerfulness of the scenery and the season. Isaac is a tall, lean, gloomy personage, with whom the clock of life seems to stand still. He has looked sixty-five for these last twenty years, although his dark hair and beard, and firm, manly stride, almost contradict the evidence of his sunken cheeks and deeply-lined forehead. The stride is awful: he hath the stalk of a ghost. His whole air and demeanour savour of one that comes from underground. His appearance is 'of the earth, earthy.' His clothes, hands, and face, are of the colour of the mould in which he delves. The little round traps which hang behind him over one shoulder, as well as the strings of dead moles which embellish the other, are encrusted with dirt like a tombstone; and the staff which he plunges into the little hillocks, by which he traces the course of his small quarry, returns a hollow sound, as if tapping on the lid of a coffin. Images of the churchyard come, one does not know how, with his presence. Indeed he does officiate as assistant to the sexton in his capacity of grave-digger, chosen, as it should seem, from a natural fitness; a fine sense of congruity in good Joseph Reed, the functionary in question, who felt, without knowing why, that, of all men in the parish, Isaac Bint was best fitted to that solemn office.

His remarkable gift of silence adds much to the impression produced by his remarkable figure. I don't think that I ever heard him speak three words in my life. An approach of that bony hand to that earthy leather cap was the greatest effort of courtesy that my daily salutations could extort from him. For this silence Isaac has good reasons. He hath a reputation to support. His words are too precious to be wasted. Our mole-catcher, ragged as he looks, is the wise man of the village, the oracle of the village inn, foresees the weather, charms away agues, tells fortunes by the stars, and writes notes upon the almanac—turning and twisting about the predictions after a fashion so ingenious that it is a moot point which is oftenest wrong—Isaac Bint, or Francis Moore. In one eminent instance our friend was, however, eminently right. He had the good luck to prophesy, before sundry witnesses—some of them sober—in the tap-room of the 'Bell'; he then sitting, pipe in mouth, on the settle at the right-hand side of the fire, whilst Jacob Frost occupied the left—he had the good fortune to foretell, on New Year's Day, 1812, the downfall of Napoleon Bonaparte—a piece of soothsayership which has established his reputation, and dumbfounded all doubters and cavillers ever since; but which would certainly have been more striking if he had not annually uttered the same prediction, from the same place, from the time that the aforesaid Napoleon became first consul. But this small circumstance is entirely overlooked by Isaac and his admirers, and they believe in him, and he believes in the stars, more firmly than ever.

Our mole-catcher is, as might be conjectured, an old bachelor. Your married man hath more of this world about him—is less, so to say, planet-struck. A thorough old bachelor is Isaac, a contemner and maligner of the sex, a complete and decided woman-hater. Female frailty is the only subject on which he hath ever been known to dilate; he will not even charm away their agues, or tell their fortunes, and, indeed, holds them to be unworthy the notice of the stars.

No woman contaminates his household. He lives on the edge of a pretty bit of woodland scenery, called the Penge, in a snug cottage of two rooms, of his own building, surrounded by a garden cribbed from the waste, well fenced with quickset, and well stocked with fruit-trees, herbs, and flowers. One large apple-tree extends over the roof—a pretty bit of colour when in blossom, contrasted with the thatch of the little dwelling, and relieved by the dark wood behind. Although the owner be solitary, his demesne is sufficiently populous. A long row of beehives extends along the warmest side of the garden—for Isaac's honey is celebrated far and near; a pig occupies a commodious sty at one corner; and large flocks of ducks and geese (for which the Penge, whose glades are intersected by water,

is famous) are generally waiting round a back gate leading
to a spacious shed, far larger than Isaac's own cottage,
which serves for their feeding- and roosting-place. The
great tameness of all these creatures—for the ducks and
geese flutter round him the moment he approaches, and the
very pig follows him like a dog—gives no equivocal testimony of the kindness of our mole-catcher's nature. A
circumstance of recent occurrence puts his humanity
beyond doubt.

Amongst the probable causes of Isaac's dislike to women
may be reckoned the fact of his living in a female neighbourhood (for the Penge is almost peopled with duck-
rearers and goose-crammers of the duck and goose gender),
and being himself exceedingly unpopular amongst the fair
poultry-feeders of that watery vicinity. He beat them
at their own weapons; produced at Midsummer geese fit
for Michaelmas; and raised ducks so precocious that the
gardeners complained of them as forerunning their vegetable
accompaniments; 'panting *peas* toiled after them in vain.'
In short, the naiads of the Penge had the mortification to
find themselves driven out of B—— market by an interloper, and that interloper a man, who had no manner of
right to possess any skill in an accomplishment so exclusively feminine as duck-rearing; and being no ways
inferior in another female accomplishment, called scolding,
to their sister-nymphs of Billingsgate, they set up a clamour
and a cackle which might rival the din of their own gooseries
at feeding-time, and would inevitably have frightened from
the field any competitor less impenetrable than our hero.
But Isaac is not a man to shrink from so small an evil as
female objurgation. He stalked through it all in mute
disdain—looking now at his mole-traps, and now at the
stars, pretending not to hear, and very probably not hearing. At first this scorn, more provoking than any retort,
only excited his enemies to fresh attacks; but one cannot be
always answering another person's silence. The flame which
had blazed so fiercely at last burnt itself out, and peace
reigned once more in the green alleys of Penge Wood.

One, however, of his adversaries—his nearest neighbour—
still remained unsilenced.

Margery Grover was a very old and poor woman, whom

age and disease had bent almost to the earth; shaken by palsy, pinched by penury, and soured by misfortune—a moving bundle of misery and rags. Two centuries ago she would have been burnt for a witch; now she starved and grumbled on the parish allowance; trying to eke out a scanty subsistence by the dubious profits gained from the produce of two geese and a lame gander, once the unmolested tenants of a greenish pool, situate right between her dwelling and Isaac's, but whose watery dominion had been invaded by his flourishing colony.

This was the cause of feud; and although Isaac would willingly, from a mingled sense of justice and of pity, have yielded the point to the poor old creature, especially as ponds are there almost as plentiful as blackberries, yet it was not so easy to control the habits and inclinations of their feathered subjects, who all perversely fancied that particular pool; and various accidents and skirmishes occurred, in which the ill-fed and weak birds of Margery had generally the worst of the fray. One of her early goslings was drowned—an accident which may happen even to waterfowl; and her lame gander, a sort of pet with the poor old woman, injured in his well leg; and Margery vented curses as bitter as those of Sycorax; and Isaac, certainly the most superstitious personage in the parish—the most thorough believer in his own gifts and predictions—was fain to nail a horseshoe on his door for the defence of his property, and to wear one of his own ague charms about his neck for his personal protection.

Poor old Margery! A hard winter came; and the feeble, tottering creature shook in the frosty air like an aspen leaf; and the hovel in which she dwelt—for nothing could prevail on her to try the shelter of the workhouse—shook like herself at every blast. She was not quite alone either in the world or in her poor hut: husband, children, and grandchildren had passed away; but one young and innocent being, a great-grandson, the last of her descendants, remained, a helpless dependant on one almost as helpless as himself.

Little Harry Grover was a shrunken, stunted boy of five years old; tattered and squalid, like his grandam, and, at first sight, presented almost as miserable a specimen of childhood as Margery herself did of age. There was even a

likeness between them; although the fierce blue eye of
Margery had, in the boy, a mild appealing look, which
entirely changed the whole expression of the countenance.
A gentle and a peaceful boy was Harry, and, above all, a
useful. It was wonderful how many ears of corn in the
autumn, and sticks in the winter, his little hands could
pick up! how well he could make a fire, and boil the kettle,
and sweep the hearth, and cram the goslings! Never was a
handier boy or a trustier; and when the united effects of
cold, and age, and rheumatism confined poor Margery to her
poor bed, the child continued to perform his accustomed
offices; fetching the money from the vestry, buying the loaf
at the baker's, keeping house, and nursing the sick woman,
with a kindness and thoughtfulness which none but those
who know the careful ways to which necessity trains
cottage children would deem credible; and Margery, a
woman of strong passions, strong prejudices, and strong
affections, who had lived in and for the desolate boy, felt
the approach of death embittered by the certainty that the
workhouse, always the scene of her dread and loathing,
would be the only refuge for the poor orphan.

Death, however, came on visibly and rapidly; and she
sent for the overseer to beseech him to put Harry to board
in some decent cottage; she could not die in peace until he
had promised; the fear of the innocent child's being con-
taminated by wicked boys and godless women preyed upon
her soul; she implored, she conjured. The overseer, a kind
but timid man, hesitated, and was beginning a puzzled
speech about the bench and the vestry, when another voice
was heard from the door of the cottage.

'Margery,' said our friend Isaac, 'will you trust Harry to
me? I am a poor man, to be sure; but, between earning
and saving, there'll be enough for me and little Harry. 'Tis as
good a boy as ever lived, and I'll try to keep him so. Trust
him to me, and I'll be a father to him. I can't say more.'

'God bless thee, Isaac Bint! God bless thee!' was all
poor Margery could reply.

They were the last words she ever spoke. And little
Harry is living with our good mole-catcher, and is growing
plump and rosy; and Margery's other pet, the lame gander,
lives and thrives with them too.

CHAPTER XXXIV

COTTAGE NAMES

'Why Lonicera wilt thou name thy child?'
I ask'd the gardener's wife in accents mild.
'We have a right,' replied the sturdy dame,
And Lonicera was the infant's name.

CRABBE.

A commodity of good names.—SHAKESPEARE.

FROM the time of Goldsmith down to the present day fine names have been the ridicule of comic authors, and the aversion of sensible people, notwithstanding which the evil has increased almost in proportion to its reprobation. Miss Clementina Wilhelmina Stubbs was but a type of the Julias, the Isabels, and the Helens of this accomplished age. I should not, however, so much mind if this folly were comprised in that domain of cold gentility to which affectation usually confines itself. One does not regard seeing Miss Arabella seated at the piano, or her little sister Leonora tottling across the carpet to show her new pink shoes. That is in the usual course of events. But the fashion spreads deeper and wider; the village is infected, and the village green; Amelias and Claras sweep your rooms and cook your dinners, gentle Sophias milk your cows, and if you ask a pretty smiling girl at a cottage door to tell you her name, the rosy lips lisp out Caroline.[1] It was but the other day that I went into a neighbour's to procure a messenger, and found the errand disputed by a gentle Georgina without a shoe, and a fair Augusta with half a frock. Now this is a sad thing. One looks upon cottage names as a part of cottage furniture, of the costume, and is as much discomposed by the change as a painter of interiors would be who should find a Grecian couch instead of an oaken settle by the

---

[1] A great number of children, amongst the lower orders, are Carolines. That does not, however, wholly proceed from a love of the appellation; though I believe that a Queen Margery or a Queen Sarah would have had fewer namesakes. A clergyman in my neighbourhood used to mistake the sound, and christen the babies Catherine—a wise error, for Kate is a noble abbreviation.

side of the wide open hearth. In fine houses fine names do
not signify; though I would humbly suggest to godfathers
and godmothers, papas, mammas, maiden aunts, nurses, and
gossips in general, the unconscious injury that they are
doing to novelists, poets, dramatic writers, and the whole
fraternity of authors, by trespassing on their (nominal)
property, infringing their patent, encroaching on their
privilege, underselling their stock-in-trade, depreciating
their currency, and finally robbing poor heroes and heroines
of their solitary possession, the only thing they can call
their own. Shakespeare has an admonition much to the purpose: 'he who filches from me my *good name*,' and so forth.
Did they never hear *that*? never see *Othello*? never read
Elegant Extracts? never learn the speech by rote out of En-
field's *Speaker*? If they did, I must say the lesson has been
as completely thrown away as lessons of morality commonly
are. Sponsors in these days think no more harm of 'filching a name' than a sparrow does of robbing a cherry-tree.

This, however, is an affair of conscience or of taste, and
conscience and taste are delicate points to meddle with,
especially the latter. People will please their fancies, and
every lady has her favourite names. I myself have several,
and they are mostly short and simple. Jane, that queenly
name! Jane Seymour, Jane Grey, 'the noble Jane de
Montfort'; Anne, to which Lady seems to belong as of
right—a late celebrated Scottish duke is said to have caused
an illegitimate daughter to be so baptized, Lady Anne, and
my friend Allan Cunningham's beautiful ballad has joined
the name and the title still more inseparably; Mary, which
is as common as a white violet and like that has something
indestructibly sweet and simple, and fit for all wear, high or
low, suits the cottage or the palace, the garden or the field
the pretty or the ugly, the old or the young; Margaret,
Marguerite—the pearl! the daisy! Oh! name of romance
and of minstrelsy, which brings the days of chivalry to
mind, and the worship of flowers and of ladies fair; Emily,
in which all womanly sweetness seems bound up—perhaps
this is the effect of the association of ideas [1]—I know so

---

[1] There is another association which cannot be forgotten in speaking of
Emily. It belongs to *Palamon and Arcite*, that most fortunate of stories,
which comes to us consecrated by the genius of Chaucer and of Dryden,
of Fletcher and of Shakespeare.

many charming Emilys; and Susan, the sprightly, the
gentle, the home-loving, the kind—association again! But
certainly there are some names which seem to belong to
particular classes of character, to form the mind, and even
to influence the destiny: Louisa, now—is not your Louisa
necessarily a die-away damsel, who reads novels, and holds
her head on one side, languishing and given to love? Is not
Lucy a pretty soubrette, a wearer of cast gowns and cast
smiles, smart and coquettish? Must not Emma, as a matter
of course, prove epistolary, if only for the sake of her signature? And is there not great danger that Laura may go
a step farther—write poetry and publish? Oh, beware,
dear godmammas, when you call an innocent baby after
Petrarch's muse! Think of the peril! Beware!

Next to names simple in themselves, those which fall
easily into diminutives seem to me most desirable. All
abbreviations are pretty—Lizzy, Bessy, Sophy, Fanny—
the prettiest of all! There is something so familiar, so
homelike, so affectionate in the sound, it seems to tell in
one short word a story of family love, to vouch for the
amiableness of both parties. I never thought one of the
most brilliant and elegant women in England quite so
charming as she really is till I heard her call her younger
sister 'Annie.' It seemed to remove at once the almost
repellent quality which belongs to extreme polish—gave a
genial warmth to her brightness, became her like a smile.
There was a tenderness in the voice, too, a delay, a dwelling
on the double consonant, giving to English something of
the charm of Italian pronunciation, which I have noticed
only in two persons, who are, I think, the most graceful
speakers and readers of my acquaintance. 'Annie!' If
she had called her sister Anna Maria according to the
register, I should have admired, and feared, and shunned
her to my dying day. That little word made us friends
immediately. I like manly abbreviations too—who does
not?—they say so much for character. You may know what
one man thinks of another by his manner of calling him.
Thomas and James and Richard and William are stupid
young gentlemen; Tom and Jem and Dick and Will are
fine spirited fellows. Henry now, what a soft swain your
Henry is, the proper theme of gentle poesy; a name to fall

in love withal; devoted at the font to song and sonnet, and
the tender passion; a baptized inamorato; a christened
hero. Call him Harry, and see how you ameliorate his
condition. The man is free again, turned out of song and
sonnet and romance and young ladies' hearts. Shakespeare
understood this well when he wrote of Prince Hal and Harry
Hotspur. To have called them Henry would have spoiled
both characters. George and Charles are unlucky in this
respect. They have no diminutives, and what mouthfuls
of monosyllables they are! Names royal too, and therefore
unshortened. A king must be of a very rare class who
should afford to be called by shorthand—very popular to
tempt the rogues, well conditioned to endure it, wise and
strong to afford it. Our Harry the Fifth, the conqueror of
Agincourt, might and did; and the French Henri Quatre;
and now and then a usurper. Niccola Rienzi, Oliver
Cromwell, and Napoleon, the noblest of names, have all
undergone such transformation; and indeed the Roman
tribune, the least known but not perhaps the least remarkable of the three; he who, born of an innkeeper and a washerwoman, restored for a while the free republic of Rome;
the friend of Petrarch, the arbiter of princes, the summoner
of emperors, the arraigner of popes—is scarcely known even
in the grave page of history by any other appellation
than that of Cola Rienzi—as who should say *Nick*.

I have said that names sometimes form the character.
Sometimes, on the other hand, they are like dreams, and
become true by contraries; especially if you christen after
the virtues. Thus the wildest flirt of my acquaintance
happens to be a Miss Prudentia—a second sister, too, whose
elder is not likely to marry, so that the misnomer is palpable;
and the greatest scold I ever encountered, the errantest
virago, was a Mrs. Patience. The Graces are usually
awkward gawkies, and the Belles all through the alphabet,
from Annabelle downward, are a generation of frights.
The Floras are sure to be pale puny girls, and the Roses are
apt to wither on the virgin stalk. Call a boy after some
distinguished character, and the contradiction grows still
more glaring. Your Foxes and Hampdens and Sidneys
range themselves on the ministerial benches, your Pitts
and Melvilles turn out rank radicals, your Andrew Marvells

take bribes, and your Nelsons run away. There is a fatality in those Christian surnames, those baptized heathens; they are sure never to fit, never run well with other names. In the case of females especially there is a double danger; even if they seem to march evenly at first, see how they end. The most remarkable instance of this acquired incongruity I ever knew befell a fair Highlander, one of my schoolfellows. Her mother, claiming to be sprung from the Bruce family, would call her daughter after good King Robert, and nothing could be better matched than her two noble Scottish names, Bruce Campbell: they suited her like her tartan dress. She was a tall, graceful, blue-eyed girl, with high spirits and some pride, an air compounded of the palace and the mountain, a sort of wild royalty, and a step that puzzled alike our French dancing-master and our English drill-sergeant—it was so unlike what either of them taught, so un-French, so un-English, and yet so bounding and free. She left school, and for some years I heard nothing more of her than that she was happily married. Last summer I had the pleasure of meeting a cousin of hers (as near, I should think, as within the eighth degree), and began immediately to inquire for my fair friend. 'I understand,' said I, 'that she married early and well?' 'Yes, very,' was the reply; 'but she had the misfortune to lose Mr. Smith in the second year of their nuptials. She is now, however, remarried to a Mr. Brown.' I heard no more! I was petrified. Bruce Smith! Imagine such a conjunction! And now Bruce Brown! Fancy that! There is an 'apt alliteration' for you! And, even if she should take refuge in initials, think of B. B.! 'P. P., clerk of this parish,' has the advantage both in look and sound. Oh, your proper names are dangerous! It is the practice of the Americans, and with them it may perhaps be politic and patriotic to diffuse and perpetuate the memory of their Washingtons and Jeffersons amongst the descendants of the people whom they freed, to give the new generation a sort of personal interest in their fame. But why should we adopt the fashion? And why should it spread, as spread it does? Those papas and mammas who labour under the misfortune of a plebeian surname do the best to lighten the calamity to their offspring by a harmonious and dignified prenomen, sometimes taken from friends or acquaintance chosen as sponsors for the good gift of a seemly appellation; sometimes culled from history; sometimes from that pseudo-history called a novel; sometimes from the Peerage; sometimes from the Racing Calendar, which, by the by, does not fail to return the compliment. One ingenious gentleman, in a northern county, even christened his eldest hope after the village in which he was born—Allonby of Allonby! How well it looks! and what a pity that the wretched little word 'Short' should have a right to intrude! Allonby Short: 'oh, what a falling off was there!' If the son should have half his father's genius, he will get an Act of Parliament and discard it altogether.

The prefixing of a little miserable name to another of the same class is also exceedingly fashionable amongst our parvenus. They seem to think that in names, as in figures, value increases tenfold by the addition of a cipher. Hence the unnatural and portentous union of hideous mono-syllables on name-tickets and door-plates, where two 'low words oft creep in one dull line.' Hence your White Sharps, your Ford Greens, your Hall Gills, and other appellations of the same calibre, which stare you in the face go where you will, and are clung to with a jealous tenacity of which the Percys and Howards and Cavendishes (for whom one name is enough) never dream. Hence all varieties in spelling, devices to turn the vulgar to the genteel by the mere change of a letter: [1] hence the De's and the Fitz's, by which good common English is transmogrified into bad French, to be mispronounced by the ignorant and laughed at by the wise—the deserved and inevitable fate of pretension, ridiculous in everything, and most of all in cottage names.

[1] It is a pity that the hero of Mr. Lamb's excellent farce, *Mr. H.*, did not possess a little of this sort of ingenuity. I am convinced that the addition or omission of a few letters, or even the transposition, the making an ana-gram of the word, or some such quip or quiddity, would have converted 'Hog's-flesh' into a very respectable appellation. Did not Miss Hannah K——, for instance, make herself at once genteel and happy by merely striking out the first letter and the last—vile useless aspirates? And did not Martha D—— become a fashionable lady at a stroke by one bold erratum, 'For Martha read Matilda,' in the first leaf of that domestic register, the family Bible? There is nothing so ingenious under the sun as your genuine name-coiner! A forger by profession is less dexterous, a coat-of-arms maker less imaginative. It is the very triumph of invention.

CHAPTER XXXV

THE SHAW

Sept. 9th. A bright sunshiny afternoon. What a comfort it is to get out again—to see once more that rarity of rarities, a fine day! We English people are accused of talking overmuch of the weather; but the weather, this summer, has forced people to talk of it. 'Summer,' did I say? Oh, season most unworthy of that sweet, sunny name! Season of coldness and cloudiness, of gloom and rain! A worse November!—for in November the days are short; and shut up in a warm room, lighted by that household sun, a lamp, one feels through the long evenings comfortably independent of the out-of-door tempests. But though we may have, and did have, fires all through the dog-days, there is no shutting out daylight; and sixteen hours of rain, pattering against the windows and dripping from the eaves—sixteen hours of rain, not merely audible but visible, for seven days in the week—would be enough to exhaust the patience of Job or Grizel; especially if Job were a farmer, and Grizel a country gentlewoman. Never was known such a season! Hay swimming, cattle drowning, fruit rotting, corn spoiling! and that naughty river, the Loddon, who never can take Puff's advice and 'keep between its banks,' running about the country, fields, roads, gardens and houses, like mad! The weather would be talked of. Indeed, it was not easy to talk of anything else. A friend of mine having occasion to write me a letter, thought it worth abusing in rhyme, and bepommelled it through three pages of *Bath Guide* verse; of which I subjoin a specimen:

> Aquarius surely *reigns* over the world,
> And of late he his water-pot strangely has twirled;
> Or he's taken a colander up by mistake,
> And unceasingly dips it in some mighty lake:
> Though it is not in Lethe—for who can forget
> The annoyance of getting most thoroughly wet?

It must be in the river called Styx, I declare,
For the moment it drizzles it makes the men swear.
'It did rain to-morrow,' is growing good grammar;
Vauxhall and camp-stools have been brought to the hammer;
A pony-gondola is all I can keep,
And I use my umbrella and pattens in sleep:
Row out of my window, whene'er 'tis my whim
To visit a friend, and just ask, 'Can you swim?'

So far my friend.[1]   In short, whether in prose or in verse,
everybody railed at the weather.   But this is over now.
The sun has come to dry the world; mud is turned into
dust; rivers have retreated to their proper limits; farmers
have left off grumbling; and we are about to take a walk, as
usual, as far as the Shaw, a pretty wood about a mile off.
But one of our companions being a stranger to the gentle
reader, we must do him the honour of an introduction.

Dogs, when they are sure of having their own way, have
sometimes ways as odd as those of the unfurred, unfeathered
animals who walk on two legs, and talk, and are called
rational.   My beautiful white greyhound, Mayflower,[2] for
instance, is as whimsical as the finest lady in the land.
Amongst her other fancies, she has taken a violent affection for a most hideous stray dog, who made his appearance
here about six months ago, and contrived to pick up a
living in the village, one can hardly tell how.   Now appealing to the charity of old Rachel Strong, the laundress—a
dog-lover by profession; now winning a meal from the
light-footed and open-hearted lasses at the 'Rose'; now
standing on his hind-legs, to extort by sheer beggary a
scanty morsel from some pair of 'drouthy cronies,' or

---

[1] This friend of mine is a person of great quickness and talent, who, if she
were not a beauty and a woman of fortune—that is to say, if she were
prompted by either of those two powerful stimuli, want of money or want of
admiration, to take due pains—would inevitably become a clever writer.
As it is, her notes and *jeux d'esprit*, struck off *à trait de plume*, have great
point and neatness.   Take the following billet, which formed the label to a
closed basket, containing the ponderous present alluded to, last Michaelmas
Day:

To Miss M——
'When this you see
Remember me,'
Was long a phrase in use;
And so I send
To you, dear friend,
My proxy.   'What?'—A goose!

[2] Dead, alas, since this was written!

solitary drover, discussing his dinner or supper on the ale-house bench; now catching a mouthful, flung to him in pure contempt by some scornful gentleman of the shoulder-knot, mounted on his throne, the coach-box, whose notice he had attracted by dint of ugliness; now sharing the commons of Master Keep the shoemaker's pigs; now succeeding to the reversion of the well-gnawed bone of Master Brown the shopkeeper's fierce house-dog; now filching the skim milk of Dame Wheeler's cat—spit at by the cat; worried by the mastiff; chased by the pigs; screamed at by the dame; stormed at by the shoemaker; flogged by the shopkeeper; teased by all the children, and scouted by all the animals of the parish, but yet living through his griefs, and bearing them patiently, 'for sufferance is the badge of all his tribe' —and even seeming to find, in an occasional full meal, or a gleam of sunshine, or a wisp of dry straw on which to repose his sorry carcass, some comfort in his disconsolate condition.

In this plight was he found by May, the most high-blooded and aristocratic of greyhounds; and from this plight did May rescue him—invited him into her territory, the stable; resisted all attempts to turn him out; reinstated him there, in spite of maid and boy, and mistress and master; wore out everybody's opposition, by the activity of her protection and the pertinacity of her self-will; made him sharer of her bed and of her mess; and, finally, established him as one of the family as firmly as herself.

Dash—for he has even won himself a name amongst us; before, he was anonymous—Dash is a sort of a kind of a spaniel; at least there is in his mongrel composition some sign of that beautiful race. Besides his ugliness, which is of the worst sort—that is to say, the shabbiest—he has a limp on one leg that gives a peculiarly one-sided awkward-ness to his gait; but independently of his great merit in being May's pet, he has other merits which serve to account for that phenomenon, being, beyond all comparison, the most faithful, attached, and affectionate animal that I have ever known; and that is saying much. He seems to think it necessary to atone for his ugliness by extra good conduct, and does so dance on his lame leg, and so wag his scrubby tail, that it does any one who has a taste for happi-ness good to look at him—so that he may now be said to

stand on his own footing. We are all rather ashamed of
him when strangers come in the way, and think it necessary
to explain that he is May's pet; but amongst ourselves, and
those who are used to his appearance, he has reached the
point of favouritism in his own person. I have, in common
with wiser women, the feminine weakness of loving whatever loves me—and, therefore, I like Dash. His master
has found out that he is a capital finder, and in spite of his
lameness will hunt a field or beat a cover with any spaniel
in England—and, therefore, *he* likes Dash. The boy has
fought a battle, in defence of his beauty, with another boy,
bigger than himself, and beat his opponent most handsomely
—and, therefore, *he* likes Dash; and the maids like him,
or pretend to like him, because we do—as is the fashion of
that pliant and imitative class. And now Dash and May
follow us everywhere, and are going with us to the Shaw,
as I said before—or rather to the cottage by the Shaw, to
bespeak milk and butter of our little dairy-woman, Hannah
Bint; a housewifely occupation, to which we owe some of
our pleasantest rambles.

And now we pass the sunny, dusty village street—who
would have thought, a month ago, that we should complain
of sun and dust again!—and turn the corner where the two
great oaks hang so beautifully over the clear deep pond,
mixing their cold green shadows with the bright blue sky,
and the white clouds that flit over it: and loiter at the
wheeler's shop, always picturesque, with its tools, and its
work, and its materials, all so various in form, and so
harmonious in colour; and its noisy, merry workmen,
hammering and singing, and making a various harmony
also. The shop is rather empty to-day, for its usual inmates
are busy on the green beyond the pond—one set building
a cart, another painting a wagon. And then we leave the
village quite behind, and proceed slowly up the cool, quiet
lane, between tall hedgerows of the darkest verdure, over-
shadowing banks green and fresh as an emerald.

Not so quick as I expected, though—for they are shooting
here to-day, as Dash and I have both discovered; he with
great delight, for a gun to him is as a trumpet to a war-
horse; I with no less annoyance, for I don't think that a
partridge itself, barring the accident of being killed, can

be more startled than I at that abominable explosion. Dash has certainly better blood in his veins than any one would guess to look at him. He even shows some inclination to elope into the fields, in pursuit of those noisy iniquities. But he is an orderly person after all, and a word has checked him.

Ah! here is a shriller din mingling with the small artillery —a shriller and more continuous. We are not yet arrived within sight of Master Weston's cottage, snugly hidden behind a clump of elms; but we are in full hearing of Dame Weston's tongue, raised as usual to scolding-pitch. The Westons are new arrivals in our neighbourhood, and the first thing heard of them was a complaint from the wife to our magistrate of her husband's beating her: it was a regular charge of assault—an information in full form. A most piteous case did Dame Weston make of it, softening her voice for the nonce into a shrill, tremulous whine, and exciting the mingled pity and anger—pity towards herself, anger towards her husband—of the whole female world, pitiful and indignant as the female world is wont to be on such occasions. Every woman in the parish railed at Master Weston; and poor Master Weston was summoned to attend the bench on the ensuing Saturday, and answer the charge; and such was the clamour abroad and at home, that the unlucky culprit, terrified at the sound of a warrant and a constable, ran away, and was not heard of for a fortnight.

At the end of that time he was discovered, and brought to the bench; and Dame Weston again told her story, and, as before, on the full cry. She had no witnesses, and the bruises of which she made complaint had disappeared, and there were no women present to make common cause with the sex. Still, however, the general feeling was against Master Weston; and it would have gone hard with him when he was called in, if a most unexpected witness had not risen up in his favour. His wife had brought in her arms a little girl about eighteen months old, partly perhaps to move compassion in her favour; for a woman with a child in her arms is always an object that excites kind feelings. The little girl had looked shy and frightened, and had been as quiet as a lamb during her mother's examination; but she no sooner saw her father, from whom she had been a fortnight separated, than she clapped her hands, and laughed, and cried, 'Daddy! daddy!' and sprang into his arms, and hung round his neck, and covered him with kisses, again shouting, 'Daddy, come home! daddy! daddy!'—and finally nestled her little head in his bosom, with a fullness of contentment, an assurance of tenderness and protection such as no wife-beating tyrant ever did inspire, or ever could inspire, since the days of King Solomon. Our magistrates acted in the very spirit of the Jewish monarch: they accepted the evidence of nature, and dismissed the complaint. And subsequent events have fully justified their decision; Mistress Weston proving not only renowned for the feminine accomplishment of scolding (tongue-banging, it is called in our parts, a compound word which deserves to be Greek), but is actually herself addicted to administering the conjugal discipline, the infliction of which she was pleased to impute to her luckless husband.

Now we cross the stile, and walk up the fields to the Shaw. How beautifully green this pasture looks! and how finely the evening sun glances between the boles of that clump of trees, beech, and ash, and aspen! and how sweet the hedgerows are with woodbine and wild scabious, or, as the country people call it, the gipsy-rose! Here is little Dolly Weston, the unconscious witness, with cheeks as red as a real rose, tottering up the path to meet her father. And here is the carroty-polled urchin, George Coper, returning from work, and singing, *Home! Sweet Home!* at the top of his voice; and then, when the notes prove too high for him, continuing the air in a whistle, until he has turned the impassable corner; then taking up again the song and the words, *Home! Sweet Home!* and looking as if he felt their full import, ploughboy though he be. And so he does; for he is one of a large, an honest, a kind, and an industrious family, where all goes well, and where the poor ploughboy is sure of finding cheerful faces and coarse comforts—all that he has learned to desire. Oh, to be as cheaply and as thoroughly contented as George Coper! All his luxuries, a cricket match!—all his wants satisfied in 'home! sweet home!'

Nothing but noises to-day! They are clearing Farmer Brooke's great bean-field, and crying the *Harvest Home!*

in a chorus before which all other sounds—the song, the scolding, the gunnery—fade away, and become faint echoes. A pleasant noise is that! though, for one's ears' sake, one makes some haste to get away from it. And here, in happy time, is that pretty wood, the Shaw, with its broad pathway, its tangled dingles, its nuts, and its honeysuckles—and, carrying away a faggot of those sweetest flowers, we reach Hannah Bint's; of whom, and of whose doings, we shall say more another time.

NOTE.—Poor Dash is also dead. We did not keep him long, indeed I believe that he died of the transition from starvation to good feed, as dangerous to a dog's stomach, and to most stomachs, as the less agreeable change from good feed to starvation. He has been succeeded in place and favour by another Dash, not less amiable in demeanour, and far more creditable in appearance, bearing no small resemblance to the pet spaniel of my friend Master Dinely, he who stole the bone from the magpies, and who figures as the first Dash of this volume. Let not the unwary reader opine, that in assigning the same name to three several individuals I am acting as a humble imitator of the inimitable writer who has given immortality to the Peppers and the Mustards, on the one hand; or showing a poverty of invention or a want of acquaintance with the bead-roll of canine appellations, on the other. I merely, with my usual scrupulous fidelity, take the names as I find them. The fact is that half the handsome spaniels in England are called Dash, just as half the tall footmen are called Thomas. The name belongs to the species. Sitting in an open carriage one day last summer at the door of a farm-house where my father had some business, I saw a noble and beautiful animal of this kind lying in great state and laziness on the steps, and felt an immediate desire to make acquaintance with him. My father, who had had the same fancy, had patted him, and called him 'poor fellow' in passing, without eliciting the smallest notice in return. 'Dash!' cried I at a venture; 'good Dash! noble Dash!' and up he started in a moment, making but one spring from the door into the gig. Of course I was right in my guess. The gentleman's name was Dash.

CHAPTER XXXVI

HANNAH BINT

THE Shaw, leading to Hannah Bint's habitation, is, as I perhaps have said before, a very pretty mixture of wood and coppice; that is to say, a track of thirty or forty acres covered with fine growing timber—ash, and oak, and elm— very regularly planted; and interspersed here and there with large patches of underwood, hazel, maple, birch, holly, and hawthorn, woven into almost impenetrable thickets by long wreaths of the bramble, the bryony, and the brier-rose, or by the pliant and twisting garlands of the wild honey-suckle. In other parts, the Shaw is quite clear of its bosky undergrowth, and clothed only with large beds of feathery fern, or carpets of flowers, primroses, orchises, cowslips, ground-ivy, crane's-bill, cotton-grass, Solomon's seal, and forget-me-not, crowded together with a profusion and brilliancy of colour such as I have rarely seen equalled even in a garden. Here the wild hyacinth really enamels the ground with its fresh and lovely purple; there,

> On aged roots, with bright green mosses clad,
> Dwells the wood-sorrel, with its bright thin leaves
> Heart-shaped and triply folded, and its root
> Creeping like beaded coral; whilst around
> Flourish the copse's pride, anemones,
> With rays like golden studs on ivory laid
> Most delicate; but touched with purple clouds,
> Fit crown for April's fair but changeful brow.

The variety is much greater than I have enumerated; for the ground is so unequal, now swelling in gentle ascents, now dimpling into dells and hollows, and the soil so different in different parts, that the sylvan flora is unusually extensive and complete.

The season is, however, now too late for this floweriness; and except the tufted woodbines, which have continued in bloom during the whole of this lovely autumn, and some

lingering garlands of the purple wild vetch, wreathing
round the thickets, and uniting with the ruddy leaves of the
bramble, and the pale festoons of the bryony, there is little
to call one's attention from the grander beauties of the trees
—the sycamore, its broad leaves already spotted; the oak,
heavy with acorns; and the delicate, shining rind of the
weeping birch, 'the lady of the woods,' thrown out in strong
relief from a background of holly and hawthorn, each
studded with coral berries, and backed with old beeches,
beginning to assume the rich tawny hue which makes them
perhaps the most picturesque of autumnal trees, as the
transparent freshness of their young foliage is undoubtedly
the choicest ornament of the forest in spring.

A sudden turn round one of these magnificent beeches
brings us to the boundary of the Shaw, and leaning upon
a rude gate, we look over an open space of about ten acres
of ground, still more varied and broken than that which we
have passed, and surrounded on all sides by thick woodland.
As a piece of colour, nothing can be well finer. The ruddy
glow of the heath - flower contrasting, on the one hand,
with the golden-blossomed furze; on the other, with a
patch of buckwheat, of which the bloom is not past,
although the grain be ripening—the beautiful buckwheat,
whose transparent leaves and stalks are so brightly tinged
with vermilion, while the delicate pink-white of the flower,
a paler persicaria, has a feathery fall, at once so rich and so
graceful, and a fresh and reviving odour, like that of birch-
trees in the dew of a May evening. The bank that sur-
mounts this attempt at cultivation is crowned with the
late foxglove and the stately mullein; the pasture, of
which so great a part of the waste consists, looks as green as
an emerald; a clear pond, with the bright sky reflected in it,
lets light into the picture; the white cottage of the keeper
peeps from the opposite coppice; and the vine-covered
dwelling of Hannah Bint rises from amidst the pretty
garden, which lies bathed in the sunshine around it.

The living and moving accessories are all in keeping with
the cheerfulness and repose of the landscape. Hannah's
cow grazing quietly beside the keeper's pony; a brace of fat
pointer puppies holding amicable intercourse with a litter
of young pigs; ducks, geese, cocks, hens, and chickens

scattered over the turf; Hannah herself sallying forth from the cottage door, with her milk bucket in her hand, and her little brother following with the milking-stool.

My friend, Hannah Bint, is by no means an ordinary person. Her father, Jack Bint (for in all his life he never arrived at the dignity of being called John—indeed in our parts he was commonly known by the cognomen of London Jack), was a drover of high repute in his profession. No man between Salisbury Plain and Smithfield was thought to conduct a flock of sheep so skilfully through all the difficulties of lanes and commons, streets and high roads, as Jack Bint, aided by Jack Bint's famous dog, Watch; for Watch's rough, honest face, black, with a little white about the muzzle, and one white ear, was as well known at fairs and markets as his master's equally honest and weather-beaten visage. Lucky was the dealer that could secure their services: Watch being renowned for keeping a flock together better than any shepherd's dog on the road; Jack, for delivering them more punctually, and in better condition. No man had a more thorough knowledge of the proper night stations, where good feed might be procured for his charge, and good liquor for Watch and himself; Watch, like other sheep-dogs, being accustomed to live chiefly on bread and beer. His master, although not averse to a pot of good double X, preferred gin; and they who plod slowly along, through wet and weary days, in frost and in fog, have undoubtedly a stronger temptation to indulge in that cordial and reviving stimulus than we water-drinkers, sitting in warm and comfortable rooms, can readily imagine. For certain, our drover could never resist the gentle seduction of the gin-bottle, and being of a free, merry, jovial temperament, one of those persons commonly called good fellows, who like to see others happy in the same way with themselves, he was apt to circulate it at his own expense, to the great improvement of his popularity, and the great detriment of his finances.

All this did vastly well whilst his earnings continued proportionate to his spendings, and the little family at home were comfortably supported by his industry; but when a rheumatic fever came on, one hard winter, and finally settled in his limbs, reducing the most active and hardy man in the parish to the state of a confirmed cripple, then his reckless improvidence stared him in the face; and poor Jack, a thoughtless, but kind creature, and a most affectionate father, looked at his three motherless children with the acute misery of a parent who has brought those whom he loves best in the world to abject destitution. He found help, where he probably least expected it, in the sense and spirit of his young daughter, a girl of twelve years old.

Hannah was the eldest of the family, and had, ever since her mother's death, which event had occurred two or three years before, been accustomed to take the direction of their domestic concerns, to manage her two brothers, to feed the pigs and the poultry, and to keep house during the almost constant absence of her father. She was a quick, clever lass, of a high spirit, a firm temper, some pride, and a horror of accepting parochial relief, which is every day becoming rarer amongst the peasantry, but which forms the surest safeguard to the sturdy independence of the English character. Our little damsel possessed this quality in perfection; and when her father talked of giving up their comfortable cottage, and removing to the workhouse, whilst she and her brothers must go to service, Hannah formed a bold resolution, and, without disturbing the sick man by any participation of her hopes and fears, proceeded after settling their trifling affairs to act at once on her own plans and designs.

Careless of the future as the poor drover had seemed, he had yet kept clear of debt, and by subscribing constantly to a benefit club had secured a pittance that might at least assist in supporting him during the long years of sickness and helplessness to which he was doomed to look forward. This his daughter knew. She knew, also, that the employer in whose service his health had suffered so severely was a rich and liberal cattle-dealer in the neighbourhood, who would willingly aid an old and faithful servant, and had, indeed, come forward with offers of money. To assistance from such a quarter Hannah saw no objection. Farmer Oakley and the parish were quite distinct things. Of him, accordingly, she asked, not money, but something much more in his own way—'a cow! any cow! old or lame, or what not, so that it were a cow! she would be bound to keep

it well; if she did not, he might take it back again. She
even hoped to pay for it by and by, by instalments, but
that she would not promise!' and partly amused, partly
interested by the child's earnestness, the wealthy yeoman
gave her, not as a purchase, but as a present, a very fine
young Alderney. She then went to the lord of the manor,
and, with equal knowledge of character, begged his permission to keep her cow on the Shaw common. 'Farmer
Oakley had given her a fine Alderney, and she would be
bound to pay the rent and keep her father off the parish if
he would only let it graze on the waste'; and he, too, half
from real good nature, half not to be outdone in liberality
by his tenant, not only granted the requested permission, but
reduced the rent so much, that the produce of the vine
seldom fails to satisfy their kind landlord.

Now Hannah showed great judgment in setting up as a
dairy-woman. She could not have chosen an occupation
more completely unoccupied, or more loudly called for.
One of the most provoking of the petty difficulties which
beset people with a small establishment in this neighbourhood, is the trouble, almost the impossibility, of procuring
the pastoral luxuries of milk, eggs, and butter, which rank,
unfortunately, amongst the indispensable necessaries of
housekeeping. To your thorough-bred Londoner, who,
whilst grumbling over his own breakfast, is apt to fancy
that thick cream and fresh butter and new-laid eggs
grow, so to say, in the country—form an actual part of its
natural produce—it may be some comfort to learn, that in
this great grazing district, however the calves and the
farmers may be the better for cows, nobody else is; that
farmers' wives have ceased to keep poultry; and that we
unlucky villagers sit down often to our first meal in a state
of destitution, which may well make him content with his
thin milk and his Cambridge butter, when compared to our
imputed pastoralities.

Hannah's Alderney restored us to one rural privilege.
Never was so cleanly a little milk-maid. She changed
away some of the cottage finery (which, in his prosperous
days, poor Jack had pleased himself with bringing home), the
china tea-service, the gilded mugs, and the painted waiters,
for the more useful utensils of the dairy, and speedily

established a regular and gainful trade in milk, eggs, butter, honey, and poultry—for poultry they had always kept.

Her domestic management prospered equally. Her father, who retained the perfect use of his hands, began a manufacture of mats and baskets, which he constructed with great nicety and adroitness; the eldest boy, a sharp and clever lad, cut for him his rushes and osiers; erected, under his sister's direction, a shed for the cow, and enlarged and cultivated the garden (always with the good leave of her kind patron the lord of the manor) until it became so ample, that the produce not only kept the pig and half kept the family, but afforded another branch of merchandise to the indefatigable directress of the establishment. For the younger boy, less quick and active, Hannah contrived to obtain an admission to the charity-school, where he made great progress—retaining him at home, however, in the hay-making and leasing season, or whenever his services could be made available, to the great annoyance of the schoolmaster, whose favourite he is, and who piques himself so much on George's scholarship (your heavy sluggish boy at country work often turns out quick at his book), that it is the general opinion that this much-vaunted pupil will, in process of time, be promoted to the post of assistant, and may, possibly, in course of years rise to the dignity of a parish pedagogue in his own person; so that his sister, although still making him useful at odd times, now considers George as pretty well off her hands, whilst his elder brother, Tom, could take an under-gardener's place directly, if he were not too important at home to be spared even for a day.

In short, during the five years that she has ruled at the Shaw cottage, the world has gone well with Hannah Bint. Her cow, her calves, her pigs, her bees, her poultry, have each, in their several ways, thriven and prospered. She has even brought Watch to like buttermilk, as well as strong beer, and has nearly persuaded her father (to whose wants and wishes she is most anxiously attentive) to accept of milk as a substitute for gin. Not but Hannah hath had her enemies as well as her betters. Why should she not? The old woman at the lodge, who always piqued herself on being spiteful and crying down new ways, foretold from the first she would come to no good, and could not forgive her for falsifying her prediction; and Betty Barnes, the slatternly widow of a tippling farmer, who rented a field and set up a cow herself, and was universally discarded for insufferable dirt, said all that the wit of an envious woman could devise against Hannah and her Alderney; nay, even Ned Miles, the keeper, her next neighbour, who had whilom held entire sway over the Shaw common, as well as its coppices, grumbled as much as so good-natured and genial a person could grumble, when he found a little girl sharing his dominion, a cow grazing beside his pony, and vulgar cocks and hens hovering around the buckwheat destined to feed his noble pheasants. Nobody that had been accustomed to see that paragon of keepers, so tall and manly and pleasant looking, with his merry eye and his knowing smile, striding daily along, in his green coat and his gold-laced hat, with Neptune, his noble Newfoundland dog (a retriever is the sporting word), and his beautiful spaniel Flirt at his heels, could conceive how askew he looked when he first found Hannah and Watch holding equal reign over his old territory, the Shaw common.

Yes! Hannah hath had her enemies; but they are passing away. The old woman at the lodge is dead, poor creature; and Betty Barnes, having herself taken to tippling, has lost the few friends she once possessed, and looks, luckless wretch, as if she would soon die too! And the keeper? Why, he is not dead, or likely to die; but the change that has taken place there is the most astonishing of all—except perhaps the change in Hannah herself.

Few damsels of twelve years old, generally a very pretty age, were less pretty than Hannah Bint. Short and stunted in her figure, thin in face, sharp in feature, with a muddled complexion, wild sunburnt hair, and eyes whose very brightness had in them something startling, over-informed, super-subtle, too clever for her age—at twelve years old she had quite the air of a little old fairy. Now, at seventeen, matters are mended. Her complexion has cleared; her countenance has developed itself; her figure has shot up into height and lightness and a sort of rustic grace; her bright, acute eye is softened and sweetened by the womanly wish to please; her hair is trimmed and curled and brushed with exquisite neatness; and her whole dress arranged with that nice attention to the becoming, the suitable both in form and texture, which would be called the highest degree of coquetry if it did not deserve the better name of propriety. Never was such a transmogrification beheld. The lass is really pretty, and Ned Miles has discovered that she is so. There he stands, the rogue, close at her side (for he hath joined her whilst we have been telling her little story, and the milking is over)—there he stands—holding her milk-pail in one hand and stroking Watch with the other, whilst she is returning the compliment by patting Neptune's magnificent head. There they stand as much like lovers as may be; he smiling and she blushing—he never looking so handsome, nor she so pretty in all their lives. There they stand, in blessed forgetfulness of all except each other; as happy a couple as ever trod the earth. There they stand, and one would not disturb them for all the milk and butter in Christendom. I should not wonder if they were fixing the wedding-day.

CHAPTER XXXVII

THE GENERAL AND HIS LADY

ALL persons of a certain standing in life remember—for
certainly nothing was ever more unforgettable—the great
scarlet fever of England, when volunteering was the order of
the day; when you could scarcely meet with a man who was
not under some denomination or other a soldier; when a civil
topic could hardly find a listener; when little boys played at
reviewing, and young ladies learned the sword exercise. It
was a fine ebullition of national feeling—of loyalty and of
public spirit, and cannot be looked back to without respect;
but, at the moment, the strange contrasts—the perpetual
discrepancies—and the comical self-importance which it
produced and exhibited, were infinitely diverting. I was a
very little girl at the time, but even now I cannot recollect
without laughing the appearance of a cornet of yeomanry
cavalry, who might have played Falstaff without stuffing,
and was obliged to complete his military decorations by
wearing (and he how contrived to keep up the slippery girdle
one can hardly imagine) three silken sashes sewed into one!
To this day, too, I remember the chuckling delight with which
a worthy linen-draper of my acquaintance heard himself
addressed as Captain while measuring a yard of ribbon,
pretending to make light of the appellation, but evidently
as proud of his title as a newly-dubbed knight, or a peer of
the last edition; and I never shall forget the astonishment
with which I beheld a field-officer, in his double epaulets,
advance obsequiously to the carriage-door, to receive an
order for five shillings' worth of stationery! The prevailing
spirit fell in exactly with the national character—loyal,
patriotic, sturdy, and independent; very proud and a little
vain; fond of excitement and not indifferent to personal
distinction; the whole population borne along by one

laudable and powerful impulse, and yet each man preserving, in the midst of that great leveller, military discipline,
his individual peculiarities and blameless self-importance.
It was a most amusing era!

In large country towns, especially where they mustered
two or three different corps, and the powerful stimulant of
emulation was superadded to the original martial fury, the
goings-on of these Captain Pattypans furnished a standing
comedy, particularly when aided by the solemn etiquette
and strong military spirit of their wives, who took precedence according to the rank of their husbands, from the
colonel's lady down to the corporal's, and were as complete
martialists, as proud of the services of their respective
regiments, and as much impressed with the importance of
field-days and reviews, as if they had actually mounted the
cockade and handled the firelock in their own proper persons.
Foote's inimitable farce was more than realized; and the
ridicules of that period have only escaped being perpetuated
in a new *Mayor of Garratt*, by the circumstance of the
whole world, dramatist and all, being involved in them.
'The lunacy was so ordinary, that the whippers were in
arms too.'

That day is past. Even the yeomanry cavalry, the last
lingering remnant of the volunteer system, whom I have
been accustomed to see annually parade through the town
of B——, with my pleasant friend Captain M—— at their
head—that respectable body, of which the band always
appeared to me so much more numerous than the corps—
even that respectable body is dissolved; whilst the latest
rag of the infantry service—the long preserved uniform and
cocked hat of my old acquaintance, Dr. R——, whilom
physician to the B—— Association, figured last summer as
a scarecrow, stuffed with straw, and perched on a gate, an
old gun tucked under its arm, to frighten the sparrows from
his cherry-orchard! Except the real soldiers, and every
now and then some dozen of foxhunters at a hunt ball
(whose usual dress uniform, by the way, scarlet over black,
makes them look just like a flight of ladybirds)—excepting
these gallant sportsmen, and the real bona fide officers, one
cannot now see a red coat for love or money. The glory of
the volunteers is departed!

In the meantime I owe to them one of the pleasantest recollections of my early life.

It was towards the beginning of the last war, when the novelty and freshness of the volunteering spirit had somewhat subsided, and the government was beginning to organize a more regular defensive force, under the name of local militia, that our old friend Colonel Sanford was appointed, with the rank of brigadier-general, to the command of the district in which we resided. Ever since I could recollect, I had known Colonel Sanford—indeed a little brother of mine, who died at the age of six months, had had the honour to be his godson; and from my earliest remembrance, the good Colonel—fie upon me to forget his brigadiership!—the good General had been set down by myself, as well as by the rest of the world, for a confirmed old bachelor. His visits to our house had, indeed, been only occasional, since he had been almost constantly on active service in different quarters of the globe; so that we had merely caught a sight of him as he passed from the East Indies to the West, or in his still more rapid transit from Gibraltar to Canada. For full a dozen years, however (and further the recollection of a young lady of sixteen could hardly be expected to extend), he had seemed to be a gentleman very considerably on the wrong side of fifty—'or by 'r Lady inclining to threescore'—and that will constitute an old bachelor, in the eyes of any young lady in Christendom.

His appearance was not calculated to diminish that impression. In his person, General Sanford was tall, thin, and erect; as stiff and perpendicular as a ramrod, with a bald head, most exactly powdered; a military queue; a grave formal countenance; and a complexion, partly tanned and partly frozen by frequent exposure to the vicissitudes of different climates, into one universal and uniform tint of reddish brown or brownish red.

His disposition was in good keeping with this solemn exterior—grave and saturnine. He entered little into ladies' conversation, with whom, indeed, he seldom came much in contact, and for whose intellect he was apt to profess a slight shade of contempt—an unhappy trick, to which your solemn wiseacre is sometimes addicted. All men, I fear, entertain the opinion, but the clever ones discreetly keep it to themselves. With other gentlemen he did hold grave converse, on politics, the weather, the state of the roads, the news of the day, and other gentlemanly topics; and when much at ease in his company, he would favour them with a few prosing stories, civil and military. One, in particular, was of formidable length. I have seen a friend of his wince as he began, 'When I was in Antigua——.' For the rest, the good General was an admirable person; a gentleman by birth, education, and character, a man of the highest honour, the firmest principles, and the purest benevolence. He was an excellent officer, also, of the old school; one who had seen much service; was a rigid disciplinarian, and somewhat of a martinet. Just the man to bring the new levies into order, although not unlikely to look with considerable scorn on the holiday soldiers, who had never seen anything more nearly resembling a battle than a sham fight at a review.

He paid us a visit, of course, when he came to be installed into his new office, and to take a house at B——, his destined headquarters; and after the first hearty congratulations on his promotion, his old friend, a joker by profession, began rallying him, as usual, on the necessity of taking a wife; on which, instead of returning his customary grave negative, the General stammered, looked foolish, and, incredible as it may seem that a blush could be seen through such a complexion, actually blushed; and when left alone with his host, after dinner, in lieu of the much dreaded words, 'When I was in Antigua,' seriously requested his advice on the subject of matrimony, which that sage counsellor, certain that a marriage was settled, and not quite sure that it had not already taken place, immediately gave, in the most satisfactory manner; and before the conversation was finished was invited to attend the wedding on the succeeding Thursday.

The next time that we saw the General, he was accompanied by a lovely little girl, whom he introduced as his wife, but who might readily have passed for his grand-daughter. I wanted a month of sixteen; and I was then, and am now, perfectly convinced that Mrs. Sanford was my junior. The fair bride had been a ward of the bride-groom's, the orphan and, I believe, destitute daughter of a brother officer. He had placed her, many years back, at a respectable country boarding-school, where she remained until his new appointment, and, as he was pleased to say, his friends' suggestions induced him to resolve upon matrimony, and look about for a wife as a necessary appendage to his official situation.

It is probable that his wife's exceeding beauty might have had something to do with his resolution as well as with his choice. I have never seen a lovelier creature. Her figure was small, round, and girlish; full of grace and symmetry. Her face had a child-like purity and brilliancy of colouring; an alternation of blush and smile, a sweetness and innocence of expression, such as might beseem a Hebe —only still more youthful than the goddess of youth. Her manners were exactly those of a child come home for the holidays—shy and bashful, and shrinking from strangers; playful and affectionate with those whom she loved, especially her husband, who doted on her, and of whom she was very fond—and showing, in the midst of her timidity and childishness, considerable acuteness and power of observation.

At first she seemed, as well she might be, quite bewildered by the number of persons who came to visit her. For living in a large town, and holding, in right of her husband's office, a station of no small importance in the county, every person of the slightest gentility in the town and neighbourhood, the whole visiting population of these, in general, very distinct and separate societies, thought proper to wait upon Mrs. Sanford. Mrs. Sanford was the fashion of B——, and of B——shire. 'Not to know her, argued yourself unknown.' All the town and all the county called, and all the town invited her to tea, and all the county requested her company to dinner; and she, puzzled, perplexed, and amazed, hardly knowing by sight one individual of her innumerable acquaintance; unable to distinguish between one person and another; often forgetting titles; never remembering names; and ignorant as an infant of artificial distinctions, made twenty blunders in an hour, and kept the poor General, as punctilious an observer of the duties of society as of the duties of the service, in a perpetual state of fidget and alarm. Her mistakes were past all count—she mislaid invitations; forgot engagements; mismatched her company; gave the mayor of B—— the precedence of the county member; and hath been heard to ask an old bachelor after his wife, and an old maid after her children. There was no end to Mrs. Sanford's blunders. The old Brigade-Major, a veteran of the General's own standing, lame of a leg and with a prodigious scar across his forehead, was kept on the constant stump with explanatory messages and conciliatory embassies—and declared that he underwent much harder duty in that service than ever he had performed in his official capacity of drilling the awkward squad. The General, not content with dispatching his aide-de-camp, exhausted himself in elaborate apologies, but embassies, apologies, and explanations were all unnecessary. Nobody could be angry with Mrs. Sanford. There was no resisting the charm of her blushing youthfulness, her pleading voice, her ready confession of error, and her evident sorrow for all her little sins, whether of ignorance or heedlessness—no withstanding her sweetness and simplicity. Even offended self-love, the hardest to appease of all the passions, yielded to the artlessness of Mrs. Sanford.

She, on her part, liked nothing so well as to steal away from her troublesome popularity, her visitors, and her fine clothes, to the ease and freedom of the country; to put on a white frock and a straw bonnet, and run about the woods and fields with some young female friend, primrosing or bird's-nesting, according to the season. I was her usual companion in these rambles, and enjoyed them perhaps as much as she did, but in a far quieter way. Her animal spirits seemed inexhaustible; I never knew her weary; and strong, agile, and entirely devoid of bodily fear, the thought of danger never seemed to come across her. How she enjoyed spending a long day at our house! now bounding over a ditch to gather a tuft of wild flowers; now climbing a pollard to look for a bird's nest; now driving through the lanes in a donkey chaise; now galloping across the common on a pony; now feeding the chickens; now milking the cows; now weeding the gravel walks; now making hay; and now reaping. These were her delights! All her pleasures were equally childish: she cherished abundance of pets, such as schoolgirls love; kept silk-worms, dormice, and canary birds; a parrot, a squirrel, and a monkey; three lap-dogs

and a Persian cat; enjoyed a fair, and was enchanted with
a pantomime; always supposing that her party did not
consist of fine people or of strangers, but was composed
of those to whom she was accustomed, and who were as
well disposed to merriment and good humour as herself.

With regard to accomplishments, she knew what was
commonly taught in a country school above twenty years
ago, and nothing more: played a little, sang a little, talked
a little indifferent French; painted shells and roses, not
particularly like nature, on card-racks and hand-screens;
danced admirably; and was the best player at battledore
and shuttlecock, hunt-the-slipper, and blind-man's-buff in
the county. Nothing could exceed the glee with which,
in any family where she was intimate, she would join the
children in a game of romps, herself the gayest and happiest
child of the party.

For cards she had no genius. Even the noise and
nonsense of a round-table could not reconcile her to those
bits of painted pasteboard. This was unlucky; it is true
that the General, who played a good rubber, and looked
upon it, next to a review or a battle, as the most serious
business of life, and who had moreover a settled opinion
that no woman had intellect enough to master the game,
would hardly have wished to have been her partner at the
whist table, but he also loved a snug party at piquet, just to
keep him awake after dinner, and would have liked exceedingly that Mrs. Sanford should have known enough of
the rules to become a decent antagonist. He was not
unreasonable in his expectations; he did not desire that
she should play well enough to win. He only wanted her
to understand sufficient of the game to lose in a creditable
manner. But it would not do; she was unconquerably
stupid: never dealt the right number of cards; never showed
her point; was ignorant even of the common terms of the
art; did not know a quart from a quint, or a pique from a
repique; could not tell when she was capotted. There was
no comfort in beating her, so the poor General was fain to
accept his old Brigade-Major as a substitute, who gave him
three points and beat him.

In other respects she was an excellent wife; gentle,
affectionate, and sweet - tempered. She accommodated

herself admirably to all the General's ways; listened to his admonitions with deference, and to his stories with attention—the formidable one, beginning, 'When I was in Antigua,' not excepted; was kind to the old Brigade-Major; and when he, a confirmed old bachelor, joined his patron in certain dissertations on the natural inferiority of the sex, heard them patiently, and if she smiled took good care they should not find her out.

To be sure, her carelessness did occasionally get her husband into a scrape. Once, for instance, he being inspecting certain corps twenty miles off, she undertook to bring his dress clothes, for the purpose of attending a ball given in his honour, and forgot his new inexpressibles, thereby putting the poor General to the trouble and expense of sending an express after the missing garment, and keeping him a close prisoner till midnight, in expectation of the return of his messenger. Another time, he being in London, and the trusty Major also absent, she was commissioned to inform him of the day fixed for a grand review; sat down for the purpose, wrote a long letter full of chit-chat—and he could not abide long letters—never mentioned military affairs, and on being reminded of her omission, crammed the important intelligence into a crossed postscript under the seal, which the General, with his best spectacles, could not have deciphered in a month, so that the unlucky commander never made his appearance on the ground, and but for a forty years' reputation for exactness and punctuality, which made any excuse look like truth, would have fallen into sad disgrace at headquarters.

In process of time, however, even these little errors ceased. She grew tall, and her mind developed itself with her person; still lively, ardent, and mercurial in her temperament, with an untiring spirit of life and motion, and a passionate love of novelty and gaiety, her playfulness ripened into intelligence, her curiosity became rational, and her delight in the country deepened into an intense feeling of the beauties of nature. Thrown amidst a large and varying circle, she became, in every laudable sense of the phrase, a perfect woman of the world. Before a change in the volunteer system and a well-merited promotion took the General from B——, she had learned to manage her town visits and her country visits, to arrange soirées and dinner-parties, to give balls, and to plan picnics, and was the life and charm of the neighbourhood. I would not even be sure that she had not learned piquet; for lovely as she was, and many as there were to tell her that she was lovely, her husband was always her first object, and her whole conduct seemed guided by the spirit of that beautiful line in the most beautiful of ballads:

> For auld Robin Gray 's been a gude man to me.

Since his death—for she has been long a widow—Lady Sanford—have I not said that the good General became Sir Thomas before his decease!—has lived mostly on the Continent, indulging, but always with the highest reputation, her strong taste for what is gayest in artificial life and grandest in natural scenery. I have heard of her sometimes amongst the brilliant crowds of the Roman carnival, sometimes amidst the wildest recesses of the Pyrenees; now looking down the crater of Vesuvius; now waltzing at a court ball at Vienna. She had made a trip to Athens, and had talked of attempting the ascent of Mont Blanc! At present she is in England, for a friend of mine saw her the other day at the Cowes regatta, full of life and glee, almost as pretty as ever, and quite as delightful. Of course, being also a well-dowered and childless widow, she has had lovers by the hundred and offers by the score, but she always says that she has made up her mind not to marry again, and I have no doubt of her keeping her resolution. She loves her liberty too dearly to part with the blessing; and well as she got on with Sir Thomas, I think she has had enough of matrimony. Besides, she has now reached a sedate age, and there would be a want of discretion, which hitherto she never has wanted, in venturing——

'What was that you said, ma'am?' The newspaper! Have I read the newspaper? People will always talk to me when I am writing! Have I read to-day's paper? No; what do you wish me to look at? This column: police reports—new publications—births? Oh, the marriages! 'Yesterday, at Bow Church, Mr. Smith to Miss Brown.' Not that? Oh, the next! 'On Friday last, at Cheltenham, by the Venerable the Archdeacon P——, Dennis O'Brien,

Esq., of the – th regiment '—But what do I care for
Dennis O'Brien, Esq.? 'What's Hecuba to me, or I to
Hecuba?' I never heard of the gentleman before in my
days. Oh, it's the lady—'Dennis O'Brien, Esq., to Lady
Sanford'—'Angels and ministers of grace defend us!' here
is a surprise!—'to Lady Sanford'!—Aye, my eyes did not
deceive me, it's no mistake—'relict of the late Major-
General Sir Thomas Sanford, K.C.B.' And so much for a
widow's resolution—and a gay widow's too! I would not
have answered for one of the demure. A General's widow
at the ripe age of forty (oh, age of indiscretion!) married
to an ensign in a marching regiment; young enough to be
her son, I warrant me, and as poor as a church mouse! If
her old husband could but know what was going forward,
he would chuckle in his grave, at so notable a proof of the
weakness of the sex—so irresistible a confirmation of his
theory. Lady Sanford married again! Who, after this,
shall put faith in woman! Lady Sanford married again!

CHAPTER XXXVIII

GOING TO THE RACES

A MEMORABLE day was the third of last June to Mary and
Henrietta Coxe, the young daughters of Simon Coxe, the
carpenter of Aberleigh; for it was the first day of Ascot
Races, and the first time of their going to that celebrated
union of sport and fashion. There is no pleasure so great
in the eyes of our country damsels as a jaunt to Ascot. In
the first place, it is, when you get there, a genuine English
amusement, open alike to rich and poor, elegant as an
opera, and merry as a fair; in the second, this village of
Aberleigh is situate about fourteen miles from the course,
just within distance, almost out of distance, so that there
is commonly enough of suspense and difficulty—the slight
difficulty, the short suspense, which add such zest to
pleasure; finally, at Ascot you are sure to see the King, to
see him in his graciousness and his dignity, the finest
gentleman in Europe, the greatest sovereign of the world.
Truly it is nothing extraordinary that his liege subjects
should flock to indulge their feelings of loyalty by the sight
of such a monarch, and that the announcement of his
presence should cover a barren heath with a dense and
crowded population of all ranks and all ages, from the
duchess to the gipsy, from the old man of eighty to the
child in its mother's arms.

All people love Ascot Races; but our country lasses love
them above all. It is their favourite wedding jaunt, for
half our young couples are married in the race week, and
one or two matches have seemed to me got up purposely
for the occasion; and of all the attentions that can be
offered by a lover, a drive to the races is the most irresistible. In short, so congenial is that gay scene to love, that
it is a moot point which are most numerous, the courtships
that conclude there in the shape of bridal excursions, or

those which begin on that favoured spot in the shape of
parties of pleasure; and the delicate experiment called
'popping the question' is so often put in practice on the
very course itself, that when Robert Hewitt, the young
farmer at the Holt, asked Master Coxe's permission to escort
his daughters, not only the good carpenter, but his neighbours the blacksmith and the shoemaker, looked on this
mark of rustic gallantry as the precursor of a declaration in
form; and all the village cried out on Hetta Coxe's extreme
good luck, Hetta being supposed, and with some reason, to
be the chief object of this attention.

Robert Hewitt was a young farmer of the old school,
honest, frugal, and industrious; thrifty, thriving, and likely
to thrive; one of a fine yeomanly spirit, not ashamed of his
station, and fond of following the habits of his forefathers,
sowing his own corn, driving his own team, and occasionally
ploughing his own land; as proud, perhaps, of his blunt
speech and homely ways as some of his brother farmers
of their superior refinement and gentility. Nothing could
exceed the scorn with which Robert Hewitt, in his market
cart, drawn by his good horse Dobbin, would look down on
one neighbour on his hunter, and another in his gig. To the
full as proud as any of them was Robert, but in a different
way, and perhaps a safer. He piqued himself, like a good
Englishman, on wearing a smock-frock, smoking his pipe,
and hating foreigners, to our intercourse with whom he was
wont to ascribe all the airs and graces, the new fashions,
and the effeminacy, which annoyed him in his own countrymen. He hated the French, he detested dandies, and he
abhorred fine ladies, fine ways, and finery of any sort.
Such was Robert Hewitt.

Henrietta Coxe was a pretty girl of seventeen, and had
passed the greater part of her life with an aunt in the next
town, who had been a lady's maid in her youth, and had
retired thither on a small annuity. To this aunt, who
had been dead about a twelvemonth, she was indebted for
a name, rather too fine for common wear — I believe she
wrote herself Henrietta Matilda; a large wardrobe, pretty
much in the same predicament; an abundant stock of superfine notions, some skill in mantua-making and millinery,
and a legacy of a hundred pounds to be paid on her wedding-

day. Her beauty was quite in the style of a wax doll: blue
eyes, flaxen hair, delicate features, and a pink and white
complexion, much resembling that sweet-pea which is
known by the name of the painted lady. Very pretty she
was certainly, with all her airs and graces; and very pretty,
in spite of her airs and graces, did Robert Hewitt think her;
and love, who delights in contrasts, and has an especial
pleasure in oversetting wise resolutions, and bending the
haughty self-will of the lords of the creation, was beginning
to make strange havoc in the stout yeoman's heart. His
operations, too, found a very unintentional coadjutrix in
old Mrs. Hewitt, who, taking alarm at her son's frequent
visits to the carpenter's shop, unwarily expressed a hope
that if her son did intend to marry one of the Coxes, he
would have nothing to do with the fine lady, but would
choose Mary, the elder sister, a dark-haired, pleasant-look-
ing young woman of two-and-twenty, who kept the house
as clean as a palace, and was the boast of the village for
industry and good humour. Now this unlucky caution
gave Robert, who loved his mother, but did not choose to
be managed by her, an additional motive for his lurking
preference, by piquing his self-will; add to which the little
damsel herself, in the absence of other admirers, took visible
pleasure in his admiration, so that affairs seemed drawing
to a crisis, and the party to Ascot appeared likely to end,
like other jaunts to the same place, in a wedding. It is
true that the invitation, which had been readily and
gratefully accepted by her sister, had been received by
Miss Hetta with some little demur. 'Going to the races
was delightful, but to ride in a cart behind Dobbin was
odious. Could not Mr. Hewitt hire a phaeton, or borrow a
gig? However, as her sister seemed to wish it, she might
perhaps go, if she could find no better conveyance.' And
with this concession the lover was contented; the more
especially as the destined finery was in active preparation.
Flounces, furbelows, and frippery of all descriptions,
enough to stock a milliner's shop, did Hetta produce for
the adornment of her fair person; and Robert looked on in
silence, sometimes thinking how pretty she would look,
sometimes how soon he would put an end to such nonsense when once they were married, and sometimes how

odd a figure he and Dobbin should cut by the side of so much beauty and fashion.

Neither Dobbin nor his master were fated to be so honoured. The evening before the races there happened to be a revel at Whitley Wood; thither Hetta repaired, and there she had the ill fortune to be introduced to Monsieur Auguste, a young Frenchman, who had lately hired a room at B—— where he vended eau-de-Cologne and French toys and essences, and did himself the honour, as his bills expressed, to cut the hair and the corns of the nobility and gentry of the town and neighbourhood. Monsieur was a dark, sallow, foreign-looking personage, with tremendous whiskers, who looked at once fierce and foppish, was curled and perfumed in a manner that did honour to his double profession, and wore gold rings in his ears and on his fingers, a huge bunch of seals at his side, and a gaudy brooch at his bosom. Small chance had Robert Hewitt against such a rival, especially when, smitten with her beauty or her hundred pounds, he devoted himself to Hetta's service, made fine speeches in most bewitching broken English, braved for her sake the barbarities of a country dance, and promised to initiate her into the mysteries of the waltz and the quadrille; and, finally, requested the honour to conduct her in a cabriolet the next day to Ascot Races. Small chance had our poor farmer against such a monsieur.

The morning arrived, gloomy, showery, and cold, and at the appointed hour up drove the punctual Robert, in a new market cart, painted blue with red wheels, and his heavy but handsome horse Dobbin (who was indeed upon occasion the fore horse of the team) as sleek and shining as good feed and good dressing could make him. Up drove Robert with his little sister (a child of eleven years old, who was to form one of the party) sitting at his side; whilst equally punctual, at Master Coxe's door, stood the sisters ready dressed, Mary in a new dark gown, a handsome shawl, and a pretty straw bonnet, with a cloth cloak hanging on her arm; Hetta in a flutter of gauze and ribbons, pink and green, and yellow and blue, looking like a parrot tulip, or a milliner's doll, or a picture of the fashions in the *Lady's Magazine*, or like anything under the sun but an English country girl. Robert looked at her and then at Mary,

who was vainly endeavouring to persuade her to put on, or
at least to take, a cloak, and thought for once without
indignation of his mother's advice; he got out, however,
and was preparing to assist them into the cart, when
suddenly, to the astonishment of everybody but Hetta, for
she had said nothing at home of her encounter at the revel,
Monsieur Auguste made his appearance in a hired gig of
the most wretched description, drawn by an equally
miserable jade, alighted at the house and claimed made-
moiselle's promise to do him the honour to accompany him
in his cabriolet. The consternation was general. Mary
remonstrated with her sister mildly but earnestly; Master
Coxe swore she should not go, but Hetta was resolute;
and Farmer Hewitt, whose first impulse had been to drub
the Frenchman, changed his purpose when he saw how
willing she was to be carried off. 'Let her go,' said he,
'monsieur is welcome to her company; for my part, I
think they are well matched. It would be a pity to part
them.' And, lifting Mary rapidly into the cart, he drove
off at a pace of which Dobbin, to judge from his weight,
appeared incapable, and to which that illustrious steed
was very little accustomed.

In the meanwhile Hetta was endeavouring to introduce
her new beau to her father, and to reconcile him to her
change of escort; and the standers-by, consisting of half the
men and boys in the village, were criticizing the Frenchman's equipage: 'I could shake the old chaise to pieces
with one jerk, it 's so ramshackle!' cried Ned Jones, Master
Coxe's foreman. 'The wheel will come to pieces long
before they get to Ascot,' added Sam the apprentice. 'The
old horse has a spavin in the off fore-leg, that 's what makes
him so lame,' said Will Forde the blacksmith. 'And he
has been down within the month. Look at his knees!'
rejoined Jem the carter. 'He 's blind of an eye!' exclaimed
one urchin. 'He shies!' cried another. 'The reins are
rotten,' observed Dick the collar-maker. 'The Frenchman
can't drive,' remarked Jack the drover, coming up to join
the crew; 'he 'd as nearly as possible run foul of my pigs.'
'He 'll certainly overturn her, poor thing!' cried one kind
friend, as, overcome by her importunities, her father at
length consented to her departure. 'The chaise will break

down,' said another. 'Break! he 'll break her neck,' added a third. 'They 'll be drenched to the skin in this shower!' exclaimed a fourth—and amidst these consoling predictions the happy couple departed.

Robert and Mary, on their side, proceeded for some time in almost total silence—Robert too angry for speech, and Mary feeling herself, however innocent, involved in the consequences of her sister's delinquency; so that little passed beyond Anne Hewitt's delighted remarks on the beauty of the country and the hedgerows, bright with the young leaves of the oak, and gay with the pearly thorn blossoms and the delicate brier-rose; and her occasional exclamations at the sudden appearance of some tiny wren, or the peculiar interrupted flight of some water-wagtail, as he threw himself forward, then rested for a moment, self-poised in the air, then started on again with an up-and-down motion, like a ball tossed from the hand, keeping by the side of the cart for half a mile or more, as is frequently the way with that sociable bird. Little passed beyond trifles such as these, until Robert turned suddenly round to his companion with the abrupt question: 'Pray, Miss Mary, do you like Frenchmen?' 'I never was acquainted with any,' replied Mary; 'but I think I should like Englishmen best. It seems natural to prefer one's own countrymen.' 'Aye, to be sure!' replied Robert, 'to be sure it is! You are a sensible girl, Mary Coxe, and a good girl. It would be well for your sister if she had some of your sense.' 'Hetta is a good girl, I assure you, Farmer Hewitt—a very good girl,' rejoined Mary warmly, 'and does not want sense. But only consider how young she is, and her having no mother, and being a little spoilt by my poor aunt, and so pretty, and everybody talking nonsense to her—no wonder that she should sometimes be a little wrong, as she was this morning. But I hope that we shall meet her on the course, and that all will go right again. Hetta is a good girl, and will make a good wife.' 'To a Frenchman,' replied Robert dryly; and the conversation turned to other subjects, and was kept up with cheerfulness and good humour till they reached Ascot.

Anne and Mary enjoyed the races much. They saw the line of carriages, nine deep—more carriages than they thought ever were built; and the people—more people than they thought the whole world could hold; had a confused view of the horses and a distinct one of the riders' jackets; and Anne, whose notions on the subject of racing had been rather puzzled, so far enlarged her knowledge and improved her mind as to comprehend that yellow, crimson, green, and blue, in short, all the colours of the rainbow, were trying which should come first to the winning-post; they saw Punch, a puppet-show, several peep-shows, and the dancing dogs; admired the matchless display of beauty and elegance, when the weather allowed the ladies to walk up and down the course; were amused at the bustle and hurry-scurry when a sudden shower drove them to the shelter of their carriages; saw the Duke of Wellington; had a merry nod from the lively boy, Prince George; and had the honour of sharing, with some thousands of his subjects, a most graceful bow and most gracious smile from His Majesty. In short, they had seen everything and everybody, except Hetta and her beau; and nothing had been wanting to Mary's gratification, but the assurance of her sister's safety; for Mary had that prime qualification for a sight-seer, the habit of thinking much of what she came to see and little of herself. She made light of all inconveniences, covered little Anne (a delicate child) with her own cloak during the showers, and contrived, in spite of Robert's gallant attention to his guest, that Anne should have the best place under the umbrella and the most tempting portion of the provisions; so that our farmer, by no means wanting in moral taste, was charmed with her cheerfulness, her good humour, and the total absence of vanity and selfishness; and when, on her ascending the cart to return, he caught a glimpse of a pretty foot and ankle, and saw how much exercise and pleasure had heightened her complexion and brightened her hazel eyes, he could not help thinking to himself: 'My mother was right. She's ten times handsomer than her sister, and has twenty times more sense—and, besides, she does not like Frenchmen.'

But where could Hetta be? What had become of poor Hetta? This question, which had pressed so frequently on Mary's mind during the races, became still more painful as they proceeded on their road home, which, leading

through cross-country lanes, far away from the general
throng of the visitors, left more leisure for her affectionate
fears. They had driven about two miles, and Robert
was endeavouring to comfort her with hopes that their
horse's lameness had forced them back again, and that her
sister would be found safe at Aberleigh, when a sudden
turn in the lane discovered a disabled gig, without a horse
or driver, in the middle of the road, and a woman seated on a
bank by the side of a ditch—a miserable object, tattered,
dirty, shivering, drenched, and crying as if her heart would
break. Was it, could it be, Hetta? Yes, Hetta it was. All
the misfortunes that had been severally predicted at their
outset had befallen the unfortunate pair. Before they had
travelled three miles, their wretched horse had fallen lame
in his near foreleg, and had cast the off-hind shoe, which,
as the blacksmith of the place was gone to the races, and
nobody seemed willing to put himself out of the way to
oblige a Frenchman, had nearly stopped them at the
beginning of their expedition. At last, however, they met
with a man who undertook to shoe their steed, and whose
want of skill added a prick to their other calamities; then
Monsieur Auguste broke a shaft of the cabriolet by driving
against a post, the setting and bandaging of which broken
limb made another long delay; then came a pelting shower,
during which they were forced to stand under a tree; then
they lost their way, and owing to the people of whom
monsieur inquired not understanding his English, and
monsieur not understanding theirs, went full five miles
round about; then they arrived at the 'Chequers' public-
house, which no effort could induce their horse to pass, so
there they stopped perforce to bait and feed; then, when
they were getting on as well as could be expected of a horse
with three lame legs and a French driver, a wagon came
past them, carried away their wheel, threw Monsieur
Auguste into the hedge, and lodged Miss Henrietta in the
ditch; so now the beau was gone to the next village for
assistance, and the belle was waiting his return on the bank;
and poor Hetta was evidently tired of her fine lover and the
manifold misadventures which his unlucky gallantry had
brought upon her, and accepted very thankfully the offer
which Anne and Mary made, and Robert did not oppose, of

taking her into the cart and leaving a line written in pencil on a leaf of Mary's pocket-book, to inform monsieur of her safety. Heartily glad was poor Hetta to find herself behind the good steed Dobbin, under cover of her sister's warm cloak, pitied and comforted and in a fair way to get home. Heartily glad would she have been, too, to have found herself reinstated in the good graces of her old admirer. But of that she saw no sign. Indeed, the good yeoman took some pains to show that, although he bore no malice, his courtship was over. He goes, however, oftener than ever to the carpenter's house, and the gossips of Aberleigh say that this jaunt to Ascot will have its proper and usual catastrophe, a merry wedding; that Robert Hewitt will be the happy bridegroom, but that Hetta Coxe will not be the bride.

CHAPTER XXXIX

THE CHINA JUG

ONE of the prettiest rustic dwellings in our pretty neighbourhood is the picturesque farm-house which stands on the edge of Wokefield Common, so completely in a bottom that the passengers who traverse the high road see indeed the smoke from the chimneys floating like a vapour over the woody hill which forms the background, but cannot even catch a glimpse of the roof, so high does the turfy common rise above it; whilst so steeply does the ground decline to the door that it seems as if no animal less accustomed to tread the hill-side than a goat or a chamois could venture to descend the narrow foot-path which winds round the declivity, and forms the nearest way to the village. The cart-track, threading the mazes of the hills, leads to the house by a far longer but very beautiful road; the smooth fine turf of the common, varied by large tufts of furze and broom, rising in an abrupt bank on one side; on the other a narrow well-timbered valley, bordered by hanging woods, and terminated by a large sheet of water, close beside which stands the farm, a low irregular cottage snugly thatched, and its different out-buildings, all on the smallest scale, but giving the air of comfort and habitation to the spot that nothing can so thoroughly convey as an English barn-yard with its complement of cows, pigs, horses, chickens, and children.

One part of the way thither is singularly beautiful. It is where a bright and sparkling spring has formed itself into a clear pond in a deep broken hollow by the roadside: the bank all around covered with rich grass, and descending in unequal terraces to the pool, whilst on every side around it, and at different heights, stand ten or twelve noble elms, casting their green shadows mixed with the light clouds and the blue summer sky on the calm and glassy

water, and giving (especially when the evening sun lights
up the little grove, causing the rugged trunks to shine like
gold, and the pendent leaves to glitter like the burnished
wings of the rose-beetle) a sort of pillared and columnar
dignity to the scene.

Seldom, too, would that fountain, famous for the purity
and sweetness of its waters, be without some figure suited
to the landscape: child, woman, or country girl, leaning
from the plank extended over the spring, to fill her pitcher,
or returning with it, supported by one arm on her head,
recalling all classical and pastoral images, the beautiful
sculptures of Greece, the poetry of Homer and of Sophocles,
and even more than these, the habits of oriental life, and
the Rachels and Rebeccas of Scripture.

Seldom would that spring be without some such figure
ascending the turfy steps into the lane, of whom one might
inquire respecting the sequestered farm-house, whose rose-
covered porch was seen so prettily from a turn in the road;
and often it would be one of the farmer's children who
would answer you, for in spite of the vicinity of the great
pond, all the water for domestic use was regularly brought
from the Elmin spring.

Wokefield Pond Farm was a territory of some thirty
acres; one of the 'little bargains,' as they are called, which
once abounded, but are now seldom found, in Berkshire;
and at the time to which our story refers, that is to say,
about twenty years ago, its inhabitants were amongst the
poorest and most industrious people in the country.

George Mearing was the only son of a rich yeoman in the
parish, who held this 'little bargain' in addition to the
manor farm. George was an honest, thoughtless, kind-
hearted, good-humoured lad, quite unlike his father, who,
shrewd, hard, and money-getting, often regretted his son's
deficiency in the qualities by which he had risen in the
world, and reserved all his favour and affection for one
who possessed them in full perfection—his only daughter,
Martha. Martha was a dozen years older than her brother,
with a large bony figure, a visage far from prepossessing, a
harsh voice, and a constitutional scold, which, scrupulous
in her cleanliness, and vigilant in her economy, was in full
activity all day long. She seemed to go about the house

for no other purpose than that of finding fault, maundering now at one and now at another—her brother, the carters, the odd boy, the maid—every one, in short, except her father, who, connecting the ideas of scolding and of good housewifery, thought that he gained or at least saved money by the constant exercise of this accomplishment, and listened to her accordingly with great delight and admiration. 'Her mother,' thought he to himself, 'was a clever managing woman, and sorry enough was I to lose her; but gracious me, she was nothing to Martha! Where she spoke one word, Martha speaks ten.'

The rest of the family heard this eternal din with far less complacency. They agreed, indeed, that she could not help scolding, that it was her way, and that they were all fools to take notice of it; but yet they would flee, one and all, before the outpouring of her wrath, like birds before a thunder shower.

The person on whom the storm fell oftenest and loudest was of course her own immediate subject, the maid; and of the many damsels who had undergone the discipline of Martha's tongue, none was ever more the object of her objurgation, or deserved it less, than Dinah Moore. But Dinah had many sins in her stern mistress's eyes, which would hardly have been accounted such elsewhere. In the first place she was young and pretty, and to youth and beauty Martha had strong objections; then she was somewhat addicted to rustic finery, especially in the article of pink top-knots—and to rosy ribbons Martha had almost as great an aversion as to rosy cheeks; then again the young lass had a spirit, and when unjustly accused would vindicate herself with more wit than prudence, and better tempered persons than Martha cannot abide that qualification; moreover the little damsel had an irresistible lightness of heart and a gaiety of temper which no rebuke could tame, no severity repress; laughter was as natural to her as chiding to her mistress; all her labours went merrily on: she would sing over the mashing-tub, and smile through the washing week, outsinging Martha's scolding, and out-smiling Martha's frowns.

This in itself would have been sufficient cause of offence; but when Martha fancied, and fancied truly, that the pink top-knots, the smiles, and the songs were all aimed at the heart of her brother George, of whom, in her own rough way, she was both fond and proud, the pretty songstress became insupportable; and when George, in despite of her repeated warnings, did actually one fine morning espouse Dinah Moore, causing her in her agitation to let fall an old-fashioned china wash-hand basin, the gift of a long deceased godmother, which, with the jug belonging to it, she valued more than any other of her earthly possessions, no wonder that she made a vow never to speak to her brother while she lived, or that more in resentment than in covetousness (for Martha Mearing was rather a harsh and violent, than an avaricious woman) she encouraged her father in his angry resolution of banishing the culprit from his house, and disinheriting him from his property.

Old Farmer Mearing was not, however, a wicked man, although in many respects a hard one. He did not turn his son out to starve; on the contrary, he settled him in the Pond Farm, with a decent though scanty plenishing—put twenty pounds in his pocket, and told him that he had nothing more to expect from him, and that he must make his own way in the world, as he had done forty years before.

George's heart would have sunk under this denunciation, for he was of a kind but weak and indolent nature, and wholly accustomed to depend on his father, obey his orders, and rely on him for support; but he was sustained by the bolder and firmer spirit of his wife, who, strong, active, lively, and sanguine, finding herself for the first time in her life her own mistress, in possession of a comfortable home, and married to the man of her heart, saw nothing but sunshine before them. Dinah had risen in the world, and George had fallen; and this circumstance, in addition to an original difference of temperament, may sufficiently account for their difference of feeling.

During the first year or two, Dinah's prognostics seemed likely to be verified. George ploughed and sowed and reaped, and she made butter, reared poultry, and fatted pigs, and their industry prospered, and the world went well with the young couple. But a bad harvest, the death of their best cow, the lameness of their most serviceable horse, and more than all, perhaps, the birth of four little

girls in four successive years, crippled them sadly, and
brought poverty and the fear of poverty to their happy
fire-side.

Still, however, Dinah's spirit continued undiminished.
Her children, although, to use her own phrase, 'of the
wrong sort,' grew and flourished, as the children of poor
people do grow and flourish, one hardly knows how; and
by the time that the long-wished-for boy made his appearance in the world, the elder girls had become almost as
useful to their father as if they had been 'of the right sort'
themselves. Never were seen such hardy and handy little
elves! They drove the plough, tended the kine, folded
the sheep, fed the pigs, worked in the garden, made the hay,
hoed the turnips, reaped the corn, hacked the beans, and
drove the market cart to B—— on occasion, and sold the
butter, eggs, and poultry as well as their mother could
have done.

Strong, active, and serviceable as boys were the little
lasses, and pretty withal, though as brown as so many
gipsies, and as untrained as wild colts. They had their
mother's bright and sparkling countenance, and her gay
and sunny temper, a heritage more valuable than house or
land—a gift more precious than ever was bestowed on a
favoured princess by beneficent fairy. But the mother's
darling was one who bore no resemblance to her either in
mind or person: her only son and younger child Moses, so
called after his grandfather, in a lurking hope, which was,
however, disappointed, that the name might propitiate the
offended and wealthy yeoman.

Little Moses was a fair, mild, quiet boy, who seemed at
first sight far fitter to wear petticoats than any one of his
madcap sisters; but there was an occasional expression in
his deep grey eye that gave token of sense and spirit, and
an unfailing steadiness and diligence about the child that
promised to vindicate his mother's partiality. She was
determined that Moses should be, to use the country phrase,
'a good scholar'; the meaning of which is, by the way,
not a little dissimilar from that which the same words bear
at Oxford or at Cambridge. Poor Dinah was no 'scholar'
herself, as the parish register can testify, where her mark
stands below George's signature in the record of her mar-

riage; and the girls bade fair to emulate their mother's ignorance, Dinah having given to each of the four the half of a year's schooling, upon the principle of ride and tie, little Lucy going one day and little Patty the next, and so on with the succeeding pair; in this way adroitly educating two children for the price of one, their mother in her secret soul holding it for girls a waste of time. But when Moses came in question, the case was altered. He was destined to enjoy the benefit of an entire education, and to imbibe unshared all the learning that the parish pedagogue could bestow. An admission to the Wokefield free-school ensured him this advantage, together with the right of wearing the long primitive blue cloth coat and leathern girdle, as well as the blue cap and yellow tassel, by which the boys were distinguished; and by the time he was eight years old he had made such progress in the arts of writing and ciphering, that he was pronounced by the master to be the most promising pupil in the school.

At this period, misfortunes, greater than they had hitherto known, began to crowd around this family. Old Farmer Mearing died, leaving all his property to Martha, and George, a broken-hearted toil-worn man, who had been only supported in his vain efforts to make head against ill fortune by the hope of his father's at last relenting, followed him to the grave in less than two months. Debt and difficulty beset the widow, and even her health and spirits began to fail. Her only resource seemed to be to leave her pleasant home, give up everything to the creditors, get her girls out to service, and try to maintain herself and Moses by washing or charing, or whatever work her failing strength would allow her to perform.

Martha, or, as she was now called, Mrs. Martha, lived on in lonely and apparently comfortless affluence at the Manor Farm. She had taken no notice of Dinah's humble supplications, sent injudiciously by Patty, a girl whose dark and sparkling beauty exactly resembled what her mother had been before her unfortunate marriage; but on Moses, so like his father, she had been seen to gaze wistfully and tenderly when the little procession of charity boys passed her on their way to church, though on finding herself observed, or perhaps on detecting herself in such an indulgence, the softened eye was immediately withdrawn, and the stern spirit seemed to gather itself into a resolution only the stronger for its momentary weakness.

Mrs. Martha, now long past the middle of life, and a confirmed old maid, had imbibed a few of the habits and peculiarities which are supposed, and perhaps justly, to characterize that condition. Amongst other things she had a peculiar fancy for the water from the Elmin spring, and could not relish her temperate supper if washed down by any other beverage; and she was accustomed to fetch it herself in the identical china jug, the present of her godmother, the basin belonging to which she had broken from the shock she underwent when hearing of George's wedding. It is even possible, so much are we the creatures of association, that the constant sight of this favourite piece of porcelain, which was really of very curious and beautiful Nankin china, might be perpetually reminding her of her loss, and the occasion serve to confirm her inveterate aversion to poor George and his family.

However this might be, it chanced that one summer evening Mrs. Martha sallied forth to fetch the sparkling draught from the Elmin spring. She filled her jug as usual, but much rain had fallen, and the dame, no longer so active as she had been, slipped when about to reascend the bank with her burthen, and found herself compelled either to throw herself forward and grasp the trunk of the nearest tree, to the imminent peril of her china jug, of which she was compelled to let go, or to slide back to the already tottering and slippery plank, at the risk, almost the certainty, of plunging head foremost into the water. If Mrs. Martha had been asked, on level ground and out of danger, whether she preferred to be soused in her own person, or to break her china jug, she would, most undoubtedly, theoretically have chosen the ducking; but theory and practice are different matters, and following the instinct of self-preservation, she let the dear jug go, and clung to the tree.

As soon as she was perfectly safe she began to lament, in her usual vituperative strain, over her irreparable loss, scolding the tottering plank and the slippery bank, and finally, there being no one else to bear the blame, her own heedless haste, which had cost her the commodity she valued most in the world. Swinging herself round, however, still supported by the tree, she had the satisfaction to perceive that the dear jug was not yet either sunken or broken. It rested most precariously on a tuft of bulrushes towards the centre of the pool, in instant danger of both these calamities, and, indeed, appeared to her to be visibly sinking under its own weight. What could she do? She could never reach it, and whilst she went to summon assistance, the precious porcelain would vanish. What more could she do?

Just as she was asking herself this question, she had the satisfaction to hear footsteps in the lane. She called, and a small voice was heard singing, and the little man Moses, with his satchel at his back, made his appearance, returning from school. He had not heard her, and she would not call him, not even to preserve her china treasure. Moses, however, saw the dilemma, and pausing only to pull off his coat, plunged into the water, to rescue the sinking cup.

The summer had been wet, and the pool was unusually high, and Mrs. Martha, startled to perceive that he was almost immediately beyond his depth, called to him earnestly and vehemently to return. The resolute boy, however, accustomed from infancy to dabble like the young water-fowl amidst the sedges and islets of the great pond, was not to be frightened by the puny waters of the Elmin spring. He reached, though at some peril, the tuft of bulrushes—brought the jug triumphantly to land—washed it—filled it at the fountain-head, and finally offered it, with his own sweet and gracious smile, to Mrs. Martha. And she—oh! what had she not suffered during the last few moments whilst the poor orphan—her brother George's only boy—was risking his life to preserve for her a paltry bit of earthenware! What had she not felt during those few but long moments! Her woman's heart melted within her, and instead of seizing the precious porcelain, she caught the dripping boy in her arms—half smothered him with kisses, and vowed that her home should be his home, and her fortune his fortune.

And she kept her word—she provided amply and kindly for Dinah and her daughters; but Moses is her heir, and he lives at the Manor Farm, and is married to the prettiest woman in the country; and Mrs. Martha has betaken herself to the pond-side, with a temper so much ameliorated that the good farmer declares the greatest risk his children run is of being spoilt by Aunt Martha: one in particular, her godson, who has inherited the name and the favour of his father, and is her own especial little Moses.

CHAPTER XL

ROSEDALE

I DON'T know how it happened when we were house-hunting the other day, that nobody ever thought of Rosedale. I should have objected to it, both as out of distance—it's a good six miles off—and as being utterly unrecommendable by one rational person to another. Rosedale! The very name smacks of the Minerva Press, and gives token of the nonsense and trumpery thereunto belonging. Rosedale Cottage! The man who, under that portentous title, takes that house, cannot complain of lack of warning.

Nevertheless is Rosedale one of the prettiest cottages that ever sprung into existence in brick or on paper. All strangers go to see it, and few 'cots of spruce gentility' are so well worth seeing. Fancy a low irregular white rough-cast building thatched with reeds, covered with roses, clematis, and passion-flowers, standing on a knoll of fine turf, amidst flower-beds and shrubberies and magnificent elms, backed by an abrupt hill, and looking over lawny fields to a green common, which is intersected by a gay high road, dappled with ponds of water, and terminated by a pretty village edging off into rich woodlands: imagine this picture of a place tricked out with ornaments of all sorts, conservatories, roseries, rustic seats, American borders, Gothic dairies, Spanish hermitages, and flowers stuck as close as pins in a pincushion, with everything, in short, that might best become the walls of an exhibition room, or the back scene of a play: conceive the interior adorned in a style of elegance still more fanciful, and it will hardly appear surprising that this 'unique bijou,' as the advertisement calls it, should seldom want a tenant. The rapid succession of these occupiers is the more extraordinary matter. Everybody is willing to come to Rosedale, but nobody stays.

For this, however, it is not difficult to assign very sufficient cause. In the first place, the house has the original sin of most ornamented cottages, that of being built on the foundation of a real labourer's dwelling—by

which notable piece of economy the owner saved some
thirty pounds, at the expense of making half his rooms
mere nutshells, and the house incurably damp — to say
nothing of the inconvenience of the many apartments which
were erected as after-thoughts, the addenda of the work,
and are only to be come at by outside passages and french
window doors. Secondly, that necessary part of a two-
story mansion, the staircase, was utterly forgotten by
architect, proprietor, and builder, and never missed by any
person, till the ladder being one day taken away at the
dinner hour, an Irish labourer, accidentally left behind, was
discovered by the workmen on their return, perched like a
bird on the top of the roof, he having taken the method of
going up the chimney as the quickest way of getting down.
This adventure occasioned a call for the staircase, which
was at length inserted by the by, and is as much like a step-
ladder in a dark corner as anything well can be.[1] Thirdly
and lastly, this beautiful abode is in every way most
thoroughly inconvenient and uncomfortable. In the
winter one might find as much protection in the hollow
of a tree—cold, gusty, sleety, wet; snow threatening from
above like an avalanche; water gushing up from below like
a fountain; a house of card-paper would be the solider
refuge, a gipsy's tent by far the more snug. In summer it
is proportionably close and hot, giving little shade and no
shelter; and all the year round it is overdone with frippery
and finery, a toy-shop in action, a Brobdingnagian baby-
house.

Every room is in masquerade: the saloon Chinese, full of
jars and mandarins and pagodas; the library Egyptian,
all covered with hieroglyphics, and swarming with furniture
crocodiles and sphinxes. Only think of a crocodile couch
and a sphinx sofa! They sleep in Turkish tents, and dine
in a Gothic chapel.[2] Now English ladies and gentlemen

---

[1] This instance of forgetfulness is not unexampled. A similar accident
is said to have happened to Madame d'Arblay in the erection of a cottage
built from the profits of her admirable *Camilla*.

[2] Some of the pleasantest days of my life have been spent in a house
so furnished. But then it was of fitting dimensions, and the delightful
persons to whom it belonged had a house in London and a mansion in the
country, and used their fancy villa much as one would use a marquee or a
pleasure-boat, for gay parties in fine weather. Rosedale, unlucky place,
was built to be lived in.

in their everyday apparel look exceedingly out of place amongst such mummery. The costume won't do. It is not in keeping. Besides, the properties themselves are apt to get shifted from one scene to another, and all manner of anomalies are the consequence. The mitred chairs and screens of the chapel, for instance, so very upright and tall, and carved and priestly, were mixed up oddly enough with the squat Chinese bronzes, whilst by some strange transposition a pair of nodding mandarins figured amongst the Egyptian monsters, and by the aid of their supernatural ugliness really looked human.

Then the room taken up by the various knick-knackery, the unnamed and unnameable generation of gewgaws! It always seemed to me to require more housemaids than the house would hold. And the same with the garden. You are so begirt with garlands and festoons, flowers above and flowers below, that you walk about under a perpetual sense of trespass, of taking care, of doing mischief, now bobbing against a sweet-brier, in which rencontre you have the worst; now flapped in the face by a woodbine to the discomfiture of both parties; now revenging these vegetable wrongs by tripping up an unfortunate balsam; bonnets, coatskirts, and flounces in equal peril! The very gardeners step gingerly, and tuck their aprons tightly round them before they venture into that fair demesne of theirs, which is, so to say, over-peopled. In short, Rosedale is a place to look at rather than live in; a fact which will be received without dispute by some score of tenants, by the proprietor of the county newspaper, who keeps the advertisement of this matchless villa constantly set, to his no small emolument, and by the neighbourhood at large, to whom the succession of new faces, new liveries, and new equipages driving about our rustic lanes, and sometimes occupying a very tasty pew in the parish church, has long supplied a source of conversation as unfailing and as various as the weather.

The first person who ascertained, by painful experience, that Rosedale was uninhabitable, was the proprietor, a simple young man from the next town, who unluckily took it into his head that he had a taste for architecture and landscape gardening and so forth; and falling into the hands of a London upholsterer and a country nurseryman, produced the effort of genius that I have endeavoured to describe. At the end of a month he found that nobody could live there, and with the advice of the nurseryman and the upholsterer began to talk of rebuilding and new-modelling; nay, he actually went so far as to send for the bricklayer, but fortunately for our man of taste he had a wife of more sense than himself, who seized the moment of disappointment to disgust him with improvements and improvers, in which feat she was greatly aided by the bills of his late associates; put a stop at once to his projects and his complaints; removed with all speed to their old residence, an ugly, roomy, comfortable red-brick house in the market place at B——; drew up a flaming advertisement, and turned the grumbling occupant into a thriving landlord. Lucky for him was the day in which William Walker, Esquire, married Miss Bridget Tomkins, second daughter of Mr. Samuel Tomkins, attorney-at-law! And lucky for Mr. Samuel Tomkins was the hour in which he acquired a son-in-law more profitable in the article of leases than the two lords to whom he acted as steward both put together!

First on the list of tenants was a bride and bridegroom come to spend the early months of their nuptial life in this sweet retirement. They arrived towards the end of August with a great retinue of servants, horses, dogs, and carriages, well bedecked with bridal favours. The very pointers had white ribbons round their necks, so splendid was their rejoicing, and had each, as we were credibly informed, eaten a huge slice of wedding cake when the happy couple returned from church. The bride, whom everybody except myself called plain, and whom I thought pretty, had been a great heiress, and had married for love the day she came of age. She was slight of form and pale of complexion, with a profusion of brown hair, mild hazel eyes, a sweet smile, a soft voice, and an air of modesty that clung about her like a veil. I never saw a more lovable creature. He was dark and tall and stout and bold, with an assured yet gentlemanly air, a loud voice, a confident manner, and a real passion for shooting. They stayed just a fortnight, during which time he contrived to get warned off half the manors in the neighbourhood, and cut down the finest elm on the lawn one wet morning to open a view of the high road. I hope the marriage has turned out a happy one, for she was a sweet gentle creature. I used to see her leaning over the gate watching his return from shooting with such a fond patience! And her bound to meet him when he did appear! And the pretty coaxing playfulness with which she patted and chided her rivals the dogs! Oh, I hope she is happy, but I fear, I fear.

Next succeeded a couple from India, before whom floated reports golden and gorgeous as the clouds at sunset. Inexhaustible riches; profuse expenditure; tremendous ostentation; unheard-of luxury; ortolans; beccaficos; French beans at Christmas; green peas at Easter; strawberries always; a chariot and six; twelve black footmen; and parrots and monkeys beyond all count. These were amongst the most moderate of the rumours that preceded them; and every idle person in the country was preparing to be a hanger-on, and every shopkeeper in B—— on the watch for a customer, when up drove a quiet-looking old gentleman in a pony-chaise, with a quiet-looking old lady at his side, and took possession, their retinue following in a hack postchaise. Whether the habits of this Eastern Croesus corresponded with his modest début, or his magnificent reputation, we had not time to discover, although, from certain indications, I conceive that much might be said on both sides. They arrived in the middle of a fine October, while the China roses covered the walls, and the China asters and dahlias and fuschias and geraniums in full blow gave a summer brilliancy to the lawn; but scarcely had a pair of superb Common Prayer Books, bound in velvet, and a Bible with gold clasps, entered in possession of the pew at church, before 'there came a frost, a nipping frost,' which turned the China asters and the China roses brown, and the dahlias and geraniums black, and the nabob and the nabobess blue. They disappeared the next day, and have never been seen or heard of since.

Then arrived a fox-hunting baronet, with a splendid stud and a splendid fortune. A young man, a single man, a handsome man! Every speculating mamma in the country

fixed her eyes on Sir Robert for a son-in-law; papas were
sent to call; brothers were enjoined to go out hunting and
get acquainted; nay, even certain of the young ladies
themselves (I grieve to say it!) showed symptoms of
condescension which might almost have made their grand-
mothers start from their graves. But what could they do?
How could they help it, poor pretty things? The baronet,
with the instinct of a determined bachelor, avoided a young
lady as a sparrow does a hawk, and discovering this shyness
they followed their instinct as the hawk would do in a
similar case, and pursued the coy bird. It was what
sportsmen call a fine open season, which, being translated,
means every variety of wintry weather except frost —
dirty, foggy, sleety, wet; so such of our belles as looked well
on horseback took the opportunity to ride to cover and
see the hounds throw off; and such as shone more as
pedestrians would take an early walk, exquisitely dressed,
for their health's sake, towards the general rendezvous.
Still Sir Robert was immovable. He made no morning
calls, accepted no invitations, spoke to no mortal till he had
ascertained that there was neither sister, daughter, aunt,
nor cousin in the case. He kept from every petticoat as
if it contained the contagion of the plague, shunned ball-
rooms and drawing-rooms as if they were pest-houses, and
finally had the comfort of leaving Rosedale without having
even bowed to a female during his stay. The final cause of
his departure has been differently reported; some hold that
he was frightened away by Miss Amelia Singleton, who had
nearly caused him to commit involuntary homicide (is that
the word for killing a woman?) by crossing and recrossing
before his hunter in Sallowfield Lane, thereby putting him
in danger of a coroner's inquest, whilst others assert that
his landlord, Mr. Walker, happening to call one day, found
his tenant in dirty boots on the sphinx sofa, and a Newfoundland dog dripping with mud on the crocodile couch,
and gave him notice to quit on the spot. For my part I
regard this legend as altogether apocryphal, invented to
save the credit of the house, by assuming that one of its
many inhabitants was turned out, contrary to his own wish.
My faith goes entirely with the Miss Amelia version of the
history; the more so, as that gentle damsel was so incon-

solable as to marry a former beau, a small squire of the
neighbourhood, rather weather-beaten, and not quite so
young as he had been, within a month after she had the ill
luck not to be run over by Sir Robert.

However that may have been, 'thence ensued a vacancy'
in Rosedale, which was supplied the same week by a
musical family, a travelling band—drums, trumpets, harps,
pianos, violins, violoncellos, trombones, and German flutes—
noise personified—an incarnation of din! The family consisted of three young ladies who practised regularly six
hours a day; a governess who played on some instrument
or other from morning till night; one fluting brother; one
fiddling ditto; a violoncelloing music-master; and a singing
papa. The only quiet person among them, the 'one poor
halfpennyworth of bread to this monstrous quantity of
sack,' was the unfortunate mamma, sole listener, as it
seemed, of her innumerous choir. Oh, how we pitied her!
She was a sweet, placid-looking woman, and younger in
appearance than either of her daughters, with a fair open
forehead, full dark eyes, lips that seemed waiting to smile,
a deep yet cool colour, and a heavenly composure of
countenance, resembling in features, expression, and complexion the small Madonnas of Raphael. We never ceased
to wonder at her happy serenity until we found out that the
good lady was deaf, a discovery which somewhat diminished
the ardour of our admiration. How this enviable calamity
befell her I did not hear—but of course that din! The
very jars and mandarins cracked under the incessant
vibration; I only wonder that the poor house did not
break the drum of its ears; did not burst from its own
report, and explode like an overloaded gun. One could not
see that unlucky habitation half a mile off, without such a
feeling of noise as comes over one in looking at Hogarth's
enraged musician. To pass it was really dangerous. One
stage-coach was overturned and two postchaises ran away
in consequence of their uproarious doings; and a sturdy
old-fashioned country gentleman, who rode a particularly
anti-musical, startlish blood-horse, began to talk of in-
dicting Rosedale as a nuisance, when just at the critical
moment its tenants had the good fortune to discover
that although the hermitage with its vaulted roof made a

capital concert-room, yet that there was not space enough within doors for their several practisings, that the apartments were too small, and the partitions too thin, so that concord was turned into discord, and harmonies went crossing each other all over the house—Mozart jostled by Rossini, and Handel put down by Weber. And away they went also.

Our next neighbours were two ladies, not sisters, except, as one of them said, in soul; kindred spirits determined to retire from the world, and emulate in this sweet retreat the immortal friendship of the ladies of Llangollen.[1] The names of our pair of friends were Jackson and Jennings, Miss Laura Jackson (I wonder whether Laura really was her name! She signed herself so in prose and in verse, and would certainly for more reasons than one have disliked an appeal to the register! Besides, she ought to know, so Laura it shall be!)—Miss Laura Jackson and Miss Barbara Jennings, commonly called Bab. Both were of that unfortunate class of young ladies, whom the malicious world is apt to call old maids; both rich, both independent, and both in the fullest sense of the word Cockneys. Laura was tall and lean and scraggy and yellow, dressing in an Arcadian sort of way, pretty much like an opera shepherdess without a crook, singing pastoral songs prodigiously out of tune, and talking in a deep voice, with much emphasis and astounding fluency, all sorts of sentimentalities all the day long. Miss Barbara on the other hand was short and plump and round-faced and ruddy, inclining to vulgarity as Laura to affectation, with a great love of dancing, a pleasant chuckling laugh, and a most agreeable habit of assentation. Altogether Bab was a likeable person in spite of some nonsense, which is more than could honestly be said for her companion.

Juxtaposition laid the corner - stone of this immortal

[1] I need not, I trust, disclaim any intention of casting the lightest shade of ridicule on the remarkable instance of female friendship to which I have alluded in the text. A union enduring, as that has done, from youth to age, adorned by rank, talent, and beauty, cemented by cheerfulness and good humour, and consecrated by benevolence and virtue, can fear no one's censure, and soars far beyond my feeble praise. Such a friendship is the very poetry of life. But the heartless imitation, the absurd parody of the noble elevating romance is surely fair game, the more so, as it tends like all parodies to bring the original into undeserved disrepute.

friendship, which had already lasted four months and a
half, and, cemented by resemblance of situation and dis-
similarity of character, really bade fair to continue some
months longer. Both had been heartily weary of their
previous situations: Laura keeping house for a brother in
Aldersgate Street, where, as she said, she was overwhelmed
by odious vulgar business; Barbara living with an aunt on
Fish Street Hill, where she was tired to death of having
nothing to do. Both had a passion for the country: Laura,
who, except one jaunt to Margate, had never been out of the
sound of Bow Bell, that she might ruralize after the fashion
of the poets, sit under trees and gather roses all day long;
Bab, who, in spite of yearly trips to Paris and Brussels and
Amsterdam and Brighton, had hardly seen a green field
except through a coach window, was on her side possessed
with a mania for notability and management; *she yearned
to keep cows*, fatten pigs, breed poultry, grow cabbages,
make hay, brew and bake, and wash and churn. Visions
of killing her own mutton flitted over her delighted fancy;
and, when one evening at a ball in the Borough her favourite
partner had deserted her to dance with her niece, and
Miss Laura, who had been reading Miss Seward's letters,
proposed to her to retire from the world and its vanities in
imitation of the illustrious recluses of Llangollen, Miss
Barbara, caught above all things with the prospect of making her own butter every morning for breakfast,[1] acceded
to the proposal most joyfully.

The vow of friendship was taken, and nothing remained
but to look out for a house. Barbara wanted a farm, Laura
a cottage; Barbara talked of cows and clover, Laura of
nightingales and violets; Barbara sighed for Yorkshire
pastures, Laura for Welsh mountains; and the scheme
seemed likely to go off for want of an habitation, when
Rosedale in all the glory of advertisement shone on Miss
Laura in the *Morning Post*, and was immediately engaged
by the delighted friends on a lease of seven, fourteen, or
one-and-twenty years.

It was a raw blowy March evening when the fair partners
arrived at the cottage. Miss Laura made a speech in her
usual style on taking possession—an invocation to friend-

[1] Vide Anna Seward's Correspondence.

ship and rural nature, and a deprecation of cities, society, and men—at the conclusion of which Miss Barbara underwent an *embrassade*; and, having sufficiently admired the wonders within, they sallied forth with a candle and lanthorn to view their ruralities without. Miss Laura was better satisfied with this ramble than her companion. She found at least trees and primroses, whilst the country felicities of ducks and chickens were entirely wanting. Bab, however, reconciled the matter by supposing they were gone to roost, and, a little worn out by the journey, wisely followed their example.

The next day saw Miss Laura obliged to infringe her own most sacred and inviolable rule, and admit a man—the apothecary—into this maiden abode. She had sat under a tree the night before listening not to, but for, a nightingale, and was laid up by a most unpastoral fit of the rheumatism. Barbara in the meanwhile was examining her territory by daylight, and discovering fresh cause of vexation at every step. Here she was in the country, in a cottage, 'comprising,' as the advertisement set forth, 'all manner of convenience and accommodation,' without grass or corn, or cow or sheep, or pig or chicken, or turkey or goose—no laundry, no brew-house, no pigsty, no poultry yard—not a cabbage in the garden! not a useful thing about the house! Imagine her consternation!

But Barbara was a person of activity and resource. She sallied out forthwith to the neighbouring village, bought utensils and livestock; turned the coach-house into a cow-stall; projected a pigsty in the rosery; installed her ducks and geese in the orangery; introduced the novelty of real milk-pans, churns, and butter-prints amongst the old china, Dutch tiles, and stained glass of that make-believe toy the Gothic dairy; placed her brewing vessels in 'the housekeeper's room,' which, to accord with the genius of the place, had been fitted up to represent a robber's cave; deposited her washing-tubs in the butler's pantry, which, with a similar regard to congruity, had been decorated with spars and shells like a nereid's grotto; and, finally, in spite of all warning and remonstrance, drove her sheep into the shrubbery and tethered her cows upon the lawn.

This last stroke was too much for the gardener's patience. He betook himself in all haste to B—— to apprise Mr. Walker; and Mr. Walker, armed with Mr. Samuel Tomkins and a copy of the lease, made his appearance with breathless speed at Rosedale. Barbara, in spite of her usual placidity, made good battle on this occasion. She cried and scolded and reasoned and implored. It was as much as Mr. Walker and Mr. Samuel Tomkins, aided by their mute witness the lease and that very clamorous auxiliary the gardener, could do to out-talk her. At last, however, they were victorious. Poor Miss Bab's live stock were forced to make a rapid retreat; and she would probably have marched off at the same time had not an incident occurred which brought her visions of rural felicity much nearer to reality than could have been anticipated by the liveliest imagination.

The farmer's wife, of whom she had made her purchases, and to whom she unwillingly addressed herself to resume them, seeing, to use her own words, 'how much madam seemed to take on at parting with the poor dumb things,' kindly offered to accommodate them as boarders at a moderate stipend, volunteering also lessons in the chicken-rearing and pig-feeding department, of which the lady did to be sure stand rather in need.

Of course Barbara closed with this proposal at a word. She never was so happy in her life; her cows, pigs, and poultry, *en pension*, close by, where she might see them every hour if she liked, and she herself, with both hands full, learning at the farm, and ordering at the cottage, and displaying all that can be imagined of ignorance and good humour at both.

Her mistakes were innumerable. Once, for instance, she carried away by main force from a turkey, whose nest she had the ill luck to discover, thirteen eggs, just ready to hatch, and after a severe combat with the furious and injured hen, brought them home to Rosedale as fresh laid—under a notion rather new in natural history, that turkeys lay all their eggs in one day. Another time she discovered a hoard of choice double dahlia roots in a tool-house belonging to her old enemy the gardener, and delivered them to the cook for Jerusalem artichokes, who dressed them as such accordingly. No end to Barbara's blunders, but her good humour, her cheerfulness, her liberality, and the happy frankness with which she laughed at her own mistakes, carried her triumphantly through. Everybody liked her, especially a smug little curate who lodged at the very farm-house where her pigs and cattle were boarded, and said twenty times a day that Miss Barbara Jennings was the pleasantest woman in England. Barbara was never so happy in her life.

Miss Laura, on her part, continued rheumatic and poorly, and kept closely to her bed-chamber, the Turkish tent, with no other consolations than novels from the next town and the daily visits of the apothecary. She was shocked at Miss Barbara's intimacy with the farm people, and took every opportunity of telling her so. Barbara, never very fond of her fair companion's harangues, and not the more reconciled to them from their being directed against her own particular favourites, ran away as often as she could. So that the two friends had nearly arrived at the point of not speaking, when they met one afternoon by mutual appointment in the Chinese saloon. Miss Barbara blushed and looked silly, and seemed trying to say something which she could not bring out. Miss Laura tried to blush rather unsuccessfully. She, however, could talk at all times, her powers of speech were never known to fail; and at the end of an oration in which she proved, as was pretty evident, that they had been mistaken in supposing the company of each all-sufficient to the other, as well as in their plan of seclusion from the world, she invited Miss Barbara, after another vain attempt at a blush, to pay the last honours to their friendship by attending her to the hymeneal altar, whither she had promised to accompany Mr. Opodeldoc on the morning after the next.

'I can't,' replied Miss Barbara.

'And why not?' resumed Miss Laura. 'Surely Mr. Opodel——'

'Now, don't be angry!' interrupted our friend Bab 'I can't be your bridesmaid the day after to-morrow because I am going to be married to-morrow myself.'

And so they left Rosedale and I shall leave them.

CHAPTER XLI

THE FALL OF THE LEAF

Nov. 6th. The weather is as peaceful to-day, as calm and as mild as in early April; and perhaps an autumn afternoon and a spring morning do resemble each other more in feeling, and even in appearance, than any two periods of the year. There is in both the same freshness and dewiness of the herbage, the same balmy softness in the air, and the same pure and lovely blue sky, with white fleecy clouds floating across it. The chief difference lies in the absence of flowers, and the presence of leaves. But then the foliage of November is so rich and glowing and varied that it may well supply the place of the gay blossoms of the spring; whilst all the flowers of the field or the garden could never make amends for the want of leaves—that beautiful and graceful attire in which nature has clothed the rugged forms of trees—the verdant drapery to which the landscape owes its loveliness, and the forests their glory.

If choice must be between two seasons, each so full of charm, it is at least no bad philosophy to prefer the present good, even whilst looking gratefully back and hopefully forward to the past and the future. And, of a surety, no fairer specimen of November day could well be found than this—a day made to wander

> By yellow commons and birch-shaded hollows,
> And hedgerows bordering unfrequented lanes;

nor could a prettier country be found for our walk than this shady and yet sunny Berkshire, where the scenery, without rising into grandeur or breaking into wildness, is so peaceful, so cheerful, so varied, and so thoroughly English.

We must bend our steps towards the water-side, for I have a message to leave at Farmer Riley's: and sooth to say, it is no unpleasant necessity, for the road thither is smooth and dry, retired, as one likes a country walk to be, but not too

lonely, which women never like, leading past the Loddon—
the bright, brimming, transparent Loddon—a fitting mirror
for this bright blue sky, and terminating at one of the
prettiest and most comfortable farm-houses in the neighbourhood.

How beautiful the lane is to-day, decorated with a
thousand colours! The brown road, and the rich verdure
that borders it, strewed with the plain yellow leaves of the
elm just beginning to fall; hedgerows glowing with long
wreaths of the bramble in every variety of purplish red;
and overhead the unchanged green of the fir, contrasting
with the spotted sycamore, the tawny beech, and the dry
sere leaves of the oak, which rustle as the light wind passes
through them; a few common hardy yellow flowers (for
yellow is the common colour of flowers, whether wild or
cultivated, as blue is the rare one), flowers of many sorts,
but almost of one tint, still blowing in spite of the season,
and ruddy berries glowing through all. How very
beautiful is the lane!

And how pleasant is this hill where the road widens, with
the group of cattle by the wayside, and George Hearn, the
little post-boy, trundling his hoop at full speed, making all
the better haste in his work, because he cheats himself into
thinking it play! And how beautiful again is this patch of
common at the hill-top with the clear pool, where Martha
Pither's children—elves of three and four and five years old
—without any distinction of sex in their sunburnt faces
and tattered drapery, are dipping up water into their little
homely cups shining with cleanliness, and a small brown
pitcher with the lip broken, to fill that great kettle, which,
when it is filled, their united strength will never be able to
lift! They are quite a group for a painter, with their rosy
cheeks and chubby hands and round merry faces; and the
low cottage in the background, peeping out of its vine leaves
and China roses, with Martha at the door, tidy and comely
and smiling, preparing the potatoes for the pot, and watching the progress of dipping and filling that useful utensil,
completes the picture.

But we must get on. No time for more sketches in these
short days. It is getting cold too. We must proceed in
our walk. Dash is showing us the way and beating the

thick double hedgerow that runs along the side of the
meadows, at a rate that indicates game astir, and causes the
leaves to fly as fast as an east wind after a hard frost. Ah!
a pheasant—a superb cock pheasant! Nothing is more
certain than Dash's questing, whether in a hedgerow or
covert, for a better spaniel never went into the field; but
I fancied that it was a hare afoot, and was almost as much
startled to hear the whirring of those splendid wings, as the
princely bird himself would have been at the report of a gun.
Indeed, I believe that the way in which a pheasant goes off
does sometimes make young sportsmen a little nervous
(they don't own it very readily, but the observation may be
relied on nevertheless), until they get, as it were, broken into
the sound; and then that grand and sudden burst of wing
becomes as pleasant to them as it seems to be to Dash, who
is beating the hedgerow with might and main, and giving
tongue louder, and sending the leaves about faster than
ever—very proud of finding the pheasant, and perhaps a
little angry with me for not shooting it; at least, looking as
if he would be angry if I were a man, for Dash is a dog of
great sagacity, and has doubtless not lived four years
in the sporting world without making the discovery that
although gentlemen do shoot, ladies do not.

The Loddon at last—the beautiful Loddon! And the
bridge, where every one stops, as by instinct, to lean over
the rails, and gaze a moment on a landscape of surpassing
loveliness—the fine grounds of the Great House, with their
magnificent groups of limes and firs, and poplars grander
than ever poplars were; the green meadows opposite,
studded with oaks and elms; the clear winding river; the
mill with its picturesque old buildings bounding the scene;
all glowing with the rich colouring of autumn, and harmonized by the soft beauty of the clear blue sky, and the
delicious calmness of the hour. The very peasant whose
daily path it is cannot cross that bridge without a pause.

But the day is wearing fast, and it grows colder and colder.
I really think it will be a frost. After all, spring is the
pleasantest season. Beautiful as this scenery is, we must
get on. Down that broad yet shadowy lane, between the
park, dark with evergreens and dappled with deer, and the
meadows where sheep and cows and horses are grazing

under the tall elms—that lane, where the wild bank, clothed with fern and tufted with furze and crowned by rich berried thorn and thick shining holly on the one side, seems to vie in beauty with the picturesque old paling, the bright laurels, and the plumy cedars, on the other—down that shady lane until the sudden turn brings us to an opening where four roads meet; where a noble avenue turns down to the Great House; where the village church rears its modest spire from amidst its venerable yew-trees; and where, embosomed in orchards and gardens, and backed by barns and ricks, and all the wealth of the farm-yard, stands the spacious and comfortable abode of good Farmer Riley— the end and object of our walk.

And in happy time the message is said, and the answer given, for this beautiful mild day is edging off into a dense frosty evening; the leaves of the elm and the linden in the old avenue are quivering and vibrating and fluttering in the air, and at length falling crisply on the earth, as if Dash were beating for pheasants in the tree-tops; the sun gleams dimly through the fog, giving little more of light or heat than his fair sister the lady moon—I don't know a more disappointing person than a cold sun; and I am beginning to wrap my cloak closely round me, and to calculate the distance to my own fireside, recanting all the way my praises of November, and longing for the showery flowery April as much as if I were a half-chilled butterfly, or a dahlia knocked down by the frost.

Ah, dear me! what a climate this is, that one cannot keep in the same mind about it for half an hour together! I wonder by the way whether the fault is in the weather, which Dash does not seem to care for, or in me? If I should happen to be wet through in a shower next spring, and should catch myself longing for autumn, that would settle the question.

CHAPTER XLII

THE TWO DOLLS

A LUCKY day it was for little Fanny Elvington when her good Aunt Delmont consented to receive her into her family, and sent for her from a fine old place, six miles from hence, Burdon Park, where she had been living with her maternal grandfather, to her own comfortable house in Brunswick Square. Poor Fanny had no natural home, her father, General Elvington, being in India with his lady, and a worse residence than the Park could hardly be devised for a little girl, since Lady Burdon was dead, Sir Richard too sickly to be troubled with children, and the care of his granddaughter left entirely to a vulgar old nurse and a superfine housekeeper. A lucky day for Fanny was that in which she exchanged their misrule for the wise and gentle government of her good Aunt Delmont.

Fanny Elvington was a nice little girl, who had a great many good qualities, and like other little girls, a few faults, which had grown up like weeds under the neglect and mismanagement of the people at the Park, and threatened to require both time and pains to eradicate. For instance, she had a great many foolish antipathies and troublesome fears, some caught from the affectation of the housekeeper, some from the ignorance of the nurse. She shrieked at the sight of a mouse, squalled at a frog, was wellnigh ready to faint at an earwig, and quite as much afraid of a spider as if she had been a fly. She ran away from a quiet ox as if he had been a mad bull, and had such a horror of chimney-sweepers that she shrank her head under the bedclothes whenever she heard the deep cry of 'Sweep! sweep!' fore-running the old-clothes-man and the milkman on a frosty morning, and could hardly be persuaded to look at them, poor creatures, dressed in their tawdry tinsel, and dancing round Jack-of-the-Green on May Day. But her favourite

fear, her pet aversion, was a negro; especially a little black
footboy who lived next door, and whom she never saw without shrinking and shuddering and turning pale.

It was a most unlucky aversion for Fanny, and gave her
and her aunt more trouble than all her other mislikings
put together, inasmuch as Pompey came oftener in view
than mouse or frog, spider or earwig, ox or chimney-sweep.
How it happened nobody could tell, but Pompey was always
in Fanny Elvington's way. She saw him twice as often as
any one else in the house. If she went to the window, he
was sure to be standing on the steps; if she walked in the
Square garden, she met him crossing the pavement. She
could not water her geraniums in the little court behind the
house, but she heard his merry voice singing in broken
English as he cleaned the knives and shoes on the other side
of the wall; nay, she could not even hang out her canary
bird's cage at the back door, but he was sure to be feeding
his parrot at theirs. Go where she would, Pompey's
shining black face and broad white teeth followed her:
he haunted her very dreams; and the oftener she saw him,
whether sleeping or waking, the more her unreasonable
antipathy grew upon her. Her cousins laughed at her
without effect, and her aunt's serious remonstrances were
equally useless.

The person who, next to Fanny herself, suffered the most
from this foolish and wicked prejudice, was poor Pompey,
whose intelligence, activity, and good humour had made
him a constant favourite in his master's house, and who had
sufficient sensibility to feel deeply the horror and disgust
which he had inspired in his young neighbour. At first
he tried to propitiate her by bringing groundsel and chick-
weed for her canary bird, running to meet her with an
umbrella when she happened to be caught in the rain, and
other small attentions, which were repelled with absolute
loathing.

'Me same flesh and blood with you, missy, though skin
be black!' cried poor Pompey one day, when pushed to
extremity by Fanny's disdain, 'same flesh and blood,
missy!'—a fact which the young lady denied with more
than usual indignation. She looked at her own white skin,
and she thought of his black one, and all the reasoning of

her aunt failed to convince her that where the outside was so different the inside could by possibility be alike. At last Mrs. Delmont was fain to leave the matter to the great curer of all prejudices, called Time, who in this case seemed even slower in his operations than usual.

In the meanwhile Fanny's birthday approached, and as it was within a few days of that of her cousin Emma Delmont, it was agreed to celebrate the two festivals together. Double feasting! double holiday! double presents! Never was a gayer anniversary. Mrs. Delmont's own gifts had been reserved to the conclusion of the jollity; and, after the fruit was put on the table, two huge dolls, almost as big as real babies, were introduced to the little company. They excited and deserved universal admiration. The first was a young lady of the most delicate construction and the most elaborate ornament—a doll of the highest fashion, with sleeves like a bishop, a waist like a wasp, a magnificent bustle, and petticoats so full and so puffed out round the bottom that the question of hoop or no hoop was stoutly debated between two of the elder girls. Her cheeks were very red, and her neck very white, and her ringlets in the newest possible taste. In short, she was so completely *à la mode* that a Parisian milliner might have sent her as a pattern to her fellow-tradeswoman in London, or the London milliner might have returned the compliment to her sister artist over the water. Her glories, however, were fated to be eclipsed. The moment that the second doll made its appearance, the lady of fashion was looked at no longer.

The second doll was a young gentleman, habited in the striped and braided costume which is the ordinary transition dress of boys between leaving off petticoats and assuming the doublet and hose. It was so exactly like Willy Delmont's own attire that the astonished boy looked at himself to be sure that the doll had not stolen the clothes off his back. The apparel, however, was not the charm that fixed the attention of the young people. The attraction was the complexion, which was of as deep and shining a black, as perfect an imitation of a negro, in tint and feature, as female ingenuity could accomplish. The face, neck, arms, and legs were all covered with black silk; and much skill was shown in shaping and sewing on the broad flat nose, large ears, and pouting lips, whilst the great white teeth and bright round eyes relieved the monotony of the colour. The wig was of black worsted, knitted and then unravelled, as natural as if it had actually grown on the head. Perhaps the novelty (for none of the party had seen a black doll before) might increase the effect, but they all declared that they had never seen so accurate an imitation, so perfect an illusion. Even Fanny, who at first sight had almost taken the doll for her old enemy Pompey in little, and had shrunk back accordingly, began at last to catch some of the curiosity (for curiosity is a catching passion) that characterized her companions. She drew near—she gazed—at last she even touched the doll, and listened with some interest to Mrs. Delmont's detail of the trouble she found in constructing the young lady and gentleman.

'What are they made of, aunt?'

'Rags, my dear!' was the reply; 'nothing but rags,' continued Mrs. Delmont, unripping a little of the black gentleman's foot and the white lady's arm, and showing the linen of which they were composed. 'Both alike, Fanny,' pursued her good aunt, 'both the same colour underneath the skin, and both the work of the same hand—like Pompey and you,' added she more solemnly; 'and now choose which doll you will.'

And Fanny blushing and hesitating, chose the black one, and the next day her aunt had the pleasure to see her show it to Pompey over the wall, to his infinite delight; and, in a very few days, Mrs. Delmont had the still greater pleasure to find that Fanny Elvington had not only overcome and acknowledged her prejudice, but had given Pompey a new half-crown, and had accepted groundsel for her canary bird from the poor negro boy.

NOTE.—About a month after sitting to me for his portrait, the young black gentleman whom I have endeavoured to describe (I do not mean Pompey, but the doll) set out upon his travels. He had been constructed in this little Berkshire of ours for some children in the great county of York; and a friend of mine, travelling northwards, had the goodness to offer him a place in her carriage for the journey. My friend was a married woman accompanied by her husband and another lady, and, finding the doll cumbersome to pack, wrapped it in a large shawl and carried it in her lap, baby fashion. At the first inn where they stopped to dine, she handed it carelessly out of the carriage before alighting, and was much amused to see it received with the grave officious tenderness usually shown to a real infant, by the nicely dressed hostess, whose consternation, when, still taking it for a living child, she caught a glimpse of the complexion, is said to have been irresistibly ludicrous. Of course my friend did not undeceive her. Indeed, I believe she humoured the mistake wherever it occurred all along the north road, to the unspeakable astonishment and mystification of chambermaids and waiters.

CHAPTER XLIII

THE RAT-CATCHER

BEAUTIFULLY situated on a steep knoll, overhanging a sharp angle in the turnpike road which leads through our village of Aberleigh, stands a fantastic rustic building, with a large yew-tree on one side, a superb weeping ash hanging over it on the other, a clump of elms forming a noble background behind, and all the prettinesses of porches garlanded with clematis, windows mantled with jessamine, and chimneys wreathed with luxuriant ivy, adding grace to the picture. To form a picture, most assuredly, it was originally built—a point of view as it is called, from Allonby Park, to which the by-road that winds round this inland cape, or headland, directly leads: and most probably it was also copied from some book of tasteful designs for lodges or ornamented cottages, since not only the building itself, but the winding path that leads up the acclivity, and the gate which gives entrance to the little garden, smack of the pencil and the graver.

For a picture certainly, and probably from a picture, was that cottage erected, although its ostensible purpose was merely that of a receiving-house for letters and parcels for the Park, to which the present inhabitant, a jolly, bustling, managing dame, of great activity and enterprise in her own peculiar line, has added the profitable occupation of a thriving and well-accustomed village shop; contaminating the picturesque old-fashioned bay-window of the fancy letter-house, by the vulgarities of red-herrings, tobacco, onions, and salt butter; a sight which must have made the projector of her elegant dwelling stare again—and forcing her customers to climb up and down an ascent almost as steep as the roof of a house, whenever they wanted a pennyworth of needles, or a halfpennyworth of snuff: a toil whereat some of our poor old dames groaned aloud. Sir Harry threatened to turn her out, and her customers threatened to turn her off; but neither of these events happened.   Dinah Forde appeased her landlord and managed her customers: for Dinah Forde was a notable woman; and it is really surprising what great things, in a small way, your notable woman will compass.

Besides Mrs. Dinah Forde and her apprentice, a girl of ten years old, the letter-house had lately acquired another occupant, in the shape of Dinah's tenant or lodger—I don't know which word best expresses the nature of the arrangement — my old friend Sam Page the rat-catcher, who, together with his implements of office, two ferrets and four mongrels, inhabited a sort of shed or outhouse at the back of the premises—serving, 'especially the curs,' as Mrs. Forde was wont to express herself, 'as a sort of guard and protection to a lone woman's property.'

Sam Page was, as I have said, an old acquaintance of ours, although neither as a resident of Aberleigh, nor in his capacity of rat-catcher, both of which were recent assumptions.   It was, indeed, a novelty to see Sam Page as a resident anywhere.   His abode seemed to be the highway. One should have as soon expected to find a gipsy within stone walls, as soon have looked for a hare in her last year's form, or a bird in her old nest, as for Sam Page in the same place a month together, so completely did he belong to that order which the lawyers call vagrants, and the common people designate by the significant name of trampers; and so entirely of all rovers did he seem the most roving, of all wanderers the most unsettled.   The winds, the clouds, even our English weather, were but a type of his mutability.

Our acquaintance with him had commenced above twenty years ago, when, a lad of some fifteen or thereaway, he carried muffins and cakes about the country.   The whole house was caught by his intelligence and animation, his light active figure, his keen grey eye, and the singular mixture of shrewdness and good humour in his sharp but pleasant features.   Nobody's muffins could go down but Sam Page's.   We turned off our old stupid deaf cakeman, Simon Brown, and appointed Sam on the instant.   (N.B. This happened at the period of a general election, and Sam wore the right colour, and Simon the wrong.)   Three times a week he was to call.   Faithless wretch—he never called again! He took to selling election ballads, and carrying about handbills. We waited for him a fortnight, went muffinless for fourteen days, and then, our candidate being fairly elected, and blue and yellow returned to their original non-importance, were fain to put up once more with poor deaf old Simon Brown.

Sam's next appearance was in the character of a letter-boy, when he and a donkey set up a most spirited opposition to Thomas Hearne and the post-cart. Everybody was dissatisfied with Thomas Hearne, who had committed more sins than I can remember of forgetfulness, irregularity, and all manner of postman-like faults; and Sam, when applying for employers, made a most successful canvass, and for a week performed miracles of punctuality. At the end of that time he began to commit, with far greater vigour than his predecessor, Thomas Hearne, the several sins for which that worthy had been discarded. On Tuesday he forgot to call for the bag in the evening; on Wednesday he omitted to bring it in the morning; on Thursday he never made his appearance at all; on Friday his employers gave him warning; and on Saturday they turned him off. So ended this hopeful experiment.

Still, however, he continued to travel the country in various capacities. First, he carried a tray of casts; then a basket of Staffordshire ware; then he cried cherries; then he joined a troop of ruddlemen, and came about redder than a Red Indian; then he sported a barrel-organ, a piece of mechanism of no small pretensions, having two sets of puppets on the top, one of girls waltzing, the other of soldiers at drill; then he drove a knife-grinder's wheel; then he led a bear and a very accomplished monkey; then he escorted a celebrated company of dancing dogs; and then, for a considerable time, during which he took a trip to India and back, we lost sight of him.

He reappeared, however, at B—— Fair, where one year he was showman to the 'Living Skeleton,' and the next a performer in the tragedy of the *Edinburgh Murders*, as exhibited every half-hour at the price of a penny to each person. Sam showed so much talent for melodrama, that we fully expected to find him following his new profession, which offered all the advantage of the change of place and of character which his habits required; and on his being again, for several months, an absentee, had little doubt but he had been promoted from booth to barn, and even looked for his name amongst a party of five strollers, three men and two women, who issued play-bills at Aberleigh, and performed tragedy, comedy, opera, farce, and panto-mime, with all the degrees and compounds thereof described by Polonius, in the great room at the 'Rose,' divided for the occasion into a row of chairs called the boxes, at a shilling per seat, and two of benches called the pit, at sixpence. I even suspected that a Mr. Theodore Fitzhugh, the genius of the company, might be Sam Page fresh chris-tened. But I was mistaken. Sam, when I saw him again, and mentioned my suspicion, pleaded guilty to a turn for the drama; he confessed that he liked acting of all things especially tragedy, 'it was such fun.' But there was a small obstacle to his pursuit of the more regular branches of the histrionic art—the written drama: our poor friend could not read. To use his own words, 'he was no scholar'; and on recollecting certain small aberrations which had occurred during the three days that he carried the letter-bag, and professed to transact errands, such as the misdelivery of notes, and the non-performance of written commissions, we were fain to conclude that, instead of having, as he expressed it, 'somehow or other got rid of his learning,' learning was a blessing which Sam had never possessed, and that a great luminary was lost to the stage simply from the accident of not knowing his alphabet.

Instead of being, as we had imagined, ranting in Richard, or raving in Lear, our unlucky hero had been amusing him-self by making a voyage to the West Indies, and home by the way of America, having had some thoughts of honouring the New World by making it the scene of his residence, or rather of his peregrinations; and a country where the whole population seems movable would probably have suited him; but the yellow fever seized him and pinned him fast at the very beginning of his North American travels, and sick and weary, he returned to England, determined, as he said, 'to take a room and live respectably.'

The apartment on which he fixed was, as I have intimated, an outhouse belonging to Mrs. Dinah Forde, in which he took up his abode at the beginning of last summer, with his two ferrets, harmless, foreign-looking things (no native English animal has so outlandish an appearance as the ferret, with its long limber body, its short legs, red eyes, and ermine-looking fur), of whose venom, gentle as they looked, he was wont to boast amain; four little dogs, of every variety of mongrel ugliness, whose eminence in the same quality nobody could doubt, for one had lost an eye in battle and one an ear, the third halted in his forequarters, and the fourth limped behind; and a jay of great talent and beauty, who turned his pretty head this way and that, and bent and bowed most courteously when addressed, and then responded in words equally apt and courteous to all that was said to him. Mrs. Dinah Forde fell in love with that jay at first sight; borrowed him of his master, and hung him at one side of her door, where he soon became as famous all through the parish as the talking bird in the Arabian Tales, or the parrot Ver-Vert, immortalized by Gresset.

Sam's own appearance was as rat-catcher-like, I had almost said as venomous, as that of his retinue. His features sharper than ever, thin and worn and sallow, yet arch and good-humoured withal; his keen eye and knowing smile, his pliant active figure, and the whole turn of his equipment, from the shabby straw hat to the equally shabby long gaiters, told his calling almost as plainly as the sharp heads of the ferrets, which were generally protruded from the pockets of his dirty jean jacket, or the bunch of dead rats with which he was wont to parade the streets of B——— on a market-day. He seemed, at last, to have found his proper vocation; and having stuck to it for four or five months, with great success and reputation, there seemed every chance of his becoming stationary at Aberleigh.

In his own profession his celebrity was, as I have said, deservedly great. The usual complaint against rat-catchers, that they take care not to ruin the stock, that they are sure to leave breeders enough, could not be applied to Sam, who, poor fellow, never was suspected of forethought in his life, and who, in this case, had evidently too much delight in the chase himself to dream of checking or stopping it, whilst there was a rat left unslain. On the contrary, so strong was the feeling of his sportsmanship, and that of his poor curs, that one of his grand operations, on the taking in of a wheat-rick, for instance, or the clearing out of a barn, was sure to be attended by all the idle boys, and unemployed men in the village—by all, in short, who, under the pretence of helping, could make an excuse to their wives, their consciences, or the parish officers. The grand battue, on emptying Farmer Brookes's great barn, will be long remembered in Aberleigh; there was more noise made, and more beer drunk, than on any occasion since the happy marriage of Miss Phoebe and the patten-maker; it even emulated the shouts and tipsiness of the B—— election —and that's a bold word! The rats killed were in proportion to the din—and that is a bold word too! I am really afraid to name the number—it seemed to myself, and would appear to my readers, so incredible. Sam and Farmer Brookes were so proud of the achievement that they hung the dead game on the lower branches of the great oak outside the gate, after the fashion practised by mole-catchers, to the unspeakable consternation of a Cockney cousin of the good farmer's, a very fine lady, who had never in her life before been out of the sound of Bow Bell, and who, happening to catch sight of this portentous crop of acorns in passing under the tree, caused her husband who was driving her to turn the gig round, and notwithstanding remonstrance and persuasion, and a most faithful promise that the boughs should be dismantled before night, could not be induced to set foot in a place where the trees were, to use her own words, 'so heathenish,' and betook herself back to her own domicile at Holborn Bars, in great and evident perplexity as to the animal or vegetable quality of the oak in question. [1]

Another cause of the large assemblage at Sam's rat-hunts was, besides the certainty of good sport, the eminent popularity of the leader of the chase. Sam was a universal favourite. He had good fellowship enough to conciliate the dissipated, and yet stopped short of the licence which

[1] Moles are generally, and rats occasionally, strung on willows when killed; not much to the improvement of the beauty of the scenery. I don't know anything that astounds a Londoner more than the sight of a tree bearing such fruit. The plum-pudding tree, whereof mention is made in the pleasant and veracious travels of the Baron Munchausen, could not appear more completely a *lusus naturae*.

would have disgusted the sober—was pleasant spoken, quick, lively, and intelligent—sang a good song, told a good story, and had a kindness of temper, and a lightness of heart, which rendered him a most exhilarating and coveted companion to all in his own station. He was, moreover, a proficient in country games; and so eminent at cricket especially, that the men of Aberleigh were no sooner able, from his residence in the parish, to count him amongst their eleven, than they challenged their old rivals, the men of Hinton, and beat them forthwith.

Two nights before the return match, Sam, even shabbier than usual, and unusually out of spirits, made his appearance at the house of an old Aberleigh cricketer, still a patron and promoter of that noble game, and the following dialogue took place between them:

'Well, Sam, we are to win this match.'

'I hope so, please your honour. But I'm sorry to say I shan't be at the winning of it.'

'Not here, Sam! What, after rattling the stumps about so gloriously last time, won't you stay to finish them now? Only think how those Hinton fellows will crow! You must stay over Wednesday.'

'I can't, your honour. 'Tis not my fault. But here I've had a lawyer's letter on the part of Mrs. Forde, about the trifle of rent, and a bill that I owe her; and if I'm not off to-night, Heaven knows what she'll do with me!'

'The rent—that can't be much. Let's see if we can't manage——'

'Aye, but there's a longish bill, sir,' interrupted Sam. 'Consider, we are seven in family.'

'Seven!' interrupted, in his turn, the other interlocutor.

'Aye, sir, counting the dogs and the ferrets, poor beasts, for I suppose she has not charged for the jay's board, though 'twas that unlucky bird made the mischief.'

'The jay! What could he have to do with the matter? Dinah used to be as fond of him as if he had been her own child, and I always thought Dinah Forde a good-natured woman.'

'So she is, in the main, your honour,' replied Sam, twirling his hat, and looking half shy and half sly, at once knowing and ashamed. 'So she is, in the main; but this somehow is a particular sort of an affair. You must know, sir,' continued Sam, gathering courage as he went on, 'that at first the widow and I were very good friends, and several of these articles which are charged in the bill, such as milk for the ferrets, and tea and lump-sugar and young onions for myself, I verily thought were meant as presents; and so I do believe at the time she did mean them. But, howsoever, Jenny Dobbs, the nursery-maid at the Park (a pretty black-eyed lass—perhaps your honour may have noticed her walking with the children), she used to come out of an evening like to see us play cricket, and then she praised my bowling, and then I talked to her, and so at last we began to keep company; and the jay, owing, I suppose, to hearing me say so sometimes, began to cry out, "Pretty Jenny Dobbs!"'

'Well, and this affronted the widow?'

'Past all count, your honour. You never saw a woman in such a tantrum. She declared I had taught the bird to insult her, and posted off to Lawyer Latitat. And here I have got this letter, threatening to turn me out, and put me in jail, and what not, from the lawyer; and Jenny, a false-hearted jade, finding how badly matters are going with me, turns round and says that she never meant to have me, and is going to marry the French Mounseer (Sir Henry's French valet), a foreigner and a papist, who may have a dozen wives before for anything she can tell. These women are enough to drive a man out of his senses!' And poor Sam gave his hat a mighty swing, and looked likely to cry from a mixture of grief, anger, and vexation. 'These women are enough to drive a man mad!' reiterated Sam, with increased energy.

'So they are, Sam,' replied his host, administering a very efficient dose of consolation, in the shape of a large glass of cognac brandy, which, in spite of its coming from his rival's country, Sam swallowed with hearty good will. 'So they are. But Jenny's not worth fretting about; she's a poor feckless thing after all, fitter for a Frenchman than an Englishman. If I were you, I would make up to the widow: she's a person of property, and a fine comely woman into the bargain. Make up to the widow, Sam, and drink another glass of brandy to your success!'

And Sam followed both pieces of advice. He drank the brandy, and he made up to the widow, the former part of the prescription probably inspiring him with courage to attempt the latter; and the lady was propitious, and the wedding speedy; and the last that I heard of them was the jay's publishing the banns of marriage, under a somewhat abridged form, from his cage at the door of Mrs. Dinah's shop (a proceeding at which she seemed, outwardly, scandalized; but over which, it may be suspected, she chuckled inwardly, or why not have taken in the cage?), and the French valet's desertion of Jenny Dobbs, whom he, in his turn, jilted; and the dilemma of Lawyer Latitat, who found himself obliged to send in his bill for the threatening letter to the identical gentleman to whom it was addressed. For the rest, the cricket match was won triumphantly, the wedding went off with great éclat, and our accomplished rat-catcher is, we trust, permanently fixed in our good village of Aberleigh.

CHAPTER XLIV

THE LOST KEYS

IT was a glorious June morning, and I got up gay and bright, as the Americans say, to breakfast in the pretty summer room overlooking the garden, which, built partly for my accommodation and partly for that of my geraniums, who make it their winter residence, is as regularly called the greenhouse as if I and my several properties—sofas, chairs, tables, chiffonnières, and ottomans—did not inhabit it during the whole of the fine season; or as if it were not in its own person a well-proportioned and spacious apartment, no otherways to be distinguished from common drawing-rooms than by being nearly fronted with glass, about which out-of-door myrtles, passion-flowers, clematis, and the Persian honeysuckle, form a most graceful and varied framework, not unlike the festoons of flowers and foliage which one sees round some of the scarce and high-priced tradesmen's cards, and ridotto tickets of Hogarth and Bartolozzi. Large glass folding-doors open into the little garden, almost surrounded by old buildings of the most picturesque form—the buildings themselves partly hidden by clustering vines, and my superb bay-tree, its shining leaves glittering in the sun on one side, whilst a tall pear-tree, garlanded to the very top with an English honeysuckle in full flower, breaks the horizontal line of the low cottage roof on the other, the very pear-tree being, in its own turn, half concealed by a splendid pyramid of geraniums erected under its shade. Such geraniums! It does not become us poor mortals to be vain — but, really, my geraniums! There is certainly nothing but the garden into which Aladdin found his way, and where the fruit was composed of gems, that can compare with them. This pyramid is undoubtedly the great object from the greenhouse; but the common flower-beds which surround it, filled with roses of all sorts, and lilies of all colours, and pinks of all patterns, and campanulas of all shapes, to say nothing of the innumerable tribes of annuals, of all the outlandish names that ever were invented, are not to be despised even beside the gorgeous exotics, which, arranged with the nicest attention to colour and form, so as to combine the mingled charms of harmony and contrast, seem to look down proudly on their humble compeers.

No pleasanter place for a summer breakfast—always a pretty thing, with its cherries and strawberries, and its affluence of nosegays and posies—no pleasanter place for a summer breakfast-table than my greenhouse! And no pleasanter companion with whom to enjoy it, than the fair friend, as bright as a rosebud, and as gay as a lark—the saucy, merry, charming Kate, who was waiting to partake our country fare. The birds were singing in the branches; bees and butterflies and myriads of gay happy insects were flitting about in the flower-beds; the haymakers were crowding to their light and lively labour in the neighbouring meadow, whilst the pleasant smell of the newly-mown grass was blended with that of a bean-field in full blossom still nearer, and with the thousand odours of the garden—so that sight and sound and smell were a rare compound of all that is delightful to the sense and the feeling.

Nor were higher pleasures wanting. My pretty friend, with all her vivacity, had a keen relish of what is finest in literature and in poetry. An old folio edition of that volume of Dryden called his *Fables*, which contains the glorious *rifacimenti* of parts of Chaucer, and the best of his original poems, happened to be on the table; the fine description of spring in the opening of the *Flower and the Leaf* led to a picture of Eden in the *Paradise Lost*, and that again to *Comus*, and *Comus* to Fletcher's *Faithful Shepherdess*, and Fletcher's *Faithful Shepherdess* to Shakespeare and *As You Like It*. The bees and the butterflies, culling for pleasure or for thrift the sweets of my geraniums, were but types of Kate Leslie and myself roving amidst the poets. This does not sound much like a day of distress; but the evil is to come.

A gentle sorrow did arrive, all too soon, in the shape of Kate Leslie's pony-phaeton, which whisked off that charming person as fast as her two long-tailed Arabians could put their feet to the ground. This evil had, however, substantial consolation in the promise of another visit very soon; and I resumed in peace and quietness the usual round of idle occupation which forms the morning employment of a country gentlewoman of small fortune; ordered dinner—minced veal, cold ham, a currant-pudding, and a salad—if anybody happens to be curious on the score of my housekeeping; renewed my beau-pots; watered such of my plants as wanted most; mended my gloves; patted Dash; looked at *The Times*; and was just sitting down to work, or to pretend to work, when I was most pleasantly interrupted by the arrival of some morning visitors—friends from a distance—for whom, after a hearty welcome and some cordial chat, I ordered luncheon, with which order my miseries began.

'The keys, if you please, ma'am, for the wine and the Kennet ale,' said Anne, my female factotum, who rules, as regent, not only the cook and the undermaid and the boy, but the whole family, myself included, and is an actual housekeeper in every respect except that of keeping the keys. 'The keys, ma'am, if you please,' said Anne; and then I found that my keys were not in my right-hand pocket, where they ought to have been, nor in my left-hand pocket, where they might have been, nor in either of my apron pockets, nor in my work-basket, nor in my reticule— in short that my keys were lost!

Now these keys were only two in number, and small enough in dimensions; but then the one opened that important part of me, my writing-desk; and the other contained within itself the specific power over every lock in the house, being no other than the key of the key-drawer; and no chance of picking them—for alas! alas! the locks were Bramah's! So after a few exclamations such as, 'What can have become of my keys?' 'Has any one seen my keys?' 'Somebody must have run away with my keys!'—I recollected that however consolatory to myself such lamentations might be, they would by no means tend to quench the thirst of my guests. I applied myself vigorously to remedy the evil all I could by applications to my nearest neighbours (for time was pressing, and our horse and his master out for the day) to supply, as well as might be, my deficiency.

Accordingly I sent to the public-house for their best beer, which not being Kennet ale would not go down; and to the good-humoured wives of the shoemaker and the baker for their best wine. Fancy to yourselves a decanter of damson wine arriving from one quarter, and a jug of parsnip wine, fresh from the wood, tapped on purpose, from the other! And this for drinkers of Burgundy and champagne! Luckily the water was good, and my visitors were good-natured, and comforted me in my affliction, and made a jest of the matter. Really they are a nice family, the Sumners, especially the two young men, to whom I have, they say, taught the taste of spring water.

This trouble passed over lightly enough. But scarcely were they gone before the tax-gatherer came for money—locked up in my desk! What will the collector say? And the justice's clerk for warrants, left under my care for the chairman of the bench, and also safely lodged in the same safe repository. What will their worships say to this delinquency? It will be fortunate if they do not issue a warrant against me in my own person! My very purse was left by accident in that unlucky writing-desk; and when our kind neighbours, the Wrights, sent a melon, and I was forced to borrow a shilling to give the messenger, I could bear my loss no longer, and determined to institute a strict search on the instant.

But before the search could begin in came the pretty little roly-poly Sydneys and Murrays, brats from seven downwards, with their whole train of nurses and nursery-maids and nursery - governesses, by invitation, to eat strawberries; and the strawberries were locked up in a cupboard, the key of which was in the unopenable draw! And good Farmer Brookes, he too called, sent by his honour for a bottle of Hollands—the right Schiedam; and the Schiedam was in the cellar; and the key of the cellar was in the Bramah-locked drawer! And the worthy farmer, who behaved charmingly for a man deprived of his gin, was fain to be content with excuses, like a voter after an election; and the poor children were compelled to put up with promises, like a voter before one; to be sure, they had a few pinks and roses to sweeten their disappointment; but the strawberries were as uncomeatable as the Schiedam.

At last they were gone, and then began the search in good earnest. Every drawer not locked, every room that could be entered, every box that could be opened, was ransacked over and over again for these intolerable keys.

All my goods and chattels were flung together in heaps, and then picked over (a process which would make even new things seem disjointed and shabby), and the quantities of trumpery thereby disclosed, especially in the shape of thimbles, needle-cases, pin-cushions, and scissors, from the different work-baskets, work-boxes, and work-bags (your idle person always abounds in working materials), were astounding. I think there were seventeen pin-cushions of different patterns—beginning with an old boot and ending with a new guitar. But what was there not? It seemed to me that there were pocketable commodities enough to furnish a second-hand bazaar! Everything was there except my keys.

For four hours did I and my luckless maidens perambulate the house, whilst John, the boy, examined the garden, until we were all so tired that we were forced to sit down from mere weariness. Saving always the first night of one of my tragedies, when, though I pique myself on being composed, I can never manage to sit still; except on such an occasion, I do not think I ever walked so much at one time in my life. At last I flung myself on a sofa in the greenhouse, and began to revolve the possibility of their being still in the place where I had first missed them.

A jingle in my apron pocket afforded some hope, but it turned out to be only the clinking of a pair of garden scissors against his old companion, a silver pencil-case—and that prospect faded away. A slight opening in Dryden's heavily-bound volume gave another glimmer of sunshine, but it proved to be occasioned by a sprig of myrtle in *Palamon and Arcite*—Kate Leslie's elegant mark.

This circumstance recalled the recollection of my pretty friend. Could she have been the culprit? And I began to ponder over all the instances of unconscious key-stealing that I had heard of amongst my acquaintance. How my old friend, Aunt Martha, had been so well known for that propensity, as to be regularly sought after whenever keys were missing; and my young friend, Edward Harley, from the habit of twisting something round his fingers during his eloquent talk (people used to provide another eloquent talker, Madame de Staël, with a willow-twig for the purpose), had once caught up and carried away a key, also a Bramah, belonging to a lawyer's bureau, thereby, as the lawyer affirmed, causing the loss of divers lawsuits to himself and his clients. Neither Aunt Martha nor Edward had been near the place; but Kate Leslie might be equally subject to absent fits, and might, in a paroxysm, have abstracted my keys; at all events it was worth trying. So I wrote her a note to go by post in the evening (for Kate, I grieve to say, lives above twenty miles off), and determined to await her reply and think no more of my calamity.

A wise resolution, but, like many other wise resolves, easier made than kept. Even if I could have forgotten my loss, my own household would not have let me.

The cook, with professional callousness, came to demand sugar for the currant-pudding—and the sugar was in the store-room — and the store-room was locked; and scarcely had I recovered from this shock before Anne came to inform me that there was no oil in the cruet, and that the flask was in the cellar, snugly reposing, I suppose, by the side of the Schiedam, so that if for weariness I could have eaten, there was no dinner to eat—for without the salad who would might take the meat! However, I being alone, this signified little; much less than a circumstance of which I was reminded by my note to Kate Leslie, namely, that in my desk were two important letters, one triple, and franked for that very night, as well as a corrected proof sheet, for which the press was waiting; and that all these dispatches were to be sent off by post that evening.

Roused by this extremity, I carried my troubles and my writing-desk to my good friend the blacksmith—a civil intelligent man, who sympathized with my distress, sighed, shook his head, and uttered the word Bramah!—and I thought my perplexity was nearly at its height, when, as I was wending slowly homewards, my sorrows were brought to a climax by my being overtaken by one of the friends whom I admire and honour most in the world—a person whom all the world admires—who told me, in her prettiest way, that she was glad to see me so near my own gate, for that she was coming to drink tea with me.

Here was a calamity! The Lady Mary H——, a professed tea-drinker—a green-tea-drinker, one (it was a point of sympathy between us) who took nothing but tea and water, and therefore required that gentle and ladylike stimulant in full perfection! Lady Mary come to drink tea with me, and I with nothing better to offer her than tea from the shop—the village shop—bohea, or souchong, or whatever they might call the vile mixture. Tea from the shop for Lady Mary! Ill luck could go no farther: it was the very extremity of small distress.

Her ladyship is, however, as kind as she is charming, and bore our mutual misfortune with great fortitude; admired my garden, praised my geraniums, and tried to make me forget my calamity. Her kindness was thrown away. I could not even laugh at myself, or find beauty in my flowers, or be pleased with her for flattering them. I tried, however, to do the honours by my plants; and, in placing a large night-scented stock, which was just beginning to emit its odour, upon the table, I struck against the edge, and found something hard under my belt.

'My keys! my keys!' cried I, untying the ribbon and half laughing with delight, as I heard a most pleasant jingle on the floor; and the lost keys, sure enough, they were; deposited there, of course, by my own hand; unfelt, unseen, and unsuspected, during our long weary search. Since the adventure of my dear friend, Mrs. S——, who hunted a whole morning for her spectacles whilst they were comfortably perched upon her nose, I have met with nothing so silly and so perplexing.

But my troubles were over—my affliction was at an end.

The strawberries were sent to the dear little girls; and the Schiedam to the good farmer; and the warrants to the clerk. The tax-gatherer called for his money; letters and proof went to the post; and never in my life did I enjoy a cup of Turning's green tea so much as the one which Lady Mary and I took together after my day of distress.

CHAPTER XLV

FAREWELL TO OUR VILLAGE

Was it the gentle Addison, as quoted by Johnson, or Johnson himself, that tender heart enclosed in a rough rind, who said that he could not part without sorrow from the stump of an old tree that he had known since he was a boy? Whoever said it gave utterance to one of the deepest and most universal feelings of our common nature. The attractions of novelty are weak and powerless, in comparison with the minute but strong chains of habit, and the moment of separation is that of all others, in which, with an amiable illusion, we brighten and magnify the good qualities of the object we leave, whilst we forget or overlook whatever at another time may have displeased us. The last tone is a tone of kindness; the last look a look of regret.

The very words consecrated to parting embody this sentiment: farewell! adieu! good-bye! Why, they are benedictions, tender solemn benedictions! How poor and trivial, when measured with their intensity, seem the ordinary phrases of meeting: good day! good morrow! how d' ye do? how are you? [1] These are felt at once to be mere formal ceremonials, sentences of custom, spoken bows and curtsies as cold and as unmeaning as the compliments at the beginning of a note or the humble servant at the end of a letter. Even between the most assured friends, there is the same remarkable distinction in manner and in word. We shake hands at meeting, at parting we embrace.

The poets, faithful chroniclers of human feeling, have not failed to resort frequently to a source of sympathy so general and so true: witness the parting of Hector and Andromache in the 'tale of Troy divine,' and many of the

---

[1] Mr. Spenser's little poem, *One day Good-bye met How d'ye do?* is a pretty illustration of this difference.

338

finest passages in the finest writers, from Homer to Walter Scott. Nay, the feeling itself has made poets, as in the case of Mary Queen of Scots, whose beautiful verses, *Adieu, plaisant pays de France!* may be reckoned amongst the tenderest adieux in any language. Perhaps, at no instant of her most unhappy life did that unfortunate beauty experience a keener sensation of grief than when sighing forth that farewell! I doubt, indeed, if farewell can be spoken without some sensation of sorrow.

Nevertheless, it is a word that must, in the course of events, find utterance from us all; and just now it falls to my lot to bid a late and lingering good-bye to the snug nook called Our Village. The words must be spoken. For ten long years, for five tedious volumes, has that most multifarious and most kind personage, the public, endured to hear history, half real and half imaginary, of a half imaginary and half real little spot on the sunny side of Berkshire; but all mortal things have an end, and so must my country stories. The longest tragedy has only five acts; and since the days of *Clarissa Harlowe*, no author has dreamt of spinning out one single subject through ten weary years. I blush to think how much I have encroached on an indulgence, so patient and so kind. Sorry as I am to part from a locality which has become almost identified with myself, this volume must and shall be the last.

Farewell, then, my beloved village: the long straggling street, gay and bright in this sunny windy April morning, full of all implements of dirt and noise, men, women, children, cows, horses, wagons, carts, pigs, dogs, geese, and chickens, busy merry, stirring little world, farewell! Farewell to the winding uphill road, with its clouds of dust, as horsemen and carriages ascend the gentle eminence, its borders of turf, and its primrosy hedgerows! Farewell to the breezy common, with its islands of cottages and cottage gardens; its oaken avenues populous with rooks; its clear waters fringed with gorse, where lambs are straying; its cricket ground where children already linger, anticipating their summer revelry; its pretty boundary of field and woodland, and distant farms; and latest and best of its ornaments, the dear and pleasant mansion where dwell the

neighbours of neighbours, the friends of friends; farewell
to ye all! Ye will easily dispense with me, but what I shall
do without you, I cannot imagine. Mine own dear village,
farewell!

MARY RUSSELL MITFORD

THREE-MILE CROSS,
9 *April* 1832.